THE MODERNS

THE

MODERNS

AN ANTHOLOGY OF NEW WRITING
IN AMERICA

Edited with an introduction by

LEROI JONES

CORINTH BOOKS, INC.

NEW YORK, 1963

ACKNOWLEDGMENTS

WILLIAM EASTLAKE. "The First Bomb" from *Harper's Magazine*, by permission of Harold Matson Co. "Little Joe" from *Accent* by permission of the author.

EDWARD DORN. "C. B. & Q." from *Black Mountain Review*, "1st. Avenue," and "Beauty" by permission of the author.

DOUGLAS WOOLF. "Cougher" from *Second Coming*, and "Work in Flight Grounded" by permission of the author.

PAUL METCALF. "Indian Game" from *Will West*, published by Jonathan Williams' Jargon Press, 1955, and "The Doll" by permission of the author.

JOHN RECHY. "El Paso del Norte" from *Evergreen Review*, "The City of Lost Angels" from *Evergreen Review*, and "Chicago, Savage City" from *Nugget* by permission of the author.

MICHAEL RUMAKER. "The Teddy Bear" and "The Puppy" by permission of Harold Ober Associates; "Uses of the Unconscious" and "8 Dreams" from *Measure* by permission of the author.

ROBERT CREELEY. "Preface," "Mr Blue," "The Grace," "In the Summer," and "A Death" from *The Gold Diggers* published by Divers Press, 1954, by permission of the author. "The Dress" from *Sidewalk* (Scotland), *Prism* (Canada), and *US Poetry Taos*, by permission of the author. "The Book" from *Evergreen Review* by permission of the author. "Mr Blue" and "In the Summer" also appeared in *New Directions Anthology No. 14*.

FIELDING DAWSON. "Early in the Morning," "Invisible Glass," "Captain America," and "Bloodstar" by permission of the author.

HUBERT SELBY, JR. "Another Day Another Dollar" from *New Directions 17*, and "A Penny for Your Thoughts" by permission of the author.

CONTENTS

APPENDIX

INTRODUCTION

The "purpose" of this anthology, and from such statement ought also to be presented its design, was not merely to get together stories and pieces I happen to like, cookbook style, but to present those writers who have impressed me, over the range of say 10 years or so, as having something to say in a prose medium that was in adjunct to the artful writing of the marketplace. It was not merely in terms of a "generation" of writers, there being as much as twenty years separation between some of these writers' ages, but more towards, I think, a quality of writing that has come to clarify itself more and more at each publication as the most interesting and exciting writing that has taken place in this country since the war.

The vital and in some cases very much publicized activity that has returned American poetry to a great measure of emotional and intellectual hegemony among the world's poetries, after about thirty years of its representation as a patently unreadable graduate student verse, has certainly helped bring my selections more directly in focus. There is a definite connection between the so-called poetic renaissance and the literary environment that delineates the writers included in this volume from the thousands of other "prose writers" who live in this country. The prose and the writers in this volume are very different from the prose and the writers that would show up say in an anthology gotten together by Herbert Gold, or James Baldwin or Norman Mailer (and I mention these names in specific relief only because anyone familiar with contemporary American fiction on any but the most parochial level will know the "personalities" that inhabit the most popular literary establishment of our time). One of the reasons for such an open statement of difference is that I am most responsive to writing that shows a care for deeper involvement beyond the specific instance of its virtues as "literature."

I was interested in this volume in placing together prose that had some *future*, as literary and social phenomenon . . . and not necessarily in that work that could be called good, only with the hopeless qualification of context. That is, I am not interested in building another "establishment" but only in gathering together an intelligent body of work that is separate from the one that exists.

"It is a commonplace though always a surprising fact that, in the literary countries generally, the subtleties of poetic technique have been mastered earlier than the simplicities of prose . . . ," which was Douglas Bush talking about the differences between Chaucer's prose and his poetry. I take this to be a generalization displayed often enough to have some meaning. It has certainly been the case with recent American literature, at least in its public entrance. (Jack Kerouac's "popularity," for instance, was to a large extent the result of the social connections the popular mythologicians could make between the resurgence of a publicly identifiable poetic activity, in this country, as a social form, with the social phenomenon of a loudly disaffiliated American youth, whose "mores" were thought to be quaint or shocking. Kerouac, himself, has written volumes of poetry, and published one, *Mexico City Blues*. But as a prose writer, *per se,* Kerouac has always been thought by most critics to be absolutely *alone* and issuing from no contemporarily intelligent body of literary concern. The point is, of course, that while no one in this volume, or for that matter, no one who is a very interesting writer, writes *like* Kerouac, I would say that just about all of the writers included in this volume could make some valuable critical precis of his writing, based on its occurrence as a style of American writing. The writer who *cannot* be placed, as it were, only exists where the stimulations and emotional intentions of his writing are unknown, or worse, denied. That is, the only jungle in America is the thinking of the *New York Times,* and almost any serious writer, against this circumstance, becomes the fabled white hunter, searching for what? . . . Ayesha; a place to live and be; or the diamond mines of Union Minere.)

The possibility of a "new American poetry" meant, of course, that there was equally to be sought out, a new or fresher American prose. The concerns that made the poetry seem so new were merely that the writers who were identified with this recent poetic renaissance were continuing the tradition of twentieth century modernism that had been initiated in the early part of this century. William Carlos Williams, Ezra Pound, The Imagists, and the French symbolist poets were restored to importance as beginners of a still vital tradition of Western poetry. It was an attempt to restore American poetry to the mainstream of modern poetry after it had been cut off from that tradition by the Anglo-Eliotic domination of the academies.

The prose restoration was subtler, but it depended not a little for its impetus on the revived intellectual spirit that began to animate American poetry. (The poet, because he works finer, and at the barest origins of language, is always quickest to force or define change within the language.) Poets began "little" magazines, began to appear regularly in them and prose writers could publish in them as well. Poets who began to reassert the fact that Apollinaire was much more important to world poetry than Sidney Lanier (to paraphrase Kenneth Rexroth) immediately recognized the prose writers who could be seen in their work to understand the importance of Joyce or Stein, or for that matter, Melville and Twain. Of course some of the "new poets" wrote prose as well. Kerouac, Creeley, Dorn, DiPrima, and myself, have all published volumes of poetry. And of these five, only Kerouac is known predominantly as a prose writer.

Consequently there has developed a loose and deliberately informal rapport between many of the younger American poets and younger prose writers. And they have all benefited by the vitality of each other's concerns. Many of these prose writers have been influenced as much by poets and poetry as by other prose writers. Some of the writers in this volume owe the fashioning of their styles much more to the poems of William Carlos Williams, for example, than to Hemingway's short stories.

There is a very general, but perhaps useful, separation or placement that can be made about the writers in this book. Their work can be divided into two main "groups," as indicative of interest in at least two important concepts regarding the disposition of our local human product. *Urban* and *non-urban* would be the largest increments of division these writers' divergent concerns display, but in the loosest sense of those words. I mean them to be loose categories, implying nothing about the writing except its attentions.

In a more inexact sense, taken from the more brutal aspect of human geography, the divisions become Eastern and Western (writers). But there are cities in the West, e.g. John Rechy's cities (though the sense I mean is people with too much space as against those with too little) and there are rural areas, although of a deliberate artificiality, in the East. But space as a fact of environment, either as it becomes overwhelming in its existence, literally, as thousands of miles to contemplate (perhaps the miles between friends, &c., or whatever emotional occasion makes the saturation of space a non-human weight reflected on by the writer) or space as it has disappeared and becomes taken up, used, by people and their biographies, is the factor that provides the two most consistently possible identifications that characterize this writing, and these writers.

Environment, in these uses, becomes *total*, i.e., social, cultural, and physical, and not merely scenery. Though it is landscape, in the way the poet Charles Olson has used the word: what one can see from where one is standing. The common concern of each of these writers is local, and in a broader though vaguer sense, American. That is, the environment, so far as it is acted upon by whatever diverse ideas that might be brought to bear on it, is American. Ideas in themselves are more "abstract" than the instance of place, but they do reflect, however international or universal, &c., they might be, the exact location where they were received. Existentialism, for example, in this sense, can be reduced or extended to a way of carrying a deer back to a cabin . . . but it would be foolish, and a little Partisan Reviewish, to stick the Europe of our minds onto our local, native, closer, activities. The deer was not put there by Heidegger to help us solve a problem in Philosophy 608.

Any contemplation of the urban American environment and its philosophical antithesis, the non-urban American environment, can provide a very broad sense of *landscape* in attempting to describe what most of the writers in this collection use as their taking off place. William Eastlake, Edward Dorn, Douglas Woolf, Paul Metcalfe are all essentially non-urban writers. And of the four, only Metcalfe lives in the East, though in an out of the way place in North Carolina, which is non-urban if only in its social disposition.

Edward Dorn has approached the environmental materials of his writing very closely (in an essay on Douglas Woolf's novels): "The American West is the place men of our local civilization travel into in wide arcs to reconstruct the present version, the native version, of the Greek experience. Not Greek directly of course. American. But

there is where you will find the Stranger so dear to our whole experience. That the fear of the stranger has superseded what was once the
curiosity about him is of minor importance, it comes from the same
original well. And in the American west are denizens. It is a cultural
movement. The denizens of the East are a "product" of neo-realism.
Painters mostly are concerned with them. It is a concern and a definition that comes directly from industrialization. The American West,
still in our time, has nothing to do with industrialization. In his desire
to get out of the tight limitation of prime metals the westerner has
constructed all of the sham formalities of a world that has gone beyond
that rawness. The witness of any city between that area from 200
miles west of the Mississippi to the Pacific, can testify."

So the non-urban or Western writer is faced with resurrecting
familiar holds on a non-existent civilization, with the hopes that by
this act, and his state of separateness within the "non-civilized," he
can demand a cleaner vision of any possible civilization anyone might
like to erect. And there are erectors all over the West, that is where
they genuinely thrive. There is an openness to the West, to the non-
urban (especially as contrasted to those shabby models of Chicago, a
twenty year old New York, which dot the rest of this land so ubiqui-
tously) that might lead a man to believe in some kind of new construction. And of course there have been these new constructions, new
buildings, outside the formal frustrations of urban America, most
impressively on sliding scales like dress or language, or the size of
living quarters. But one of the most poignant descriptions these writers
make is of the reconstruction of common national futilities in
"unfamiliar" circumstances, and of such specific priggishness as to ter-
rorize even the least sensitive. (That is, *all* of America is desolated.)

I do not mean by these generalizations to infer a complete similar-
ity of style, &c., among the writers I label non-urban. Even though
they are, in a great many instances, after the same kind of "information," i.e., "Is the West really possible?" they go at the gathering of
such information in specifically diverse ways.

One characteristic that binds most of the writers in this volume
together, at least as far as a common distinction which separates them
immediately from the serious middlebrow establishment fiction of our
era, is that for the most part they are interested in those personalities
(and people) who exist outside the mainstream of the American social

organism. The urban writers like Rechy, Selby, Kerouac (whose characters reveal a great deal about the non-urban, but who are usually
en route, at full speed, to another city), Burroughs, Rumaker (his
earlier stories), &c., do not focus on the handsome urbanized (a state
of mind) middleclass either. The non-urban writers are usually much
more interested in the typical prosperous American because of the
rude surprise they experience in finding such lives even in the most
beat up parts of America. Only in the stories by Robert Creeley,
Fielding Dawson, and the later Rumaker, could any of the central personnae of this fiction be connected in some sense to the American
majority. Creeley, Dawson and Rumaker are writing literally about
anybody, but the terms of their description, even in the non-literal
environment of, say, the Creeley stories, is closer to people who somehow inhabit at least the fringe of mainstream American life. The
"people" in Creeley's stories are perhaps more intense than the "average American," certainly more tortured; but their difference from our
mainstream is one that Creeley has proposed aesthetically. They are
people better revealed, but they are not *different* people, as the characters in a Rechy story or a Selby story are. Dawson and Rumaker are
also, for the most part, concerned with an intelligent and provocatively
sensitive kind of middleclass American. But Selby's hoodlums, Rechy's
homosexuals, Burroughs' addicts, Kerouac's mobile young voyeurs, my
own Negroes, are literally not included in the mainstream of American
life. These characters are people whom Spengler called *Fellaheen,*
people living on the ruins of a civilization. They are Americans no
character in a John Updike novel would be happy to meet, but they
are nonetheless Americans, formed out of the conspicuously tragic
evolution of modern American life. The last romantics of our age.

Jack Kerouac and William Burroughs are writers whose names
came into prominence about the same time, though of course, Kerouac's
was much more public. I mention them together in this instance because
they both seem to have paid homage to similar literary traditions,
though their final uses of these traditions have moved quite evidently
apart. For one thing, both seem to have benefited consciously by the
model of the James Joyce of *Ulysses* (and Burroughs, of late, e.g. the
"cut-ups" and "fold-ins," has even moved into the relatively unknown
concerns of *Finnegan's Wake*). Even though Burroughs is relatively a
formalist when compared with Kerouac, they both depend on the

Joycean mode in its various expressions for very definite character-istics of their styles. Burroughs is interested not only in the linguistic innovations, as for example the Molly Bloom soliloquy can propose, but in the whole social reconstruction that should have taken place in order for one to write intelligent fiction after reading Joyce. Joyce made the novel, as a traditional literary form, almost meaningless. And more important, he destroyed its social pretensions as well simply by focusing *Ulysses* on the socio-cultural intelligence of the city Dublin, as revealed by whom? Joyce. There is no one talking in *Ulysses* but Joyce. There is no A. aged 26, the young clerk or factory worker, or squire, son of B. aged 65, the old judge or foreman or aging Lord, and their wives and children, and the long chronicle of their novelistic lives. Joyce destroyed the artificial humanity of the novel by re-focusing its concerns. The writing itself also becomes important then, in all its elements, and not merely as a *vehicle*. Samuel Butler's writing is important only insofar as it is *about* something. Joyce's writing became an event in itself.

Twentieth century Western fiction, even in its middlebrow aspects, has had to adjust to at least a superficial adaptation of the social qualities Joyce's fiction proposed. The "psychological" novel was how it was popularized. "Stream of consciousness," the middlebrow novelist thought, meant only another way of writing a traditional novel; the difference was that the characters didn't have to talk as much. But Burroughs took up the social and literary propositions and reduced his personnae to a Joycean anonymity (as Samuel Beckett did also). *Naked Lunch* is Burroughs spinning a parable in which all of existence can participate. He merely names it as it shows up, i.e., he is not necessarily "pulling for anything." Guilt in this sense, as the modern philosophers posit it, becomes anonymous. There is no one good person or one bad person, living out their lives under the auspices of the reluctantly mortal Augustan christianity; there is only the idea of good and the idea of bad and "characters" wander into these categories as they relate to the central logic of the writer's intent. Popular novels are still so popular, like Protestant jingles, because they are one place where God still exists very definitely on the side of right.

Kerouac is interested in Joyce for the most part for his innovations in word division. The spontaneous prose which Kerouac has talked so much about seeks merely to keep prose writing as personal as it ought to be. To keep even the rhythms and awkwardness of its creator as a part of its final "story": the writing as part of what is being said. This has been the essential concept the important twentieth-century writers have worked through. Joyce was just very apparent in his innovation along these lines. As Robert Creeley has said about poetry, "Form is no more than an extension of content" so *Ulysses* made this clear in prose, and so the prose writers in this volume contend, though, of course, they are not all by any means indebted specifically to Joyce. Stein, Hemingway, West, Fitzgerald, Lawrence, Wolfe, Beckett have been definite influences, but also, as I said, twentieth-century poetry has contributed equally, and in some cases even painting and music (though perhaps, in the last two cases, more specifically music, because it occurs in time, the same way a poem or a story does, and is motivated rhythmically as well).

I have not attempted to categorize "definitively" the writers and writing in this volume, merely to sketch in some of the common backgrounds and catalysts for their work, to point out, as I have insisted, that there is a body of work that seeks its identification and delineation as a departure from the main body of popular American fiction. A writer like Russell Edson, and his intense preoccupation with the surreal and fantastic, or a writer like Diane DiPrima, whose recent concerns are equally remote from the naturalist's reality, can find themselves in the same volume with a writer of such lyric realism as Edward Dorn, or a writer such as Hubert Selby whose concerns are so naturalistic as to be almost socialist-realism, because all of their work is in adjunct to the "stylish" fiction of our time, but intelligently and meaningfully so. But this volume is no "protest" against that stylish literature, nor does it seek to be compared, in any useless sense, with it. Let me just say that the work in this collection does exist out of a continuing tradition of populist modernism that has characterized the best of twentieth-century American writing. It's common stance, if one can be honestly found (and I obviously believe one can) is perhaps one of *self-reliance*, Puddin'head Wilson style.

LeRoi Jones
April 1963

THE MODERNS

WILLIAM EASTLAKE

THE FIRST BOMB

November is the month of the dead and on All Saints Day of that month yellow *flores de muerte* are hung in the doorways of the adobe huts in Tico. They are arranged carefully in the form of the cross on the many graves and they are interset with candles.

The men on horseback had ridden through the sharp yellowness of the flowers of the dead two hours before and now from the edge of the barranca in the rapid-coming darkness they could see the faint blur of the candles celebrating death. The seven men sat astride their horses without movement and without speaking. Twenty minutes before they had ridden to a point directly below them, descended abruptly from their horses and felled a tree across the highway. But now as they watched in perfect silence up the ravaged road for the American car to appear they did not breathe heavily. One of them dropped the end of a cigarette and a horse pawed into the adobe and then swung its big head before it ceased. Now the heavy roll of the bells of Tico began again.

They had been unremitting on this day of our dead since the horsemen had begun the journey. The peons will stand for hours for their turn to ring the bells on this day for their dead. If they pull long and extra hard for their dead they know the Lord will look on them with favor in his eyes.

One of the horsemen spat. It was the same horseman who—when they had ridden through Tico in the heavy tolling, he, at the head of them—had ridden differently with his back straight, riding as one not asleep, riding as the old ones remembered Black Jack's men had ridden, swinging loosely and straight up on their McClellans, pretending

19

to chase Villa and Villa asleep, bored, accommodating, pretending to
be chased.

When the seven on their rare horses had gotten into Tico as far as
the outdoor *zapateria* of Jole Ruiz, the outlander had doubled back
within the others, flowed back through the huge sombreros of the six,
ridden alone to the blinding white wedding-cake front of the Church
of Our Blessed Lady of the Immaculate Conception and allowed his
horse to drink from the heart-shaped fountain of the Blood of Our
Saviour. No one gave him their eyes. The iron beating of the bells
fell with the steadiness of almost fierce patience as the man twirled
his horse on its hind hooves with style and rode out of town, freely
yet erect, followed by the six waiting at Jole Ruiz'; they slowly
diminished into the wavy sand going fast toward the edge of low
hills faintly suggested in the shimmering dazzle of the heat waves that
shifted and began again their illusions in the recurrent dry wind of
Baja Sonora.

"Kill all the cíngaros!"

It was turning cool now. Where the seven waited at the edge of
the barranca, the scrub and thorn and cactus-dry ravine that followed
the pass, the blur of the candles of Tico became distinct as the cold
and the darkness came on.

The rider who had spoken was one of the six. He had spoken to
himself but as he reset his weight on the saddle by leaning his bulk
on the pommel he looked at the seventh. The man looked back at him
and at them. He was in advance of the others on a V-shaped promon-
tory jutting over the ravine. His eyes were on the man who had spoken.
His own eyes were of a blue like the color of the spaces between the
clouds. Still all *norte-americanos* were so afflicted, the argument had
run thus back in camp. None was an expert, none had seen too many,
and when they asked Buck (they pronounced it Book), he just laughed
as he had on many questions of equal importance. Most times with the
quick laugh there would come a sudden remark in ununderstandable
inglés and he would slap his Texas chaps and stare through them,
beyond them, with his blue eyes that were the color of between the
clouds.

"No smoking," he said in Spanish.

The glow of four cigarettes arched through the dusk. With the night had come the coldness of the hills. One of the *Indios* rubbed his gun and cursed to himself in his own language. The bandits sat now like the rocks as big as houses around them and stared at the pass.

Their first victim, a long, low, heavy and hand-rubbed, august black limousine emitting almost no sound curled patiently through the quiet, pluming ocher dust of Mexico, down the long arroyos, dull-lensed with gray sediment and far above, always the continuous flag of striped cliff, gaudy and endless and wavering above an exquisite water-and-wind-eroded hell of purple sharp banded clay slopes, abrupt and blinding white limestone faults, twisted convolutions of a billion years, wind-ripped, naked, and shot red-bright with iron; now the soft folded dark mounds of clay and shale and now the cacti, abstract and bizarre, gesturing. Ahead, the fresh and quick, man-felled barricade. But a really perfect barricade.

Inside the hushed black car that made toward the barricade and away from something behind them, the pristine, blue-black, and tailored chauffeur heard the receiver click on.

"Ulysses."

"Yes, Mr. Elphick?"

The voices came over the car's intercommunication with the wiry dissonance of a medium's performance.

"Do you think we might have missed a turn back there somewhere, Ulysses?"

"I'm sure I did not," the Negro chauffeur said without accent.

The man in the rear pressed the button and broke off contact, settled back and said in a voice that obviated the need for wires to anywhere, "Did we miss the turn, I said, putting my foot in it. I did not miss the turn, he said, putting me in my place. He's always catching me up like that."

"Now, Tom," his wife, sitting cool and immaculate alongside him said, "now, Tom," and she touched his knee gently.

"Yes," Mr. Elphick said, "and you'd think if the government down here wanted to keep any business they'd mark their roads, and surface them while they're at it. This is a cow pasture. It may lead to Rhodesia for all I know."

"That's in Africa, isn't it, Father?" his daughter said.

"Yes," the man said, rubbing his polished forehead. "It's somewhere over there and it's where we get our chromite to make into chrome to make ours cars bright to make into money so you can primp your face, for God knows why, in Huatabampo."

Bozzie had turned on the corner light, pressed another button that revealed a built-in silver make-up kit, and was dabbing at her well shaped nose with a pink puff.

"It's time for Father's medicine," she said.

Mr. Elphick winced.

"It's Huatabampo, a small village filled with Indian fisherfolk. It is not Cap d'Ail or Sun Valley. There's no use powdering your nose."

The three Elphicks were seated on the rear seat of the seven-passenger limousine. Mr. Elphick wore a loose-fitting, faint-plaid suit that his tailor had been enthusiastic about, a pale blue bow tie that he had selected himself. A web of fine red veins covered his soft face. His mother, who was still alive, told him he was beginning to look the way he did the day he was born. Mr. Elphick was fifty-nine. His wife alongside him was less and looked much less. She had a long and once very beautiful face. Age hung on it well and gave it a dignity and assurance. She allowed her hair to turn gray when and where it wanted to and the streaks of it were attractive. She was not keen about the prospects of Huatabampo, especially now that Charles was trans-planting from the green houses at Rancho Paraíso and the bougain-villaea would be in purple battle over the guest houses. Still she endured easily and comforted herself with the knowledge that Charles would be alert at zinnia time.

Bozzie continued to busy herself with the make-up kit. She had the features of her mother but without their strength. Her dark blue eyes were overlarge; her heavy lips on a short mouth and her up-tilted nose gave her face a constant, amazed, wondering quality. Her breasts were heavy for her age, nineteen, but were in keeping with the dust-jacket pictures on contemporary American fiction, which she knew.

Bozzie had just returned from a little tour of the continent. She had spent most of her time in Paris. It had been planned that she stay in Switzerland but she had hated, hated, hated it. It was like a church with the radiators turned off she said. Now Paris—Paris was *très, très chic*. She wanted to go there again soon, she said. She was engaged to Choo Choo Traine, possible All-American half-back at USC. Now she thought Choo Choo cute but dull, Paris and Creighton sophisticated and exciting. Creighton had been on his way to the international auto races at Monte Carlo. He drove for the British team. The Italians in their Maseratis ran away with it but Creighton got drunk and made a joke of the defeat. Then they had gone to Vence, a small town in the hills back of Cannes and were very, very happy until Creighton had to go back to his wife and family in Birmingham, something he hadn't told her about. Still he hadn't not told her about it, she thought, and she stopped dabbing with the puff.

And what was so very wrong with Choo Choo? She saw Choo Choo jump off the bench in a red and gold uniform and she saw him go over the goal line standing up, his small hips swinging easily under his false shoulders and heard the feminine squeal beneath the deep roar of the stadium. She saw Choo Choo reading the comic strips on the floor with their children. She saw Choo Choo president of the Twenty-Thirty Club and an outstanding local booster. There was nothing wrong with Choo Choo, nothing wrong at all with Choo Choo. She sighed and looked unhappily into the silver inlaid mirror as the car swerved. Yes, that's what was wrong with Choo Choo—nothing.

In the twilight she watched Mexico going by the car. She repeated the word to herself—"Mexico." It had an exotic ring and the landscape was strange. The abrupt and weird attitudes of the cacti were like the pictures of modern people at the *Salon d'Automne*. Lawrence had loved it and how she had worshiped Lawrence. Or was it Huxley? Someone had filled her library hours at Vassar with the strange, blood-sacrifical rites of the Mayas, the hot blood-enduring passion of weird Indian cults. It was Lawrence, she was certain of that. Yet Aldous Huxley had written something too. Mexico, land of the *conquistadores*, land of *The Plumed Serpent* and *Beyond the Mexique Bay*.

Bozzie clicked off her light and smiled happily in the semi-darkness. Mexico was embracing her.

In front of Bozzie on the drop seat sat Mr. Williams, Mr. Elphick's secretary, holding tightly to a briefcase resting on his knees. Mr. Williams removed his gold wire spectacles from his thin, arched nose and cleared them with his handkerchief. He was a tight man and each movement was quick and tense. His spare body perched nervously on the front of the seat, his head poking as he jerked rather than turned. Now he set the wire spectacles back on his nose. Inside the car as they

rode over a smooth track it was absolutely silent. Mr. Williams had
poked his head almost against the glass and watched vacantly the
smooth going by of the desert landscape.

"Dreaming, Williams?" Mr. Elphick asked. There was a silence
while Mr. Williams shifted his briefcase and looked about the car.

"Hitchhikers," he answered. "This country reminds me of something
I read in the papers. It seems a hitchhiker murdered somebody who
gave him a lift in Arizona, then he fled down here into Mexico, got
another lift with a family of tourists and murdered them all too."

"Oh, you never told me you'd been reading the newspapers,
Williams. Never thought you read anything but the *Wall Street Journal*."

Mr. Williams didn't answer. He was looking at the man sitting on
the drop seat beside him, Mr. Elphick had cultivated him in the hotel
bar at Hermosillo. While in the car, outside of small talk about the
rainy season and the possibility of sailfish out of Huatabampo, he
had been silent. The man's legs were too long for his position; he was
able to rest his chin on his arms folded over his knees. While it was
still light he looked at the landscape carefully from this position, watching the cliffs and the vari-colored formations intently. His features
were regular yet all slightly overlarge. His black hair would sometimes
fall over his long forehead when the car lurched and he would push it
back with a wiping motion. Mr. Williams guessed him at about thirty-
five, thought him concerned about something, and knew what it was.

The car shifted itself now as it began to climb for the pass and they
all braced themselves as it swung into the first cutback.

"Mr. Guthrie is looking for a horse," Mr. Elphick announced.

"Did you lose a horse, Mr. Guthrie?" Mr. Williams asked. He had
a New England accent.

"I don't think we did but some people do."

"And so you've come all the way down here into old Mexico to
look for a horse you don't think is missing?"

"That's right," Guthrie said.

Back in the corner Bozzie giggled and Mrs. Elphick laid a warning
hand on her thigh. Guthrie continued looking seriously at the seat in
front with his chin resting on his long legs in a forced foetal position.

"And just where did you lose the horse?" Mr. Williams asked,
patiently and spacing his words as you might to a child or an idiot.

"Eocene," Guthrie said, his voice coming from between his knees.

"And where is that?" Mr. Williams said, still spacing his words and still louder now.

"Where?" Guthrie said raising his head. "Where was the Eocene? Of course you mean when. It was fifty million years ago. Somewhere between the Paleocene and the Oligocene. About fifty million years ago."

"If you can get your knees off this panel—" Mr. Williams said over-politely to Guthrie.

Guthrie turned his knees away from the back of the front seat until they were jammed into Williams' ribs. Mr. Williams released a catch that let down a copper ledge. It held about seven cut-glass bottles fitted into holes in the copper table. In one corner was a cordova covered Thermos that held ice, and in another a velvet pouch containing silver cups.

"How about you girls?" Mr. Elphick said.

"Not on an empty stomach," his wife answered.

"Then make it three, Williams. Make it four. Don't forget the horse."

"So you are a paleontologist," Bozzie said wisely and comfortably from her corner.

"Yes," Guthrie said.

"And you can trace all of life through the rocks," Bozzie said seriously. "So you must have some pretty definite idea of what the big picture is."

"It's rye whisky and water," Mr. Elphick said, humming it.

"No," Bozzie said, embarrased again by her father and touching Guthrie. "I mean, you know, where we've been. And you must have a pretty good idea of where we're going."

"Briefly," Guthrie said, "we're not going anywhere in particular."

"And in detail?" Mr. Elphick said, gay, watching Williams pour the drinks. "We've been in sin but now we're going to Mexico."

"Oh Father!" Bozzie said, ashamed of him now and leaning forward to exclude him. "Tell me," she said intimately and seriously to Guthrie, "is this the picture or is the evolutionary process continuing in man? That is, are we still changing or is this form of man the final product?"

"And if so," Mr. Elphick said, imitating Bozzie's seriousness, "where do we go to get our money back?"

"No," Bozzie said, ignoring her father. "I mean, what, in your opinion, lies on the road ahead for us?"

"Bandittos," Mr. Elphick sang and slapped his knee.

"You know, that's true," Guthrie said. "The road is oriented yet chance plays a big part."

"I told you," Mr. Elphick said, pleased.

"I mean seriously," Bozzie said, lighting a cigarette nervously and looking big at Guthrie. "How can evolution explain away the validity of Freud's death wish?"

"I paid for her at Vassar for four years," Mr. Elphick said solemnly, "and they have now brought her to the excitement of asking the wrong questions."

"Papa can be difficult," Bozzie said, settling back.

Mr. Elphick passed around the drinks. "To the horse," he said. They all drank deeply and with some reverence, Mrs. Elphick thought, to the horse.

"Yes," Mr. Elphick said, breathing again, "Mr. Guthrie and I went deeply into the rocks in the bar. That is why I offered him a lift. I am a student of the rocks myself and I would never allow a true student to wait twenty-three hours for a train. But don't pump him. He has already earned his ride, in the bar."

Mr. Elphick leaned with the roll of the car, trying to save his drink. "That this road is slightly oriented in some direction may be true, but since the last hour I began to lean toward the entirely random school."

"Are you, Mr. Guthrie," Bozzie said abruptly, "a vitalist or a finalist?"

"What she means is, are you married," Mr. Elphick said.

"Or do you," Bozzie said, "hold the more materialistic view and deny both of them and if so," Bozzie said—

"And if so—" Mr. Elphick said.

"And if so, " Bozzie said, "what instruments does science have to disprove the metaphysical?"

"None," Guthrie said, "but we can examine the results."

"Yes," Mr. Elphick said into his drink, "yes, but this road is not oriented but truly random and Bozzie really wants to know if you are married."

"Papa, I want to get at the heart of the matter."

"Being a woman you will get at the heart and past that to the viscera and the tortilla in the viscera," Mr. Elphick said.

"I only want Mr. Guthrie to tell me what forces have been acting throughout the history of life."

"Bandits." The voice of Ulysses came back through the communication system. "We've been going by bandits for the last hundred yards."

They could see the dim skeleton shape of oil rigs among the full organ cactus.

"It's not that Ulysses is a Marxist," Mr. Elphick said, watching. "It's that I had a set-to with the oil companies and we have a private joke."

"I didn't think there was oil in this formation," Guthrie said, thinking.

"There isn't," Mr. Elphick said. "Ed Pauley's wasting his time and so is Bozzie."

Mrs. Elphick reared back her head as though surveying the scene but she was still thinking about the greenhouses at Rancho Paraíso and the camellia cross and the continuous beginning smile of the refugee Trappist monk she had tamed who had now dedicated his life to the camellia cross. His red Herbert Hoover cross had been a failure, true enough, but an interesting one and who could say that his letter to *Organic Gardening* might not create a tempest all of its own—and about his being a Trappist monk, you would never know. When people get very close to the earth they are difficult. Perhaps it was only his love of Mendel that made him think it up or it might have been a means of worming his way into the greenhouse. Still let him experiment. He might come up with an interesting cross, and they had already decided to name it after their goat who had suffered disappointment after disappointment at the San Fernando Valley Fair. Bozzie was in pursuit and Tom maybe had a little too much with that nice fossil boy and Mr. Williams didn't have any lines. Someone should write him some lines, she thought, so that he could sandwich a speech in between the speeches of the others.

"I'm sorry," Bozzie said from her corner, "but I can't buy it
without the big picture. Everyone is trying to crowd me off into the
little picture but I can't dig it without the big Darwinian picture.
Or do I sound like a square?" she said toward Guthrie.

"No," Guthrie said stunned. "No, you sound—well, you are—how
would you say it—you are all progressive. You are entitled to the
picture certainly—the big picture."

"I mean maybe my Freud is rusty," Bozzie said seriously, removing
the cigarette from her mouth. "I mean, but he did comment on paleon-
tology? He said he could not understand, in view of the validity of the
death wish, how certain species could have survived almost indefinitely.
I mean, briefly," she said, "Freud saw within man two powerful drives
—the life drive which is mostly libido and the death drive—"

"Which is mostly death," Mr. Elphick helped.

"No," Bozzie said. "So man inhibits himself to balance these instinctual drives. If he fails or succeeds anxiety is produced along with
fears—a fear of losing a part of himself—not, according to Horney,
necessarily just his sex."

"Not just what, child?" Mrs. Elphick asked cautiously.

"I was speaking scientifically, Mother," Bozzie said hopelessly.
"I was referring to Horney's extension of Freud's limited views. Horney,
Karen. *The Neurotic Personality of Our Time,* Norton, 1937."

"Oh, I thought you were referring to sex," Mrs. Elphick said.

"Dig Mother on sex referrals," Bozzie beamed. "Isn't she sensational?"

"We only want our money returned that the Vassar people took,"
Mrs. Elphick said definitely.

"Will you buy Horney or Freud?" Bozzie said, excited, to Guthrie,
"Both," Guthrie said.

"Then you're right in there, Roger, with Harry Stack Sullivan and
Frieda Fromm-Reichmann," Bozzie said, enthusiastic.

"I certainly wouldn't want to get in between Frieda Fromm-
Reichmann and Harry Stack Sullivan," Guthrie said seriously.

"Dig him," Bozzie said tilting her head back. "Isn't he sensational,
Mother? I mean you think he's all fossil and then he gives you a
yak yak."

The drinks were passed around and the men held them close to
their stomachs to keep them from spilling. When they drank it was

more like a quick look so that the drinking took on the appearance of a stiff poker game.

"Ulysses does not think it is wise for him to drink when he's driving," Mr. Elphick said, studying the neck of the Negro. "And he's been driving very silently for the last hour as though he's taking us into that country from whose bourne no traveler returns."

"Ulysses checked Father out on Shakespeare," Bozzie said quickly. "He usually recites poetry on these long drives but he's been quiet since we entered Mexico. I suppose you've been checked out on the Huxley Brothers," Bozzie said, turning to Guthrie now. "Julian, that is. You probably think Aldous is fruit, that is you're probably all Darwin."

"I'm all ears," Guthrie said.

The big car rolled heavily in the rough terrain, so they played the drinks close to their bodies.

"To the scientific attitude!" Mr. Elphick said, gesturing his glass toward Guthrie. "The organized religions are having difficulties with me," Mr. Elphick said, "so I will drink to the scientific attitude."

"The scientific attitudes are always willing," Guthrie said.

"Even if I am rich?" Mr. Elphick said.

"Because you are rich."

"Organized religion won't let me in," Mr. Elphick said soberly, "—unless I compete with a camel to get through somebody's eye. My being rich is a by-product of my work and my work I can continue efficiently because I am rich. If someone can use my money to create more work than I can he is welcome to it but I refuse—"

"Tom, don't bore the gentleman," Mrs. Elphick said coolly. "A scientific gentleman has problems but they do not include money."

"But they do include money," Guthrie said.

"You mean you too have some holy land, some boneyard, you must pilgrimage to?" Mr. Elphick said.

"That's right," Guthrie said. "We have expeditions."

"And where do you find the Holy Grail?" Mr. Elphick asked.

"We find interesting deposits in Patagonia, Mongolia, many places and at the moment, right here," Guthrie said.

"Then you don't have to go any further," Mr. Elphick said, interested. "You don't have to be financed, you're almost there. It won't cost anything."

"That's right," Guthrie said.

"Then we can really drink to the scientific attitude," Mr. Elphick said, taking a sip from his drink.

"I don't see," Bozzie said quickly, "how we can harmonize a middle-class concern for money with the scientific attitude."

"Yes," Mrs. Elphick said smiling, "you've overdrawn your account again, Bozzie."

Bozzie was silent. She had tried to elevate the conversation but she had once more come up against her mother's compulsive pattern and there is only so much pressure you can apply against an authority symbol without building a block within your own subconscious. She held no particular brief for or against the middle class, she was merely trying to elevate her parents to a position of objectivity so that they would be able to define their own position in society with not only the subsequent advantages to them of better interpersonal relationships but also a complete rejection of the neo-Lamarckian attitude into which they seemed to be drifting.

Mrs. Elphick said, guessing and disinterested, "I don't suppose your last check could have gone to pay for the new fog lights on Robert Traine's Pierce Arrow?"

"Choo Choo has plenty of money of his own and he has the same concern for it as you do, plus the fact," Bozzie added hopelessly, "that his middle-class mores would not allow him to take money from a girl, and plus the fact," she added, "that Choo Choo's car is a new Mercury. They haven't made the Pierce Arrow for years."

"Oh," Mrs. Elphick sighed. "What a pity. It's the only car that ever ran properly and it's the only car I know the name of outside of the one your father manufactures. The one your father manufactures I find difficult to get into and impossible to get out of. Still," she said in her quiet, knitting voice, "the advertisements say it has many features."

"I don't want to go interesting-features on you or even metaphysical on you," Bozzie said across to Guthrie. "You'd probably resent that, so let's say I'm going extrasensory on you." Bozzie hesitated then relaxed back into the heavy seat away from all of them before she said it—"I see an evil cloud lifting into the sky, shaped not like a horse but more like a giant white frog—"

Guthrie lost his grip on his drink and it ended up soaking the red carpet.

"The car gave no particular jolt," Bozzie said. "You know sometimes the therapist will dig for months to touch a key that will give an emotional response worth exploring. Ferenczi tried to shorten this period by urging the patient to give up all sexual indulgence, and cut down the time of the complete toilet. Even eating and drinking should be cut down during the period of therapy. He thought in this way he could increase the intensity of the therapeutic hour. Soon he came to the blind end, however, that the reaction he was observing was not the repression he was trying to explore—liberate, I suppose is better. Now a true student would find your reaction to when I said it was not so much a horse that the great shadow was more a white giant frog—"

"Bozzie Lamb."

"Yes, Mommikins."

"Shut up," her mother said.

The big car began to turn now in a great circle. When it completed its circle it was going in the opposite direction; it was going back to the United States.

Mr. Elphick picked up the inter-com and talked in quick and abrupt words with Ulysses. When he finished they were still headed back toward the States.

"He says he is willing to hitchhike back if we want to continue into Mexico," Mr. Elphick said to the others.

No one said anything, they were all studying their shoes. There was an occasional jolt from the power brakes as the car went down a sheer valley under compression.

"He said you can't walk away from anything. He doesn't get a chance to talk up there so he thinks. He believes he thinks too much alone up there but this is what he thinks—that we are getting nowhere at all and would never get anywhere at all because you can't walk away from anything at all."

Mr. Elphick looked annoyed and thoughtful at the neck of the Negro driving in the wrong direction, began to give an order, then felt someone's hand touch him and he ceased.

The car swept, careened over sharply to the right but everyone continued to examine the floor.

"But this is only a vacation," Mrs. Elphick said finally.

"Only an extended vacation," Mr. Elphick agreed as the others remained silent continuing to examine the carpet. The big car under deep throttle rocked along the floor of the valley, getting ready to hunch up the big ocher mountain, its bright chrome flashing like a heliograph in the last sun as it climbed back toward the United States.

All over the world November is the month of the dead and on All Saints Day of that month yellow *flores de muerte* are hung in the doorway of the adobe huts in Tico. They are arranged carefully in the form of the cross on the many graves and they are interset with candles. The bandits on horseback had ridden through the sharp yellowness of the flowers of the dead three hours before and now from the edge of the barranca in the rapid-coming darkness they could see the faint blur of the candles celebrating death. The seven men sat astride their horses without movement and without speaking. Some time before they had ridden to a point directly below them, descended abruptly from their horses and felled a tree across the highway. Now they watched in perfect silence up the ravaged road as the American car turned back and disappeared. One of them dropped the end of a cigarette and a horse pawed into the abode and then swung its big head before it ceased. Now the heavy toll of the bells of Tico began again. They had been unremitting on this day of our dead since the horsemen had begun the journey. The peons will stand for hours for their turn to ring the bells on this day for our dead. If they pull long and extra hard for our dead they know the Lord will look on us with courage in his eyes.

LITTLE JOE

I think we all realized that nothing, nothing at all, would ever stop Little Joe; not the drought even, because he, or his father Jonathan rather, had thought of it, but Joe executed it—the damming up of the small spring above Rye Hill, so that they had at least one crop (the oats below) when no other farmer had anything except the orchard crop; nor the mortgage foreclosure when Little Joe took his turn with the rifle because his father couldn't stay awake all the time to fend off the sheriff (who never arrived, however, because the bank had good farms coming out of its ears). It was certainly too the same madness that carried Little Joe over into helping Jonathan make a crop. They starved themselves by not selling the seed grain—planting a crop that there was no market for out of that identical madness, or maybe frenzy to work, or ornery habit, or perhaps the dark fear of thinking as the other farmers thought, knotting idle around Ferber's Grain and Storage and thinking. Harvested the crop and sold it to the government, something the thinking farmers had never thought of—never thought that some wild-eyed Biblical schemer in Washington would buy it to bury. And always Little Joe plunged right on figuring and running and investigating, and when he wasn't figuring and running and investigating—he was hiding.

Little Joe couldn't stand people. I remember one time clearly when we went to visit his family. Not that we ever had anything especially to say to our neighbors, but Father thought we should make something especially to say to them, that we should "contrive our piece of the world into something less of a wheated jungle." So on Sunday we went to see them and Joe was hiding. "He has been hiding ever since the dark night," Jonathan said. We all knew that he had been hiding before that. But that he had had particular reason to hide since the dark night was probably true. The "dark night" was the day we went underground, or the day Little Joe came out from underneath the rock.

We were all up in Charlie Peacock's tree house when we saw him come out from underneath the rock, but it wasn't until he passed close by us that we could tell it was Little Joe. "Where did you come from, Little Joe?" Gregory asked in a shout that is never so much a question with children as a challenge.

Little Joe swung his large head away from up at the tree and over to the rock as though checking certain that our point of vantage had not exposed his secret and that our question was only a challenge.

"Where did you come from, Little Joe?"

Little Joe took off into the swamp. We got down from the tree and followed him in. Little Joe had not taken off into the swamp in the manner of someone in flight but as though it were an old direction, a path to some other house or meeting-place of swamp-walkers, instead of a pathless ooze and suck, bayoneted with cattails and sword grass, circling without itself, endless because it began again without stopping after the river, which wasn't a river even here although it had channels that bled through the swamp with secret depths plumbed now by Gregory as he shot in head first and all the rest of us in after him except that we got tangled in razor brush and freed ourselves only in time to lift him out and set him on a bog. "There he goes," Gregory said, and following the turn of Gregory's head we saw through the reeds Little Joe's rear vanish down the hole he had come out of. When we got back to the hole Charlie Peacock went in first. Charlie Peacock came out again quick and said that it was so dark he couldn't see a damn thing and he wanted me to go in and then Eddie Markowitz and before they got to Gregory or Pete Nelson they said we shouldn't ought to go in without a light and before they got back to me again I said here goes the Crip and I went in.

It was much darker than Charlie Peacock said it was; that is, when you went in through a bush that hid the opening you made a quick double turn and even with that, without any doors or anything, you expected something more than absolute blackness. Then I saw a scratch of light, but surrounded by so much darkness I did not know for sure where I was, and yet it was already too late to turn back because after the first few steps I did not know which way was back and could only make towards the light that rose now and fell like some soft breathing flame, but it got all its quiet shock from the fact that every step in the now seeming floating world was a step that brought me that much nearer to Little Joe.

"Keep coming, Crip." It was Little Joe's voice, a low-pitched rasp.

"Okay, stop, Crip. You've gone far enough, Crip."

At once the light seemed to settle. It appeared to be about ten feet in front and then the face of Little Joe came into it.

"Maybe we've gone too far. That's what we've got to investigate. Be nonchalant, Crip."

Little Joe had other big words than nonchalant. He had fructify, vainglorious, persiflage, nonpareil, de trop and the Hanseatic League. He had more big words too, most of which he got from the commercials, but some he got from the Negro couple who were the cooks at the grange hall, Goldie and Gilmore; for example he had conjointly and copesetic.

"Are you here conjointly with others?" Little Joe's head cast no shadow nor did it appear to be attached to anything. It swayed in the light as though moved from above by strings that matched the darkness.

"I repeat, are you here conjointly with others? You'll have to answer that question."

"I'm conjointly here with others," I answered.

"You'll have to name names. Now whose idea was it to track me?"

A thumb and forefinger rose to the light and snuffed at it. Gasps of total darkness came and went.

"It wasn't nobody's idea," I said.

"I'll put that name down. Edward Markowitz."

"If you're going to put a name down put my name down."

"It doesn't make any difference. If you know him that makes you just as guilty."

There was a pause now, the light yellow, flickering Joe's mouth against his upper face.

"Do you think I'm being unfair?" he said.

"I think you're being nuts."

Little Joe moved the light so that it went over to the side of his face.

"We will have no more persiflage," he said, "or I will have to put out the light. I don't want any more redundancies and it's not me who's nuts. I never followed anybody down into a dark sewer."

"So it's a sewer, is it?"

"It's a kind of a sewer," Little Joe said. "But that's redundant. Will you or will you not answer the question before us?"

"I don't remember what the question is that is before us."

"Listen, my boy," Little Joe said finally, looking at me carefully now, "you don't have to remember the question because I am going to take care of you. Now come on over here and sit down."

I walked over beside the light and my knee touched something hard.

"Sit down there," Little Joe said.

I sat down on something cold.

"You wait," Little Joe said. "They'll be down and we'll find out what they're up to."

"I know what they're up to. They're not up to nothing."

"Wait till I get all the evidence and then make up your mind," Little Joe said. "You can know people all your life and not know what they're up to without knowing the evidence."

"Why do you want to know the evidence, Little Joe?"

"Because I want to have a lot of friends," Little Joe said. "And these people don't like me."

We stared out, both of us, through the yellow light that I could see now was a candle. The place had a smell like the kind of a smell you get when you put a fire out suddenly with water, more of a stench than a smell, and sharp.

"Are you going to make friends by giving the tree house boys a bad time, Little Joe?"

"They don't like me," Little Joe said. His words echoed back off some hard invisible wall.

"Why don't the boys in the tree house like you, Little Joe?"

"Well, for one thing—" Little Joe hesitated, his boy face suddenly aged and yellow in the unfair light. "For one thing I guess it's because I don't believe in known sayings."

"Well, I don't necessarily believe in known sayings myself," I said.

"Just name me one known saying you don't believe in," Little Joe said, confident.

I thought a while, even putting my hands against my head and thinking, but I couldn't think of one that wasn't perfect. I thought some more, testing many of them, but I couldn't find a hole in a single one of them. Then I even got to thinking about So Is Your Old Man and Yes We Have No Bananas which were almost known sayings at that time, and then I got to thinking what I was doing thinking at all when I didn't even know where I was except underground some place, and I got scared.

"See, you believe in all the known sayings," Little Joe said, touching me kind of clammy, and I must have moved.

"For example what known sayings don't you believe in?" I said suddenly, I guess to keep him from touching me.

"I hate them all," Little Joe said.

"For example," I said, as though saying something would keep him away, "do you hate Sink Or Swim, Paddle Your Own Canoe, Do Or Die, Survive Or Perish, Tom The Bootblack, Phil The Fiddler, From Canal Boy To President?"

"They're not known sayings," Little Joe said, patient again. "But I will tell you I hate them anyway— Hold it. I think the others are coming and I want you to do as you said you would."

"What did I say I would?"

"We must be very quiet," Little Joe said, hushed and over-gentle.

They had evidently decided to come down all at once. You could hear them fumbling in the darkness. If not encouraged by leadership or sense of direction they shared a togetherness of ignorance, groping toward the yellow spume of light in the perfect blackness, seeming, as it had seemed to me, to be set against nothing and coming from nowhere; this joined now by the stench of the cave, sour and acrid, permeating and finally by the voice of Little Joe.

"Which one is Paris France?"

They semed not only to stop out there in the darkness but to bunch up like a herd of cows caught breaking into a corn field, their leader, or the one most in advance, or the one nearest the hired hand, belted by a pitchfork across the nose, the rest not retreating, quiet, puzzled, their legs and eyes abruptly frozen in movement, their bodies hanging awkward—like sometimes when a moving picture stops and you think the cameraman is going to run the film backwards.

"I repeat, which one is Paris France?"

"I guess that's me."

Little Joe shook his head, shadowless in the pallid light, amused and tolerant and still patient.

"You guess that's you. Don't you know? Do you use other names? What are they?"

"John Joplin."

"And what is your real name?"

"I guess John Joplin is my real name."

"Why do you use the foreign name of Paris France?"

"Because the kids started calling me that."

"Why did they start calling you that?"

"I guess because when we were standing around saying what we wanted to be when we grew up someone wanted to be a fireman and I wanted to go to Paris France."

"Why did you want to go to Paris France?"

"Because I had a fight with my mother."

"And do you expect us to believe that? Why, you must think we're vapid. Why did you have a fight with your mother?"

"Because she told me never to see you again. She said you were a creep and I said maybe you were a creep but I—"

"But you admit you had a fight with your mother?"

"Yes."

"Well, I don't think we have much respect for this witness. You may step back. Now will an Edward Markowitz step forward and be sure you don't slip in the four-hundred-foot hole. Now, Edward Markowitz, a man sitting here alongside of me who used to be one of you has made what you'd call a kind of statement. In this statement he named names and he named you. He said that you—"

"Wait a minute," I said. "Wait a minute. I nev—"

"That hole," Little Joe whispered over to me huskily. "That four-hundred-foot hole I was talking about ain't alongside them. It's right alongside you. I'd advise—"

"Wait a minute," I said, and looked out into the darkness where the others must be. "This four-hundred-foot hole he's been talking about, now he says it's over by me. He's just threatening us. I don't think it exists."

There was a mutter of voices from the invisible group and I felt encouraged. Then Little Joe said in Little Joe's voice, "If it doesn't exist then all of you take one step forward."

No one took the step forward, least of all me.

"Very well," Little Joe said. "Now that we have established the bravery I will tell you how smart you are. There may be four-hundred-foot holes four hundred feet deep. They may be here, they may be there. I don't know. I only know there is a certain way out where there are no holes and if you go along with me I will lead you to the light.

Now if you would all repeat after me what I say, I would appreciate it very much. Little Joe is the Leader."

It seemed only two people repeated it after him—Pete Nelson was one, maybe Charlie Peacock, I wasn't sure or interested.

"Now, you can all do better than that," Little Joe said, friendly and very patient. "Now, if we try it again and get it right maybe we can get it over with and we won't have to spend our life down here. Now once again—Little Joe is the Leader."

"Little Joe is the Leader," they all said.

"I notice you didn't say it," Little Joe said, turning his head, the pale light yellow and faltering, catching only the highlights so that his face seemed an image thrown against nothing by a magic lantern using negatives.

I didn't answer anything and Little Joe went on without changing tone: "You're a very brave boy, still that's why you're on my team."

I still couldn't say anything.

"You were brave enough to inform on an Edward Markowitz."

"I didn't squeal on Eddie," I said. "And I'm not on your team."

"Then you would rather, be at the bottom of a four-hundred-foot hole. Okay, if that is the way you choose to want it."

The yellow candle moved toward me followed by the face that was more a mask (not the gaudy kind you buy at the five-and-dime for Hallowe'en but colorless, self-made), that wavered and then came on again toward me.

"Don't push the Crip."

The face stopped and turned with the candle toward the invisible speaker. It was Eddie.

"Maybe I didn't hear you rightly," Little Joe said carefully into the darkness toward the voice. "But if I understood your meaning you want to wind up at the bottom of that hole yourself."

"I just said don't push a crip."

The yellow light was slowly put down again.

"Let me get this clear," Little Joe said with the old patience. "Did you get that out of a book? It's important to know where you got it. Not pushing a crip could be a good thing in most every instance. Now just let me know where you got it."

"None of your business," Eddie said.

"Oh," Little Joe said, pleased, the mask coming into a smile but the ends of the mouth still not turning up. "Oh, in that case I'm afraid I'll have to ask you to take one step forward." The voice was dead again and tired.

"I'm not taking any step anyplace."

"Very well, then. If you don't want to help the Crip, if you won't cooperate, then we'll have to finish this business."

The light and face came toward me and then almost at once there was a massed movement in the darkness. Little Joe stopped. "The four-hundred-foot hole," he said toward them, but the movement continued, gaining confidence now; and then almost gently in the weak light at the edge of the darkness the faces began to gather close to Little Joe.

"Very well," Little Joe said, threatened, without any movement of the face at all. "If that's the way you have to have it, if you think you can escape this darkness yourselves, if you don't think you need a light to show you the way, if you people think you can make it alone when it is only me who understands the darkness, all right then, let us see what you won't see."

Then Little Joe made a heavy pass with his bear-like arm toward the weak light and everything went black. You could sense now only the great underground stench and the solid silence that tensed us all.

"Yes. Maybe you don't need me at all to get out of the darkness. Maybe prayer will do it." The voice was confident and smooth now in the blackness. It had even lost its straining patience as though in pitting himself against God he would forego all that; as though he could perform finally within a situation where the two of them were equal. "You can pray or take a vote."

"You think maybe he has gone nuts?" It was the voice of Pete Nelson, low and intimate.

"No, it's Little Joe's own normal self," Paris France said.

"Anyway," and I think this was the voice of Gregory now, "I think maybe taking a vote is a good idea. We got to try finding our way out of here without getting killed and I think we should find out who is going to be the leader. If we don't have a leader some of us are bound never to get out of here."

"All right," I said, wanting to get moving. "When I call out your names you tell me who you want to be leader and Eddie will keep count."

"Before you vote," Little Joe's voice commanded from nowhere, "I want to warn you that no one knows how to get out of here except me. You followed me down and now your only chance to be saved is to stick with me."

"All right," I said. "No more speeches. Let's get the vote over with. Charlie Peacock, how do you vote?"

"I guess I vote for Little Joe. He's the only one who seems to know his way around down here."

And so did all the others, including, when it came my turn, myself. I guess we all reckoned there was no alternative now that we had played his game and gotten ourselves down here.

"All right," Little Joe said. "But if I am going to accept this candidature or whatever, I have got to have some concommitments as to what you people have been up to."

"I hope that's not a sequitur," Paris France said, topping Little Joe's word.

"It's a question," Little Joe said. "And I want an answer yes or no."

"But how can I give the answer if I don't know the question?"

"It's easy," Little Joe said. "Just say what I tell you to. Now try this: Little Joe is—"

But that was the end of his first empire. While Little Joe was being carried away by the sound of his own election Charlie Peacock had figured where the voice was coming from and snuck around in back of him and was twisting his arm up as though to break it if Little Joe didn't quit.

Little Joe quit and he led us out, in his pain, up to the real light. We sat Little Joe down in the middle of us beneath the tree house to have a careful look at him.

"I won the election fair and square," Little Joe said. "You didn't play it fair."

Little Joe lay curled up in front of us like some cornered thing, fearing to move as though movement might set off some chain of something which he was now unable to stop.

"Like something that crawls out alive, white, when you turn over a rotten log," Gregory said, reaching forward to touch Little Joe with his foot.

"Okay, okay, okay," Little Joe said. "But you never gave me a chance."

"What do you mean we never gave you a chance?" Eddie said.

"Never gave me a chance to help with the tree house or nothing."

"Maybe he's got a point," Paris France said. "You can't tell, maybe he's got a point."

"I don't think he ever had a point," Gregory said. "But we'll go up in the tree house and take a vote."

We were always going up in the tree house to vote on something. I don't think there was anything we didn't vote on in the tree house. We voted on who was going to carry the secrets down; we voted where to bury the old treasure and where to dig for the new, the rules for cheating at marbles and who was the shortest and the tallest and the fattest and the most likely to succeed in cutting off all his own hair.

"Me first," Little Joe said, unwinding and waddling over to the ladder.

"No, you last," Gregory said, pushing him to one side. Gregory went up first, then Eddie, then Paris France, Charlie Peacock, and me last, not because it was my position in the pecking order but because I had to pull the right leg after me, which made me slow. I got ready to go up, and Gregory hollered from way atop the tree, "Wait a minute—you make Little Joe come up first."

"He says you promised him he could go up last," I hollered back up.

"I changed my mind," Gregory's voice rang around the forest.

"He says that your decision—" I called and then paused to confer with Little Joe on one of his words. "He says your decision is arbitrary and should be put to a vote of the others."

There was a silence from above and Little Joe hollered up, "Hear this before you vote—you still don't know your way around down there. If you don't stick to your promise that you promised me maybe you never will."

The dead silence continued from way up in the tree. I looked up. The great pine, stripped of its branches and plumed with the thatched roof of the house, appeared palmlike, tropical, a stalk, naked and queer in the dark north.

"Okay," Gregory shouted down at last. "How do you vote?"

"I think I vote to put him on his honor and let him go last."

"Okay, that does it," Gregory shouted. "You better come up."

I started crawling up the pine-barked and poplar-runged ladder, making it slowly and pulling the bad leg after me. At the top the ladder began to vibrate and then thump, and if Paris France had not reached down and grabbed me I would have gone spinning down with the ladder.

Little Joe ran and jumped until it crashed, then he waddled back and solemnly, down to the last recognizable rung, destroyed our freedom with a great rock that seemed, as he lifted it over his antic body, larger than he was.

"Little Joe!" Charlie Peacock called, and then he called again, "Little Joe!"—each time the cry becoming more feeble because Little Joe had already gone, disappeared below again with all our secrets and treasures and maybe even rules and certainly all that we had that passed for confidence in our fellow Indians.

We all stood there teetering on the edge of our stalk-borne house raft in the now sunless sky almost one hundreed feet above the soft black floor of the forest. We had carefully sheared off the branches so that the stumps would give no purchase to our enemies—the Moors and the Saracens, the Sioux, Blackfeet, and Crow.

We sailed on in the sky, seeming to have actual movement now, as though the sun westering not only brought the rawness of the night but also had left us without stability; cut off from the earth, we joined the movement of the beginning stars. As it grew darker, we shouted for a time, our voices skimming across the trees which with the blackness beneath us now seemed part of our new ocean, their big dark tops emerging and rolling softly like our raft.

At about midnight there was the noise of rough father voices beneath us, then the grunting and swearing of ladders being erected. We were informed that Little Joe had saved us, that we had invaded his tunnel and tried to force him into our house, but that in spite of this he had saved us. And four days later, which in our child's world could be four years, he still insisted he would save us again if the opportunity presented itself—and again and again and again. He would go on saving us, he said carefully across the desk-topped classroom silence to Charlie Peacock, until we were all dead.

EDWARD DORN

C. B. & Q.

In the early morning the sun whipped against the plate glass of Tiny's restaurant, reflecting the opposite side of the narrow dusty street where the printer's shop, the saloon, another restaurant waved in the quiet morning, in the distorted glass. This was Tiny's place. He was called Tiny for the usual reason. About 6:30 every morning the place was full of construction workers, and an occasional rancher who had been stranded in town the night before. At night, in front, until 8:00, were several railroad section men, with the exception of Sunday night, talking about Denver or Kansas City, or talking in cruel tones about John C. Blain the concessionaire who handled all the meals for the Burlington railroad. But most of the section men, the gandies, stayed close to their bunk cars, in a park of rough square shape and next to the tall thin grain elevator that could be seen for several miles coming from the east, from Belle Fourche, or from the west.

Back of the restaurant the half desert began. Immediately. There was a banged up incinerator fifty feet out, in the desert of short pieces of barbed wire and rusted tins. Beyond wasn't a desert, exactly. Sheep, and probably some cattle, grazed there, over on and on past the layers of soft hills. A map shows the open range to extend far into Montana.

On past Tiny's restaurant, past the hardware store and a vacant lot with an old ford grown in the rear of it, was the New Morecroft Hotel. Buck stayed there. He had new scars right under his lower lip and over farther down on his left jaw after he had washed with strong hotel soap, more bright scars stood red and looked quite becoming. He had been three days so far without paying so that Simms the thin

44

owner shifted his feet on the linoleum floor when Buck returned to
his room in the evening. Outside the low ceilinged lobby, on the front
porch, it was quitting time for the construction workers and they hung
around while their foreman took the days' count of everyone's hours
into the small office thrown up with new rough lumber next to the
hotel. It was the last building in the block and beyond it was a vacant
lot and beyond that were the bunk cars of the gandy crews on a siding
leading off to the grain elevator. To the left across the road, the gandy
crews stood in bunches or stretched out resting on the lawn. The
length of the dirt street was in shade by 5:15.

Soon after, the rain fell slowly into the street and raised quick
pockets of dust. Simms lifted his sharp elbow from the glass show
counter where he kept odds and ends, a 1952 calendar, a mail-order
catalogue, a dusty carton of aspirins, and moved to the front window
where he propped a foot on the ledge and stared with his cheek on his
hand at the increasing wind in the poplars outside and the rain that
was now hard. The park was empty and the rain drove the small border
of willow trees toward the ground. Buck came to the window all washed
up and said that them gandies could sure move when they wanted to.

Outside town, off the highway to Gillette, about four miles to the
right was a considerable mound of gravel. Except for a layer of sandy
dirt a foot or so thick on the top, the gravel below was of a varying
grade. A fleet of ford dump trucks were lined up near the contractor's
shanty and the rain spread roots of light yellow clay over the hoods
and down from the cabin tops onto the windshields. The yellow caterpillar sitting in the mouth of the pit threw steam jets up from its hot
radiator and from the tin can covering its vertical exhaust pipe. Reed,
the contractor, was frying some eggs for his supper, and he sometimes
glanced out his window to the river curving around the base of the
gravel hill where two of his workers, from South Dakota, had a trailer
hidden in the willows. The smoke from their camp stove stayed close
to the ground this evening. This was almost the end of the contract.
The gravel stockpile out by the highway across the rolling range was
lengthening day by day and the regular peaks made by the dumps were
growing dark and shiny in the rain. Virgil Reed would pass the stockpile as he turned onto the highway to town and see he would have to
hire another driver if he wanted to finish the job before the end of
June.

2

Buck would not go near the post office. And he always waited around for some time before he asked Simms if he had any mail that day. A letter from the gang at Papy's tavern in Wichita came yesterday but it only mentioned his wife and kid in Mississippi and nothing about the accident. When the car crashed at the red light intersection in Wichita Buck threw out of the car and was in K.C. the next morning. He got drunk that day and saw lots of old acquaintances who worked with him in Nebraska and others he didn't know but who knew those he did, from Denver to Omaha. It was hot that day in Daddy's tavern in Kansas City. The three piece band smiled as they sat sweating on the little band box between the two toilet doors. The heavily built man with the curly hair stood on his crutches by Buck's stool and bent his neck to hear the talk about the guitar and drum. Max was one half Cherokee and Buck thought he had known Max. Max was sure. And when Buck found out Max had nine dollars and a ride to Wyoming on the Burlington that afternoon at 4:00 he went across the street to the gandy hiring hall and hired in too. When he got back to Daddy's Max was in with a tiny old woman who had already got three dollars away from Max. Buck sat brooding in the booth under the band box and once in a while glared at Max. He snapped hard language across to the bar and asked Max if he was indian. Max weaved slowly and smiled at the little woman who pulled on his flannel shirt. He smiled into the crowd and said he was indian from way back and old Buck was going with him anytime now to Wyoming. At the last minute Buck jerked away from old Sheila and had a cab on the curb outside Daddy's.

Max sat upright and stared all night, across the aisle from Buck, out the window. The train drove through the darkness up the Kansas line to Nebraska. In the station at Kansas City they had only given their names to the man at the gate with a list. In the car there were no white tabs on the windowshades by their seats. They rode free to the job in Wyoming. At Grand Island, Nebraska Max got off the train and went into a restaurant back of the depot. He thought he might go back to Daddy's. Sheila was there every day he bet. Since coming from Illinois with the man who took dogs to a hospital there, he hadn't been with a woman. In the still waiting car Buck opened his eyes. He blinked when he felt his swollen lips were tighter this morning than they had been since the accident. He licked them and wandered through the car and down the steps to the platform to look for Max. Max must have five dollars left, unless he buys too much to eat. Buck found him in the restaurant with some of the other travelers to Wyoming. Buck ordered a cup of coffee and said to Max that they might not have to gandy if there was other work there, maybe on a ranch or road work. Max thought if he didn't like the setup, the looks of things when they got there he might shove on to Oregon, he had an uncle who was a foreman in a mill at Klamuth. They came back through the depot just as the train moved off toward the border.

It was unusual to arrive on Friday afternoon because there was no work Saturday or Sunday. Buck swung up into the dining car and took the last seat for dinner, away from Max who was avoiding his eyes now that he had determined to go back to Daddy's to drink beer with old Sheila. And late in the evening Max blinded the first passenger back east. It was on Monday morning that Buck decided he wouldn't work on the section. He ate their cold fried potatoes for two days.

3

Virgil Reed came along the pavement into town, through the increasing waves of rain, between the ditches on either side and broken weeds and long grass that had been earlier in the spring burned by the hot winds pouring in from the south-east. He had shaved after finishing his supper and there were still wet nicks on his neck below his chin and he dabbed them with his handkerchief from time to time. He knew that his new catskinner was a man that would work, he knew how to push the gravel. With Boyd the matter was simple: if you are a small man, you have to use your hands and feet to move. All day on the dusty cat he had crammed the accelerator to the floor and ground into the earth, with his visor cap pulled down tight on his forehead he had ground the blade into the earth, let it up and down quickly and infuriated the truck drivers by spilling over onto their road under the gravel loader. With the engine roaring all around the small hills that surrounded the pit, the shattering engine in command of all the air and Boyd was in command of the engine, back and forth across the opening to the pit he pressed the large, dirty, yellow caterpillar and acknowledged no one's presence until the end of the day, when soon after the rain started on the hot metal covering the engine, he told Reed about the defective left brake. Reed said he would see to it.

Now Reed rounded the corner into the town, past the tight groups of willows, past the deserted filling station, went the length of the street and stopped in front of the New Morecroft Hotel. Through the glass he could see Buck standing with Simms. Buck suddenly faced Simms with his hands out of his pockets and nodding several times said some words and turned to go. Out on the porch Reed met him and they started back down the street toward Pages' saloon.

In Pages' Boyd was at the bar. It was nearly dark outside. The rain along the muddy street had slackened to a fine quiet regularity. The rain was quieter throughout the whole town. Up on the hill outside town on the highway to the east, in the filling station-grocery store where Buck was running up a small grocery bill, and saving credit stamps against a large red ornamental lamp with a white meandering shade for his mama, and beyond that, was a small opening in the grainy clouds, weak light from the sun as it went down in the north-west in back of the hill.

In the bar Boyd sat by himself away from the general noise center-ing in the last booth on the wall opposite the bar toward the back of the saloon. Some road construction workers heavily persuaded each other that the wage was bigger in North Dakota or at the white horse dam job in Montana and that you could work endless hours but it was dangerous. The big fellow with the wrinkled forehead had skinned a cat on a high bluff where the push was so inclined that you had to be quick to save the rig and yourself from going over at the last minute. Boyd listened to their tales and jerked his head as he finished his beer and looked their way with his short curled smile. Through the room of noise he shouted to the heavy-stomached man with the wrinkled forehead that he could drive any earth mover made, and that he didn't need to think that since he was such a big bastard he could talk so smart. But Curly didn't hear him then because one of the others in the booth had started to tell of a job the summer before near Butte.

Buck and Reed came through the door and took stools next to Boyd. Boyd relayed their orders down the varnished bar to the bartender, and Reed went on about the job out at the pit, how he was thinking of moving his equipment to Cheyenne as soon as this country job was done.

Through the open door Buck could see several men he recognized from some other summers and he thought again of how he could get

his mail without a direct address. They were sure to be on his trail.
Boyd asked Reed if the job down at Cheyenne would be a big one and
Reed didn't answer so Boyd turned his head away from Reed and
Buck and looked at the group in the rear booth where there was now
an argument between the large frowning man with wrinkles in his
forehead and another road worker, thinner and tall, who said that he
could cut as fine a grade with a scraper and cat as the big frowner
could with a patrol grader. The frowning man's answer to this was
to take his opponent by the khaki shirt and lift him quickly on top
of the table spilling several glasses of beer. The noise was overflowing,
even out on the street the knots of workers knew. Back of the bar
under the long slender tubes of green vapor two hula-girl lamps wiggled
their rubber bottoms and the bartender was debating his duty. Boyd
slid off his stool and took it with him as he made across the floor to
the battle. He had cracked it on the large man's back twice before it was
thrust back into his middle at the end of the third swing.

Outside on the bumper of the car with his face bleeding Boyd
wiped his small hands on his pants' legs smearing the blood in long
stripes and crying. He sobbed in jerks as he tried to clean out between
his sticky fingers. He told Buck that he always wanted to be a mason
anyway, that that was a real trade, you didn't have to worry about jobs
and the right kind of money once you made it. But they wouldn't let
him train for it when he got out and there were always so many on the
waiting list for apprentice that he couldn't see it. Buck said that he
had a good job down in Wichita but the goddamn foreman had it in
for him because he broke three springs on the truck in one day on that
bad road and he got fired. Boyd had calmed down and said that he
intended to go south for the winter, maybe to Tucson or Albuquerque
but he was sure as hell going to be south when the winter hit this
place. And he didn't see what Buck saw in Wichita. He could go anywhere anyway because he had a car that the back seat came out of and
could be used to sleep in he said.

1st AVENUE

It is about noon. Bill Elephant sits behind the wheel of the black panel truck jabbering about Alaska and fish traps, Kodiac bears, and the thinning population of Koniags amidst whose dwindling little villages sit colorful Russian Orthodox churches, the last remnant of the dreamy murders starting with the curiosity of Vitus Behring. We wait for a red light. Looking through the rain, the soft misting air, for a place to park. And then later the walk down Occidental Street. Bill is a Totemist. His mother was Klikitat. His father was Russian. He says he gets the Totemism from his mother, but I suspect he read about it in Wagnalls encyclopedia. He is a large man with a trunk of a nose. Rather small but not mean, eyes. Interested eyes.

The rain comes down softly. A soaking thing. There are colors to be seen through it, blue houses, brown office buildings standing like dumb machines along the zealously laid out streets. It is said they washed the steepness of the hills of Seattle away with pressure hoses, they drove the summits right off into Elliott Bay, such a placer mine is civic interest. Civic power, like that inimitable pimp Mercer returning east to pick up the brides those stalwart greedy men forgot in the rush to get here. When the hills were made normal the traffic started, no longer baffled. The rain would never have achieved this. The rain would never have denuded the hills, not this soft eternal rain. The city rain is quite different from the country rain and the difference doesn't all lie in where it falls. Along the wide streets that disclose their exact period, a period different than issued from the progressive brain that devised Camberra, or than was slipped from under the lid of the pompous idle brainbox that contained the boulevard of Buenos Aires, no these middling width streets of Seattle, neither narrow nor not narrow, came from under the thriving lids of merchants who would abide no width but the exact one suited for their commerce. The major streets are named for early merchants. Mercer, Yestler, etc. This is an order born of commerce, dry goods, the streets are now crowded with the feet of consumptive buyers in whose hands the grimy change of their cold northern lives is transferred in bags. An oversized

carrot, a massive cabbage, a grotesque squash, milk crackers. The
oversize cabbage & carrot comes from that lingering light and cease-
less rain which filters down from the northern curve. And the latter-day
wise men with a touch of Midas in their eyes know now that it is
Food you must turn everything to. EAT!

The truck shot forward across 1st. Avenue to the Pike Street
Market. Through the rain, moving slowly down the plate glass shine
of the store fronts, one can see the people of this world moving on
their way to and from carrying the inevitable shopping bags. The
old ones carry umbrellas. The old men have broad, flowered, disrep-
utable ties around their necks. In the plate glass reflected world are
the brisker types in blue suits standing in the entrances of shoe stores
and jewelry stores, ultimately, but they don't know it, in the hands of
all these people with so little money each, but collectively what is
referred to as a consumer power. Something, each man in flimsy slacks
is saying, will have to be done about it. But probably nothing can be
done about it. With each new man born, a jewelry store is born for
him. The terrible leveling of Malthus plods on, on this frontier which
no longer is a frontier. A dead atmosphere. Ahead, and in back, there
are no butterflies all at once swimming into view, large and black-
oranged fringed, like a weightless tiger, the great lightness, the delicacy,
the great possibility lighting here and there.

The pigeons scatter away from us as we walk along and Bill Elephant says, "First thing we'll do is check a shoe shop I know about
under the market."

All the time Bill was jabbering on, swinging his big frame upstairs
and down, pointing out people he had seen in lumber camps from
the California coast to Alaska, to those he knew to be fishermen, or
cannery workers, calling one the Bear, another a flounder because he
had one eye and was thin, pointing out the manner in which the
one-eyed flounder kept his eye down close to the botton, eyeing the
vegetables—"Yah, look at that Flounder, he's swimming along the
concrete there eyein' that swiss chard, dropping those tomatoes in
his bag, see that. He was in Florence when I had my big accident, son
of a bitch he damn near killed me, that was just after I got your card,
Mora was staying in an apartment in Florence, well, Christ when she
got out there I was layin under some blankets by the spar tree, they
had to peel the clothes off me with a razor blade, I was soaked up

with blood, I looked like a mashed beet. The godamn Flounder there, he was runnin' the donkey. Said he'd run one for years in Canada but the son of a bitch never had. He didn't know how to stop the fucking drum so he run me right up through the bull block."

"What happened," I asked.

"What happened! You crazy bastard, the bull block, the whole riggin' an me came down through the buckle guys onto the ground! 110 feet, that's all that happened. I was lucky I didn't get the whole works planted in my ass. Let's go down here. I don't want to see that prick . . ."

We turned down the steps onto a lower level of the complicated lower market. Spice shops sent their smells floating in streams down there. Into Italian groceries with buckets of strips of brittle lasagne macaroni, nets of spaghetti drying on hooks, a little underground far away mediterranean world with the bright sunshine bare bulb throwing its famous rays over the head of the famous smiling Italian shopkeeper. Gallons of olive oil. And here Bill stopped and opened a door. We went into a small shop. Back of a long red machine with several spinning wheels a bald-headed man was holding a shoe to one of the wheels. Without looking up he told Bill he could look over the cork boots. There didn't seem to be any worth what the shoemaker wanted for them and it appeared he wasn't the kind to bargain. Then on we walked through rug stalls up and down ramps and stairs poking our heads in Good Wills and Saint Vincent de Pauls, Bill pushing his hat farther and farther back on his head—"Hell, there's nothing here, let's go up and get a drink before we go down to Occidental." And then walking stiff legged and fast in front of me up to the street level and the vegetable stalls.

When we came out into the air from the brighter artificial light below I glanced over the toothpick wooden rails of the complex ramps that lead down over the whole market to the waterfront. In a narrow frame between brick buildings, dotted with the dead windows of rooms, I saw the docks, the great listless ships tied up and all around derricks and lines. Bright yellow and shiny black the vague strip of white, unreadable, near the bow, where the name . . . . . huge ships. Back of the sheds and wharves and ships the bay and beyond so dimly the faint strip of land, South Seattle. Less than a second look then we had turned into the boisterous sidewalk. Seattle is an inland town.

No indication you're in a port until you see the docks. Dry goods. The atmosphere is inland, not salt, the men you see look like workers not sailors. Scandinavians, when they are short and squat, as many are in the northwest, look like the Filipino, who is everywhere short and squat. Their headpieces distinguish them. Filipinos wear Hood hats. Swedes wear caps.

The air was still. Lifeless and grey, but the colors were vivid in this subdued wet light. We saw the rough, startling red horse meat as we walked on. An old woman was opening her snap purse to get a quarter out for a pound of ground horse meat "Wild Horses of the Montana Rockies" in big letters, "We use only," smaller, above. But the air and the light were so dim that day. The inside of an unknown shut-in hotel room, the ripped lace curtains fluttering slowly from the air passing under the window opened just 3 inches.

We went into a Salvation Army store on the way to the great battery of taverns that stand on 1st. Avenue above the market. A long room with a raised level and a door at the other end. You could pass right through and out onto the next steep street. I stopped to look at the books while Bill was turning over great piles of wool underwear. "You'll need these, boy. The rain is cold as hell sometimes even in the summer. But no matter how cold it gets, as long as you have wool next to your skin you won't get chill or pneumonia." I looked at the mystery books dumped in boxes, saw the dresses ripped open at white thigh and horrified faces of blondes covering their cherry red mouths with their perfect hands. And then on the shelf at the travels of George Stoddard. Who is Stoddard? I have seen him many times. His travels were very wide. How did this Egyptian come to turn up so constantly on the shelves of the poor and less organized wanderers. In every Salvation Army. Every Good Will, every St. Vincent de Paul. All of the volumes are never there.

On through the rear door in to the Saturday noon, with a bundle of wool underwear. Bill was looking for certain men he knew to ask how the catches were this year. The first boats had returned from Alaska yesterday and he was always very interested in what was happening. Of course he recognized everyone. My head swam with his recognition. The reeling of totems and the names or names and their totems. Charlie, the sea horse was standing at the bar grinning. But he was never out on the boats anymore so Bill simply slugged him in

the arm and said, "Hows it going you old horse, seen Dick the seal?"
Yes, he had, down the street at the Ketchikan Saloon, he was drunk,
had fallen under a booth and was probably being stepped on, puked
on, spat on by now and the 3 thousand dollars he had in his pocket
this morning was closer to 3 dollars now. "Hell, *he* won't know anything," Bill answered.

In the Ketchikan Saloon we sat drinking beer. Bill jabbed me in
the ribs with his thumb, jerking his head toward the opposite wall.
I couldn't see anything at first, in the dark, my eyes had been on the
mirror back of the bar, the bright spot in the room. Gradually forms
began to grow and I saw booths lining the wall. "See that down there?
That's the seal." I strained my eyes and saw a man staring out from
under the booth. He looked dead or in a coma. "Ya, that's Dick," Bill
said. Then shouted, "Hey Dick, how's it going?"

The fat brown seal struggled out from under the booth in his
brand new clothes now covered with the whole wrack of the city, and
flapped slowly over to us and stood weaving, squinting at Bill then at
me, forming words on his mouth, raising his eyebrow, smiling, then
cumbersomely and gigantically frowning, all the time trying to focus
on something, finally he said, "Heh heh, look 'ere." There was silence
for three minutes. Finally Bill said, "Aw shit." Then, "What happened
to your three thousand?" The seal gestured up in the air with his hand
then began screwing up his mouth as though all the necessary words
were actually coming out and I suppose if one had that fine an ear,
they were, the travels were so mute in this human being the length
was probably the same as a Stoddard Lecture, but the muteness, so
vast, the world became a crazy abbreviation on his lips. At last he
came out with "Well . . . . ." then subsided into a weave forward and
back, catching himself. We were suddenly aboard a ship. Gesturing
now out from his side as though his hands held rigging. "Oh," . . .
something about this morning and getting off the boat. "Hey Bill,
could you let me have a quarter." Bill looked at me and said, "This
bastard had 3 thousand this morning. It usually lasts longer. Maybe
a week. Some of 'em even have a few bucks left after three weeks.
This guy's either fast as hell or he got rolled."

Where shall we go now? Bill would stay here all day. The beer
tastes very good. Tastes a little skunky though. Can't tell whether it
is the detergent they use on the glasses or maybe it's the temperature.

Not quite cold enough. More likely they dumped something awful in it in Olympia.

The seal stepped back a few feet and began railing at the customers coming and going. He suddenly produced a hat, like a magician, and put it on his head. Now his face was shadowed and the shadows gave the face a new relief. Who knows what he said but he was full of comment. Would rush to the door and shout at the prowl car driving off from the curb. Two cops with a young man between them in the front seat, the man staring straight ahead down the length of 1st. Avenue. He would shout and gesture, full of emotion. But who knows what he said? The ambulance going by would quiet him and he would speak softly, go all the way out onto the sidewalk waving his hand gently in the air. The next moment his short fingers would retch themselves into a fist and he would pound the bar like a judge, then the barkeeper in his torpor would blink silently at him. For perhaps the 500th time. Now he miraculously had a coat under his arm and his clothes generally seemed not new anymore but much older. All in these past few minutes. Back again he would go to the sidewalk just outside the door, shouting, then muffling his voice into a deep deep commentary, staring through brick walls into the eyes of people beyond, nodding his head, jerking it back. Then his lips would move giving forth no sound at all. And then he would stare. With his hands in his pockets. Finally, and quietly, I saw him walking off, as we took ourselves out into the light, down toward the leveling out of 1st. Avenue. I waved to him but he didn't wave back, only looked. I was of the compound of general image. Part of the brick cornices, electric buses. A strange inward feeling, I knew I was in that instant enclosed in this compound by this man's undistinguishing stare. He didn't wave back to me. He was a careful man, and never waved to delivery trucks, hotel signs, or brick walls.

Bill stood scratching his head wondering whether or not we should go up to his apartment to see how Mora was doing, before going on down to Occidental. It was mid-afternoon and the old dungeon shops kept by ogreish women into whose hands all the gear of the indian and eskimo loggers, and some of the less resolute swedes (as a rule the swedes are resolute) ultimately filtered, those dark shops would close soon on the boots and hats, pants and shirts and black bear underwear.

The sky was clearing in spots. There were still great blotches of clouds but the sun came through every once in a while and the rain had stopped. We decided to walk. It was about fifteen blocks to Occidental. But down hill so that we walked swiftly stopping only when something irresistible was seen in a hock shop window. Of course what Bill saw was different than what I saw so that there was a constant lagging and overtaking as we walked along. It was like a race. First he would be left behind looking momentarily at some object in a window, canned heat, a whole unbroken case 24 large cans, to be used on a trip into the mountains after uranium, Bill's dream. Then I was far ahead down the block where I would see a huge pair of binoculars, and stop for a long drawnout interval gauging the impossible price then Bill would pass me saying we had better hurry on, only to stop himself again at a surplus store sometimes even going inside where I would follow still thinking of the binoculars. The possibility of seeing all that distance. The idea of having them around your neck, and at any moment putting those mastodon eyes UP to your own smaller eyes copping distances unheard of. Bringing into creation objects not even there. A little act of anti-christ, creating a new world from this machine hanging around your neck.

And then inside the sprawling surplus store: a Hudson's Bay trading post, blankets stacked to the ceiling that made you shiver thinking of the cold they would ward off, the blizzards you would ward off inside those tents. All a fabulous playing. Only equipped like no child ever was. The whole world of exploration where the object was not discovery but living in and playing with the great brutal elements of earth. It could kill you. Equipment. Primas stoves of every size. Small cylinder stoves made by careful Swedes, small enough to hold in the hand. To keep a tentful of men warm even on the Spitzenburgs, such as Andree, the Polar Balloonist probably killed himself and his friends with, in a tent. The shelves of anti-mosquito oil, with the fragrance of eucalyptus. And the beds that fold out half size from nothing. Bill was talking to the short fat dark haired man with a mustache and gold chain on his pants who ran it all. Standing with legs apart and hands on his hip he was inquiring of the man the price of a great water keg with a spigot. One will need water high up in the mountains, or out on the desert. I was looking at an elaborate pilot's suit with tabs up and down the legs, a fur collar, sheepskin lining, when I noticed Bill was ready to go again.

Approximately seven blocks below the entrance to the Pike Street Market, 1st. Avenue levels out. When we walked out of the store we were walking along the level stretches. For a while now we were out of the territory of binoculars and blankets. Suddenly masses of people down here, the masses of legs, we were coming onto a writhing centi-pede, each jointed segment a pair of legs. Now there were night clubs and bars. But we didn't stop for blocks. Just looked hurriedly through the door in passing at pin-ball machines and penny arcades where the brooding race horse machines and hockey machines clicked peace-fully, patiently withstanding the malicious banging fists of small men in large hats wearing black shoes and pants. And occasionally far back in the dark interior, behind curtains, awfully dark and back, the vague misty outline of a hunched man his forehead against a box, in which parading for the benefit of the great longitudinal movements in his thigh, half dressed women sit lit up by a 10 watt bulb on couches, on low modern beds, on slim chairs or just stand, and sometimes smile, other times smirk on their circular way past his eyes. And yet on a similar afternoon in Chicago or L.A. they really were there. They really were on those tassled couches with those great Mediterranean white dirty legs in the air. And the man at the other end. He was hunched over the camera and he had eyes, for the rolling belly rolled then, and the fabulous long legs ending in black patent heels reeled before in the afternoon as they do now before this man two thousand sexual miles away. With pimples on his face and a blue necktie, in the darkness. Bring, in some one's soft arms, the demise of drug store scenes. The woman purchasing lotions to take off, then, in a great red convertible over hills, in fresh breezes. What is the dark? America, it is all that is hidden under your hat. Your hot tropical afternoon when all the desperate groans creep out. It is our listless powerful voyage to oceania. Brings the disease of white morning. Brings waking, blinking and the slow redawning that nothing is accomplished and already at your ears is the sound of the great raucous bells announcing a different race of men in the street, delivering truckloads of what you didn't even know existed and what you will have to patiently learn to want. "I want, I want, I want" rolls on wheels down 1st. Avenue.

Here are the black mirror stores with the box of cigars in the windows and the baseball scores on a blackboard along one side a lunch counter on the other. It is summer. On the corner we waited for the light to change. The squat grim bank, the women coming and going through its doors are of the same cast, faultless, with standard neat dress and hose, all the heels of their shoes are of like height. There is a dull brass railing in front of the windows, lettered in gold, smaller, still in gold, are listed the assets, in one corner. Bill scans the women out of the corners of his eyes. It would make your head swim. I, when I look, which one does, constantly at one miserable thing or another, don't, instead my lips curl and I envision the carports of their squalid "activities." Their early evening conversations about the copper fireplace, up, back on the hinterland hills of Seattle. They are all of the race of architects of course, and their hands constantly drip with one kind of material or another. A certain kind of precambrian stone from Oregon, limestones from elsewhere. Roman in their vulgarity and willingness to disturb the earth for even so small a thing as an outdoor fireplace, in which the weiners of the poor are gulped insensibly down down their serviceable gullets. That hinterland realm, the tops of the hills, the edges of this city that line the Sound out west, out north is just ugly. The frightening vulgarity of green, the loose ease of growth. The tiresome proliferate "views," so manifest and public, where every intimacy and loneliness and loveliness is crushed arrogantly, (but fearfully) out—this is the ugly unvaluable Seattle. The university, so hot and deserted, where the population mills. Sheer population. Gross indiscriminate, rancid population. From where these creatures creep out after sundown in their automobiles to drive across the bridges, or fast, along the overpasses and elevated highways, come on then their twinkling lights, giving the hills that effeminate starry shine, and also lighting up their miserable, unscrupulous doings, the churning of their diesel engines in the bays, lighting the sculpture in their niches, casting blinking shadows over the whole of their ungodly arrangements, birdbaths of their clarity, the woven redwood siding of their honor, the stark white west german cups and saucers of their senses.

Where they chatter ceaselessly of slowly revolving lacquered disks of Broadway plays, the length of the hair of the Japanese girl who sells jew jaws in an interesting store by day and lives in an even more interesting life by night, for whom will the warm sorrel enclosure between her fashionable thighs open tonight? Not love, but the life, of love, oh not love, but the doings of love. They never never cry for mercy. They cry for more only. An alien world lives up on the hills.

But there is a slender edge of the city around the great curve of the Bay, which is the halo of the city, the light grey rain making the shining arc, there, the poor sometimes late in the night cry silver colored tears as they paw in the garbage cans; and then look up, the blue of the eye of the Scandinavian the brown of the eye of the Esquimaux, is diluted and washed another shade lighter.

BEAUTY

Albuquerque. I quite naturally thought of lions. Not that lions are there. The sad lion shaking his mane is akin to the soft redbrick sun going down at this moment. Raw brown silent hills. The Rio Grande runs in a thin green vein of trees.

And while I am still caught by this static brocade, I notice the ants at my shoes. I had stopped the car near an ant hill. Now they are crawling over the tip of my shoe. Coming and going with their great eggs they leave and enter the hole in the hill 50,000 at a time. And they bite ferociously, Paul, my youngest son, is dancing to keep them off his bare legs. Cleverly they have built the mouth of the hole high, with fractions of pebbles, so that from a distance, on the other side of the riding earth, as they come up over what seems an insurmountable range of earth outcropped by man with a rubber wheel, they glimpse their own homemade volcano cone resting there, their sole direction. Thence, going down into, the earth. A lot is made of the instinctual qualities of such animals, ants, bees, termites, etc. But they go as you or I would. Home. Here enters the force of the will. For isn't will simply their gaining quality. Why not give them will. And be anthropomorphic. It costs us nothing. And we have qualities in abundance to share. To say instinct is so easy and gains nothing for the ant, the bee, the termite, in our eyes, the only disclosing eyes.

Then I turned and saw Beauty. She was carrying a large pan of dishwater out the door. Oh no! Yes! Hi! There was a nice laughter over everything as we greeted, and went inside the little house, leaving the ant to its continuous journeying from the edge of its territory.

Inside we sat at a round table. The room was very hot. There was no breeze anywhere and the mice flitted back and forth from the refrigerator to the cabinet, and from there through the doors into the other three rooms. The strong tock tock of the blind moths around the bare bulb hanging from the center of the ceiling was our small signalling drum in the still early night. We talked of the university and of the course Beauty was taking there. Beauty said one of the courses especially was very intense because the students split sharply into two groups, those for, and those against, certain things. There was the difference, and that one student was a teacher on an indian reservation. Where the children had no sense of time, that was the most difficult thing to instill in them the sense of time, where were you, at what time, what were you doing, the sense of being present, and not obligated in some distant abstract and unreasonable part of the Earth, how is it you arrive at 4 P.M. to start school, and if you haven't left by 7 P.M., what is the trouble. And further, is it possible to teach wild people. Will people wind up *knowing* more than they did after a given point, granted you start somewhere. Or feeling. What is it you feel, and can you, the matter of centipedes, their horror, your horror, (I heard one native woman call them eyelashes) that they are mere liquid. What is death anyway, in a given locale? Here in this southwest are the printed inventory numbers carefully inscribed on the lower foreheads, between the eyes nearly, of skulls, the ultimate life number of Folsom man, who once played with his children on these rolling juniper covered hills, brushed past flowering yucca, but what he had to place between the eyes was finally more dignified; a carefully flaked arrow point.

Still, some men act as though death and birth were not considerations, for instance the instructor was thought to be democratic, she said, he wanted everyone to have their time to say what they thought, or what they felt, if not thinking. There is time and relaxation for those activities now. Night has come over the outlying town. It appears blue through the window. Resting on the ridge of the massive bulkhead of the Sandias is the moon and instead of rising, if it chose, it could roll along the upper ridge of that fabulous rest. But it chooses to rise, lifting off, a ball of orange ice, such as you get at a county fair.

We wanted to please her. Wanted to say decent things and have the conversation happy and contented not tormented by the sense of time and remembering, or even acknowledging that we had come to see her because we wanted to see her, and be with her, to be contented with her, for there is a boredom and a danger in being contented with anyone. But there is the simple danger in being malcontented. . . . . . To sit there not wanted, when such interesting people enter the room, with six trout caught the first time they were fishing, and using a strange little red and white bobber, to keep the

bait off the bottom, but would you believe it possible to say anything
further than I was there too, no, one is immediately cut off by a remark
intended to convey the sense that you were not there at all, and that
indeed you didn't, just now, speak. And are not indeed here now. The
incredible selfishness of people. And the morbid impossibility of not
being able to leave a place where you know you aren't wanted.

We had gone to the Corn Dance at Taos thinking it would start
on time. But the indians have no sense of time; some, it is said, even
carry around alarm clocks saying, It is time to eat, it is time to
sleep, it is time to. . . . . . But I am sure they must have picked
up a volume of DHL now and then. As for their not really having
a sense of time, they observe the sun coming up, and the moon set, so
that takes care of that. There is a wheel, and it turns around. If
someone observes it, so much for the exactness, if someone doesn't,
so what? But the dance didn't start on time. We all tramped inside a
partitioned off lower room of the East House and talked with an old
man who had eaten lots of peyote when he was young. We had gone
in to get warm, away from the gale of rain coming down from the
mountain wall. Then outside again to look at the pueblo. Far up on
the fifth story of the brown pueblo the governor came out to face the
cold wind and rain. It was a small space, the intimate little court
of the top story, and there were the stalwart chimneys all around, the
smoke curling up from their pinon fires perfumed the air. Five men
accompanied the governor. They all wore striped flannel blankets,
wound around their heads like arabs. Only the eyes could be seen
peeping out from the wonderfully draped toga, and chanting, they
addressed the whole world, like Romans; but unlike the Romans with
their roads and their marching, their abominable marching without
bands and hilarity, who were too intent on those perishable things like
earth boundaries. These indians are the opposite of Romans, of course.
Their shrinking empire was overrun and sacked by civilized people.
So they chanted on, the slow long level chant ending in an abrupt
rising of the voices in a word similar to GO, although it was Pueblo.
It is said they were addressing the young, harrassing them to start
the dance of the corn, the dance of fertility, the dance of birth bringing
and coming into existence again. But for me, being no indian, having
no corn, they were lovely in existence now, in their bright green and

pink striped thin flannel blankets waving broadly in the wind. We had stood upon a massive rubbish heap when the chanting began. When the governor broke forth in his heady powerful voice, looking down at us from five stories up on the brown pueblo, we all ran in terror down the mountainous rubbish heap, Paul falling and cutting open his skin. Because we thought we were being summoned to leave a burial mound, the site of the dead. Thought it was holy. But a man later told me the indians sometimes throw afterbirth there, and to them it is a place to be avoided. There are mistakes about the holy. He, the governor, wasn't chanting to us, so we slowed down, and walked on, talking about it. Laughing. We thought it was the cops. In some places, God is a cop.

But in these indian breezeways blow the dusts of other religions. Yes. The position of gods today is a bad one. But what can they do. "The bomb is important in terms of my career, we must stockpile," we hear from the University. "The bomb is a destruction sensible human beings must not allow," we hear from the insurgent chemist. On the other hand the poet says, "The bombum is a beautiful flower sent from heavenum, suck it, with your moist lips, Oh dusky bombum." Sic. um. I ignore all three. Some of us shall don gracious diving suits and slip under the water flowing like saviour butterflies through the underwater to where the bomb rests on the bottom of the sea, not asking who slipped it there, No Morality, beware the morality of the scientist and the poet, and we amoral saviours will delicately slip the chemical pin from it there in the deep brine, the flowering sea flowers will wave around us undulating in the indigo light a revolutionary century deep, where the blackness is said to be so total there is the light of dreams, and we indeed will never return. There will be only three men left upon what was our upper earth.

There is still a picture of Benevolence, whether it comes from France out of a false Rousseau ego or not, I won't bother with. But the blue line is there. Tracing the horizon, and the tree is there, with broad green leaves, I don't want to lose them, the tree has blue limbs, and beneath its wrong colored boughs is a lion and a tiger and a horse. The saddle on the horse's back is a bird, and it is a saddle too, but it is a bird most. Black. The tiger has stripes across its face, he is in San Quentin. And the certain lion is Christ, he has his head tilted slightly up and the gentleness has nothing to do with the killing of a zebra which you will remember is not provided in the picture, this is an ideal picture. The lion has a brown body somewhat but the legs are pale yellow. There is no zebra, the lion eats nothing. And if it is desirable only to me, to have such a lion, then, I, will have to be the lion.

It was raining that night when they brought the trout in through the door. There was some trouble getting the fishing rods past the screen door, but all of us, the two women and myself, could hear the rain clearly now that the door was open, whereas before we had sensed it vaguely, and in the background. We all disagreed as to the worth of the rain. The two fishermen strode past us intent on taking the catch out of the canvas bag. They were both artists and fishing then was not merely fishing. No no. It was of course an art. One of the men wouldn't touch the slimy things, was even said by the other to have been unable to take them off the hook. Earlier, before the men came, we drank a toast, with scotch, "to the limit". Little did we two guests know then that there is no limit.

What was amazing was the way they fondled the fishing rods and the gear, like some precious and elegant stuff, as if the dreadful fish didn't stink, and it was so dainty the way the man with darker hair, the shorter squatter one, the drippier droppier one gasped, as he had to fraudulently force himself to take the fish from the deeply regarded and many times shown canvas bag. "See here," he said, "it is a creel."

Recalling it now the whole content of those few minutes seems connected and reasonable regardless of the fact they were real live people, the sense of everything was restricted to one ready plane. Sight and hearing. The mouth, out of which words came. The genitals for all other purposes were cut off, which always accounts for a certain vacancy. This was the sense of castration pervading the reality of the little room in which we sat. One man, the taller, louder man said the same thing over and over about how to clean the fish. And the woman's face was absolutely shining from emulating grasping light coming down from the well stocked Pecos River. And she smiled a great deal on the man who was cleaning the fish. The other man, the squeamish man, sat down next to me. He said that next weekend they were all going to Juarez. And then offered me a look that was both cruel and alarming. In effect saying why don't you get out! They obviously wanted to eat the fish. He then produced a sketch book with a drawing in it the woman said had social significance, and showed it to the woman and the other man, and at the last moment and hesitantly, like an afterthought, but cunningly, to me. It was a man covering a woman, the woman was a brown mass under the man, like a shadow. I said, "It looks like a shadow." Finally I looked at my wife, "For Christ's sake, let's cut!" And out the door we went but not without having to shake the hand of the tall man who said, "Have you lived here long?"

While the rain increased we continued to stroll around in back of the pueblo. It is raining still, and quite chilly, at times piercing cold, in July, the cold rain sweeping down like gentle wet hairs, raking our faces, from the Sangre de Christos. This is not to make us out courageous at all, in fact when the large black car drove up with the indian in it, saying stay out of here, get back to the plaza, we all meekly lent our arms to one another and went back. The indian in the black car too had the flannel wrapping and was very arabian, like a sheik without a chauffeur. They were all sheiks running here and there, preparing, shouting still from the top of the pueblo, and now they were atop the building on the west side, shouting down from there too. I guess in their own sense they were agitating. The wild tourists were filling the plaza which stands between the two adobe buildings. The sheiks, five stories up, shouting their chant down into the common plaza. The wet, cold wind.

Today I was looking through Katherine Coman's *Economic Beginnings of the Far West*, and there was a picture in the book of this pueblo. The same. I wanted to buy a little paper umbrella for my daughter but the vendor has sold all he had. I got her a twirly on the end of a stick instead, now she goes running with it held up above her head in the cold air. It is 4 P.M. From somewhere in the east house the dancers emerge, they are about nine men, one is carrying a heavy log drum. They assemble in front of the courtyard of the church, and huddle there chanting and revolving in a shuffling pinwheel formation. The sheiks of the air have come down from the tops of the houses. These are the elders. Then suddenly the women appear, rather girls, someone says they are all unmarried. They form in two parallel lines and start the soft dance, the old men huddled behind near the

wall chanting in old men's deep strong voices. There is one male dancing with them and he does a brisker dance, rather like a caricature,
of an indian dancing. Someone, a boy, on the shoulders of his father,
in the circling onlookers, tries to take a picture and there is much
shouting and the dance stops but the big rolling indian who comes
out to see what is going on does not take the camera away. The boy
answered that he had not taken a picture, but he had. Why he was
believed I can't say. Is this a sham? The indians are said to not abide
pictures taken of their ceremonies.

We move on, the crowd disperses led by the indians who repeat
the same dance nearly, but not quite, in front of the other houses.
We go across a narrow railless bridge, the hundreds of tourists following the indians. No one falls off the bridge, but there are some
close calls. There is one girl dressed in red who keeps laughing to
her companion. She is a large buxom very beautiful girl, a little older
and wiser than the others. She seems embarrassed by what she is doing
and the laughing and giggling is nervous and self conscious. But is far
less so in this dance than it was in the first. She has long hair. You
can see what a swell body she has underneath the red robes. Then
another male joins the dancers. The old men still chant in the background and keep an eye out for cameras.

At one point in the dance the men sustain the rattle in a long
shaking interval, one time during the dance. The earth is recalled
in the spirit of its secret sound. The brief rattle of creation. It is a
tonal recollection. The rhythm otherwise of the chanting and the dance
is stylized and the cadence is beautifully regular, and it takes the ear
no time at all to fall into the significant breaks; you know where they
are at any moment. But it is impossible to keep up an interest. The
body swings, yet you are not dancing with them. Anthropologists who
come on like: the religion of the navajo or pueblo, etc. (or whatever
primitive) is too esoteric for you, the forms are so different, but they
are a little like such and such European thing you might understand,
bore me. Understanding, of course, is not the point. It is that you are
not dancing with them, not chanting Tiwa with them. Which is much
more important. Understanding is a device used to separate us. In so
many other ways you are here. So one lapses into watching the crowd,
the nice nordic looking homosexual in a blue union suit such as
children in the midwest used to wear. He is carrying a camera. Strut-

ting around proudly, as Lucifer, his shoulders back. Knotty muscles. And there is the man in the expensive white duck trousers with a blue wool sweater who keeps looking at us. He has a beard, "a mean intellectual"? The woman with him has long hair and a suede jacket on her shoulders. But is wearing shorts, her legs are slender, and brown from lying in the sun. The indians will stop dancing it is said when the sun goes down. But it is heavily overcast. How will they know? They must use clocks. Still the cold rain is coming down with the little bursts of air. There is the cozy smell coming from the piñon fires the other indians who haven't come out to see the dances are burning in their little compartments in the pueblo. They are all inside, perhaps eating peyote, seeing the dances more finely. We are using our overstrained eyes. Following the arabs, with the Atlas Sangre mountains in the background, and the coldness, and the rain and the spirits of the long once more coming rattled interval recalling Earth's secretly sprouting corn, watchful the needful grace of the indian girl in red lipped smile who has sobered now and whose body is more akin to the dance, her weighted moment's hesitation, making the corn grow, making us all grow into one religious bigness, rolling onward, her tight brown limbs sending us hallow into silence.

. . . We were sitting at night by the round table in the kitchen listening to the high occasional chirping, to the crickets going earth earth earth earth. Beauty still is talking about the university and the education course, the stupidity of those who want to cut out all academics, in effect, not teach. And she is right as rain, of course. The slender beauty is nervous and inarticulately articulate. There are slender graciously blowing lashes around her eyes, the great beautiful arcadian grooves of the beauty's eyes. And she looks piercingly at you, so that you are uneasy, will you be taken into this opium den, will you make the jogging trip through the groves riding leisurely in the checkered sun in a carriage and two?

The slender beauty lives in the midst of poverty. And she is categorically against poverty. Her father is an aristocrat. Her mother is an indolent earth wandering Havana vacationing Mexico embarking idiot. Who won't leave her room so the servants can come in to clean. But Beauty continues to stare from the deep groves of her lashes and her red mouth continues to work like a seductive snake, making vision and revery of the conversation. Appollonio lives next door. He actually carries a loaded shotgun to the well when he gets water from the pump. His mother owned this place and he had expected to inherit it in a sense, but the mother had rented it to Beauty. There is an orchard and three acres. Living in the country is grand today, even if it is squalor. There is a certain peace unattainable anywhere else. A trumpet vine on a dead tree can come to make up in exotic reward for any amount of mosquitoes and stagnating water, the result of no plumbing. And, educated people are equipped to ignore conditions which would appall and depress a primitive. What will happen. We discuss the fact he might shoot her, he is that lunatic about its being rightfully his place. Or her children. Yes, Beauty has children. Apollonio might murder them all. Because she is trying to have him evicted from his house next door, land she thought she had rented with the house we now sit in. But he won't leave. He speaks slowly and threateningly. Calculating eyes as he stands by the pump. And she sometimes lies awake in the early morning hours thinking of a shotgun battle with Apollonio. But then goes off to summer school, nothing resolved. The Battle is strange. Once, in the early morning light and then cool air he brought her the things intended to make his birthday party meal, left over because no one came to his party. Some frijoles, and tortillas, on a plate. He knocked softly on the door, and said—no one came to her party. He meant his party. Beauty started to weep and took the tortillas. Earlier in the week he had stood in front of his own door which could be seen through her window and indeed she was looking. He stood there with a twelve year old girl, engaged in what is loosely called love, looking toward the slender beauty's window. Was this what he wanted? No. He wanted Beauty, wanted to be standing inside her house. But the confusion. How do you approach anything directly. The problem, a superficiality, which hid the deeper desire. He might murder her not because he loves her, but because he knows she doesn't love him and this is the terror, that she can't come to the love. This is a well of frustration, nothing else. Love and Hate are not similar.

This is Beauty's simplicity, her confusion over Apollonio, whom she would like to please, though she hates the man intensely. She says, "Oh I am guilty," and the guilt she expresses comes up from the deep well of herself. The guilt is real. Beauty was sitting there with her children. Staring out from the groves her lovely lashes, thinking it was when she had called the justice of the peace the trouble had started.

It was on this legal ground that Apollonio should be thrown out with his public carnage. The menace of the eyes. Could a justice of the peace fix this? Could moving fix this? Or would he eventually seek all of them out, her and the children, for murder. The mexican revenge.

Apollonio stole through the night to Beauty, through the kitchen door with long slender words under the window in the stifling New Mexican night and came to her a shotgun around his neck and hundreds of years of mexican frustration. Knowing no language but the splotches of the indian and spaniard the mexican and the gringo frustrator. What wonder! She was studying for the examinations, her children were asleep, she was afraid they would wake. And the heat! It came swirling in with Apollonio. Apollonio who plants trees, who cares in an oblique way for the world saying, see didn't I plant you trees, saying you get the hell out of here. My mother owns this property. Why do you speak spanish better than I do, why are you so pretty? Why are you here. But Apollonio had stood drunken with the twelve year old. And Apollonio was canceled by the blackness, being in the wilderness. The night whispered itself away. Through the little crack of the slightly raised window and out over the dry plain of the short ledge Apollonio stood gazing in bewilderment in the Land of Enchantment. Wondering Apollonio—gazing over the earth through the window. A part time planter of trees.

Apollonio went back to work again to the nursery, and the days passed. Tending the roots of trees. Grimy halting Apollonio. Whose marked delight is standing twelve years old girls. Yet Apollonio is a stupid ancient Plato in reverse. That's why property is such a drag. It isn't that anyone owns something, no, that is too simple. It is rather the sex of the earth and its indetermination, the possibility of the ambiguity of the night in the daytime, that throws us into the screening off of the whole exhaustible span we make, that we make one way or another a man can live dying. Useless to look for explanations.

Beauty got in her car with her laundry and went to get it washed at a laundromat only she patronized. This is her singularity and one of the things rendering her provocative presence. This is one sense in which she exists, and this is what she has of truth. And what I would pay tribute to. To the not forgotten. That she got into the car and

went to the laundromat where she had not been for two weeks, and
the woman inside said to her man, "Here she comes!" The man turned
to look, they were going bankrupt and out of business and had waited
for her two days to come to do her wash, before they closed the
place.

We sat there, by the coffee table, watching the Artist-Fisherman
take the poor slimy helpless creatures from the newly bought creel.
The tall redfaced Artist-Fisherman said, "I love to hunt birds." (The
woman looks serenely down like a Roman whore into the arena where
Christians are screaming, clawing the arm of her companion the way
modern Romans and Russians and Americans do when they are about
to witness the slaughter of all of *you*, my darlings.) He said, "I love
to shoot birds. It makes no difference to me at all that they die (oh
Hudson) it gives me no pain, if I do say so, I love to shoot them,
and I love to eat them and I may say that as a Man this is the way
it should be." Still the woman smiled down and looked serene and
uplifted, and was edified that a man should speak so. How long had
it been since she had had a man. What he was saying was her
avowal. This, with her great yearning, was her edification, and she
wanted strength, she wanted to tear the heads off the fish and eat them
raw, right then and there. She very much wanted, being withheld, to
have this man's raw manly temperament thrust into her ex-newyorker,
to know that at last she was sitting there and believing what she
heard, and she smiled benignly, for war, and the disturbances that
bring us some balance out of the dull plane of the everyday and the
lonely, where the french go marching and where the zulu perform,
the prowling of lions after the prized zebra; that neither she nor I
nor you nor anyone can lift up from the sudden relief we need, when
shall we smile and where shall we go to be both alone and surrounded?

But she didn't. She sat there quite serenely, smiling. Barbaric was
a sight to behold sitting there, with her hair down. And everyone was
talking, mostly about the indian dances, and how the best ones were
to be August 4, 1959, at Santa Domingo, New Mexico, and they were
all going, to dig the indians, dancing. "They will be all men dancing
and that's a rarity. Most of the dancing now is done by the women
and that's not nearly so lively," she said, looking down at the bird-
killer, with an exclusive little smile filled with appreciation for a
real, truthful unabashed man. Then the Squeamish Extractor of Fish

said, "I don't care, both of you say what you want, I *just can't* stand
the killing of anything, what's the point, this is what I think about
hunters: that they have to go shoot themselves in the legs, that's their
capacity, to shoot their legs off." Then the Squeamish Extractor of
Fish sat back with his drink in his hand and smiled inwardly—a satisfied defender of Nature's own warm blood. (Or a defender of Hunter's
legs.)

As it is said, life is a tinkling little fair, as we amble into it.
Into rooms, or to cities and mountains. I remember Beauty and her
husband, and my wife, were in the front seat, I was in the back with
the children, who were romping around, and looking out the windows
at the mountains and valleys below. We were going up the side of the
Sangre de Christos. A sight seeing trip. To the ski lift. Down through
the trees the skiers were coming through the emerald green and white
sprinkled trees, the snow was stark green white and the air had a chill,
we had just gotten out of the car to admire the romantic glidings
on the mountain's side. The children, like children, were demanding
to ski. Ho hum. The demands of children. It got to be too much. We
stood around staring awhile. Beauty was saying ooooo, and she said,
once, ahhh. The skiers glided so serenely down through the earthly
pines. But on another slope there were more plodding people with skis
on their feet trying to purchase the top of a small hill, and not graceful at all, they were a bore to see, and we turned our eyes away as
they all fell down. Beauty frowned and she grimaced and she said
ohh on the way down, but down we went through the coolness of,
till we returned. No one saw Beauty for some time after that.

I went to work in a restaurant. Spring had by now disclosed herself to the extent that the Cottonwoods along the river were in the
greenest part of their leaf. Still, on some April mornings the ground
had a coat of fresh wet snow. We were living then in a guest house.
But it turned out that the living in such a place is far too close to the
domain of those who own it, and that they are vivid about the demands
made on the occupants. For instance there was a patio so to speak,
and when we ventured out on to it, because it was outside our back
door, they screamed at us, "Get out of our PRIVATE PATIO!" And
we always meekly did. But we swore at them from behind the closed
door because we knew that to swear in the open and to take our own
rightful part in the matter would presuppose a new place to move

into, which we didn't have. So we lived on there for a spell, waiting it out, and I continued to work at Tommie's.

At Tommie's, the huge and powerful lesbian leader of the local legitimate gangsters, every day about sunset, the people with nothing to do save practice a kind of hard hearted, nickle biting sentimentality toward the "spanish" (these types specialized in knowing one or more "spanish" family intimately) about sunset they would begin to arrive at Tommie's. Along with them were the inevitable horde who worked but pretended to the local ideal of nothing to do. The "private income" pretenders. It goes without saying all of them were "artists." Very loose definition there. An imported dog with perfume dumped on it, an indian pot with something in it. An old, unpainted door. Many other things of that nature assured the owner that identity. But of course the greatest proof of all—the private, or hidden, income. A very local peculiarity. For instance if an "artist" were actually hard pressed— rent, food, clothes, etc., these were very good signs that he wasn't playing the game, and was probably taking the whole thing too seriously. The standard remedy for such a case would be to become an indian, or a "spanish", move into an interesting old adobe house, live with someone who had lots of money, buy a sports car (a cheap one; for some reason there weren't many expensive sports cars about), shoot a young "spanish" boy between the shoulder blades as he crosses your back yard (patio). This last device should be explained briefly. It's only the very old servile "spanish" who are "simpatico". The young ones boast too much property and are therefore (tacitly of course, this word is never breathed openly), Mexican.

Tommie kept about her a ring of bull dikes. She drank with them often and sometimes they would join her for dinner. She had a bull fight motif in the bar and the food was, well lousy, but tried to be continental. It all tasted the same. Her customers were too drunk, always, to realize how bad the food was so that was never a problem. One had to change their tablecloths often because they slopped their soups and lasagne, or whatever, wherever. Changing tablecloths as frequently as changing courses.

Beauty's husband had been the entertainer there all winter, play- ing the piano. But when spring came, Tommie decided she was paying him too much money. She went on a trip and while gone, phoned Jaurez and hired some mexican musicians. One night he came to work.

There was a group of Mexicans playing, and he was without a job. "Well you know, I guess I'll have to take my piano and go home. You know, man, what else can I do?" I helped him roll it out the front door and lift it into his V.W. bus. When I went back inside the mexican musicians were standing around.

Much later, in the summer, an old friend from Phoenix came to town. I wasn't there. I heard he was drinking at the bar, talking to Tommie. The conversation grew tiresome and he ups and spits on the old bull fight poster Tommie had hung between the bar and dining room. She turned various shades of purple and chartreuse and her hyper-thyroid eyes revolved rapidly in her head like plums in a slot machine. Thirty seconds later three of her henchmen, still chewing food, held him while she beat him limp and then kicked him out the front door and into the street. Some one found him later, lying crumpled where she had left him, by a little red sports car.

Beauty did come again, with her children in the back of the car. Now that I am writing this there is a peace and I have longed to be off again, to cease being Robinson Crusoe. It is fall. I am sad because Beauty has gone. There never seemed to be anything settled about her, yet there are far away calls that appeal to us for no reason at all, her unsettledness, her lovely sympathetic inner turmoil was the means by which she largely held you. It always seemed slightly as though a trick had been performed but one never minded. It is a relief to cry and laugh together in the company of a just woman. Remove one cherished article from a vast and arid landscape and it becomes empty.

Lately my wife and I have been whiling away some time in a small mexican tavern downtown. A cabaret, really. There are three men who sit like magpies. They sit there at the back of the room, a guitar, a banjo, and a drum. Very static, but the beat is strong, and has a strange silly dignity. Two very old ladies are there dancing usually, in utter disdain of the room. The thing that relieves one most is that nothing is in the air more offensive than a little cigarette smoke. In a striking way the two old ladies are like the two in *The Knife of the Times*. Forty years later. I don't know what gives them such seductiveness. They must be seventy, at least. There is a certain way in which deep age is repelling and lovely at once. Not the paint on their faces certainly, although that isn't badly done either.

So we sit in New Mexico drinking beer brewed anciently first in the

hills of Assam, under the bright skies of Manipur in the Khasi hills.
My wife is dancing and she just had her hand stamped by the cus-
todian. She smiles and I wave to her through the smoke. The swirling
noise of the room, where the life of the horse does exist, the horse
with a saddle on his back, like a bird, and the smiling joking tiger,
with stripes on his face like he is in prison. And a giraffe looks in at
the window smiling. That drunk Santo Domingo indian I met walks
across the plaza in the fall wind. I remember him from a tale of hard
luck he gave me one night about how he had been elected to some
council and had tried to do lots of things but couldn't get any "coopera-
tion" from the other indians. How cool and tart that air now it is
fall. Delicious. Aside from however evil the types of people are here,
there is the magnificent light. How it seems at times to come from
the ground as well as deep deep from the sky. At the edges of the
broad tablelands the rich earth plunges into silent attractive shadow.
Albuquerque always a pleasure to go down to, because the wild dry
desert mixtures of people are more reasonable and seeming. The raw
juxtaposition of the people not so important in themselves, not to
be dwelled on so selfishly. Nevertheless, we think very much these days,
to leave, as Beauty did.

DOUGLAS WOOLF

COUGHER

At the bureau early, seated on a waiting chair, he knew he would have a coughing fit. He fought with all his practiced ways and wiles to smother it, drown it with a glob of mucus in his throat, seduce, cajole, threaten it with tremulous epiglottis, blow it loose with fierce gasps of air sucked through first his nose and then his mouth: to no avail, delay at most. Still he did not attempt the evergushing water cooler five steps away, to be caught choking and spluttering there, spraying germs on the immaculate bowl, the wall, the printed four-inch SHIELD THAT COUGH! Better to sit in his chair, begging that his thumping heart might somehow reintegrate his aching chest. He still had both his lungs intact, but with the x-ray being overhauled today who would believe so in the face of, he knew, shaking evidence.

The writer at desk 3 would not. He had the wretched little office face that no man loves yet so many daily adulate, the slack neon-haunted skin, the parched tan hair with scaly part, the washable blue eyes that palest winter sun would blind were it not for polaroid. No sour breath, armpit, crotch would ever pass by his desk without a full analysis, report. From him slim girls first had their deepest fears spelled out, they weren't just off the straight and virgin path—five weeks knocked up. Old dying ones of either sex scarcely had times to rest their backs, desk 3 for them was a dispatch point. Coughs, when finally they could not help themselves, were greedily collected here and reechoed fivefold by the empty drawers. The writer waggled one short white forefinger a deadly bit.

Now they had to wait for the fit to pass, John gagging on the freshest of his pressed and folded handkerchiefs, the other dabbing a half-hidden smile with tissue plucked from the left underarm of the backward tilting writer's chair. John's chair was straight, he could not lean back, dared not advance, could not stop breathing with his lungs erect. He packed a large part of his life into that wad of wilting cloth, saving only enough to hawk his poor apologies, "Too many cigarumps!"

Unveiling his leer, the writer pressed the tissue into a tiny ball and lobbed it six feet to the wastebasket, a perfect shot. He plucked his next, held it limply afloat while studying John's long face. "John Forbes," he said, in perfect voice, "no MI or name?"

"No, they weren't obligatory then."

"I know the regulations very well," the writer said. "Your records are up to date? Spouse, Marlene T? Three issue, John A, Mary E, Susan C—John A deceased?"

"Correct."

"Spouse pregnant yet?"

"No, no, not again . . ."

"John, shall we stay with the facts? What are you looking for these days, desk work or," leering, "physical?"

"Oh, anything . . ."

"Oh? Anything?" Another ball, an almost perfect shot. "Well, first there's a new form to be filled out, you may have heard, 203?" Together they looked toward the writing rooms, saw that all the occupied lights were on. "Room 6 should be available any second now," the writer said, and at once its light blinked off. He led the way, shoulders easy and chin outthrust, fine picture of an indoor scout. But within the writer's room, the heavy soundproof door thumped shut of its own accord, the white and the infrared went on by unseen dual switch. John sank at once into the bucket-chair to roll his sleeves while the writer, perched on a writer's stool, arranged his implements. Either the man was feeling the effects of exercise, or he was finally alarmed by John's cough in this tiny airtight room. His hands trembled as he tested points, he might well have pricked himself, and he smiled at John. "Got them all rolled, through coughing now, right arm in pretty good shape today?"

"All fine and ready to go," John said. In truth he was raw from the shoulder down, as the writer knew too well, but John was brave and always *retenu*. Pride in his self-control, his one pride left, almost let John believe the writer looked on him admiringly as he wrote, enough perhaps to remove the onus of that cough. But in any event pain was brief. They had added an extra jolt to their ink this year (John had heard about that but until now had not believed) and it seemed faster too. He was riding high in the bucket by the time the writer completed his 2, his 0, his 3. "That's an awfully nice 3," John said.

The writer added a final touch to its bottom outer edge. "Well, down to work," he said, flexing his fingers against writer's cramp while John unbuttoned his shirt. "Your blue target spot's been drawn, I see."

Nodding, smiling, John spread his shirt wide to let the writer center the electrical stethoscope. Together they watched, John with retenu pride, the dials jump only an instant before they settled steadily in place. It was the writer's eyelids that flickered, if anything. "Pull your pants down, John," he said.

John was the private type, but no one could ever have guessed by the easy way he accepted the thermometer. Now they watched dials again, while the mercury made its sure climb to normalcy. The writer joggled the tube a bit, but John's temperature refused to rise, .6 right down the line. Frowning the writer probed John's chest. "The x-ray is being overhauled today."

"Oh? No matter, I checked out 100 percent in May."

"Hm. Well, where are we going to put form 203? You're pretty well filled up, it seems."

"No no," John said. "Plenty of room in back."

"In back?" The writer swung the bucket semi-circle. "How long since you checked back here?"

"It's been a while . . ."

"Wait a minute, what's this," the writer said, "I find some gaps in your records here."

"They've all been checked out many times."

"Still, we'll want to go over these thoroughly," and John could feel the writer's breath warm on his back. "Form 203 is a resume, a digest of the entire history, for ready reference. Now then, what were you doing in winter 1951-2, fall *and* winter 1953-4?"

"Right off I don't recall."

"You don't?"

"I believe I was traveling."

"Traveling to where, what for?"

"Just here and there," John said and, very retenu, "I used to be a writer then, before we had to register."

"A what?" John could feel a forefinger running studiously over his back. Now his bucket swung. They were face to face, the writer's face thrust forward in an intent scholarly way, checking cross-references. "A writer, you used to be?"

"I wrote books. People used to read them," John explained. "Some people did."

The writer's smile became a nearly perfect thing. "I know my history very well," he said, whether with reverence or derision who could say? "John Forbes. Right off, I don't recall having seen any of your books in the museum, John."

"No no, you haven't. I was very low on the list."

"Ah? You didn't have your heart in the work?"

"Yes. Yes, I loved it well. Somehow . . . For one thing, to tell the truth, I had my license suspended for a year. I had to look for other work."

"Suspended? Why?"

"Failure to register."

"What year was that?"

"Let me think."

The writer, rearranging his implements, let John think. But as soon as he began to write again, John knew that he was using a more potent ink. There was absolutely no pain at all, only an irresistible lassitude, like downward flight, and John no longer had even remote control over his replies. He answered everything asked, candidly, at terrible length. The writer wrote down every word of it, long-forgotten names, titles, plots, inconsequential dates, old family jokes, prides, plaints, countless trivialities that had no place in a history. John saw all this yet could not stop himself, evade, invent, no more than he could make the needle stop. He could only go on and on until finally he found himself looking up, still talking, from his rocking bucket to the writer's smiling face. "Well now, John, old man," he heard the writer interrupting him, "where are we going to put 203?"

"There must be room."

"Where, John? I've looked."

"There's lots of room."

No, the writer shook his head. "If you were a little more bald perhaps . . ."

"I had room when I came in, lots of room. You did this deliberately," John said, but his voice like his limp body was unthreatening.

"We might have put 203 right here," the writer said, patting John's left inner thigh, "if you had remained a single man. But you're all filled up there with family. No, John, you shouldn't have been such a lady's man. You've dug your own grave, you might say, John, with your overeager stick. Here we are running short of room, all of us, and just look at your family history."

"I know," John said, "but I was retenu."

"Two spouses, three issue, John? No, I'm afraid you've been fighting us, John, with all your girls and your books. Look here, I had to use valuable space listing those little stories you said you wrote." Raising John's bare feet aloft, one at a time, he briefly scanned the soles. Letting the second one drop he said, "You're finished, John."

"No."

"Yes, John, you are."

"No," John said again in his tranquil voice. "My father wasn't finished until he was 83. My mother . . ."

"Yes yes." The writer patted John's high forehead. "All there, John," he said. His hands were gentle as he detached the stethoscope and the thermometer, guided the bucket across the tiny room, skidded John talentedly into the finishing chute head-end first.

"Could I have a pencil . . . a graphite stick?" John asked, but it was dark.

WORK IN FLIGHT GROUNDED

Tossed rudely together, two floating kidneys in Beantown, they braced themselves against a spin round all the back bays of the city. Back here, where the houses were seldom less than ten-roomed, two-storied and the vines and the trees for generations had intermarried, the neighborhoods, fastidiously shaggy, all but glassless, seemed impervious to all outsiders not excepting the sun. One saw little in those cool shadows, nothing behind those small dark windows, absolutely no intimate glimpses of anything, especially while under the sway of a driver in a rush to connect with an airplane. He *had* to drive fast, the route he had chosen, if he hoped to get there this morning. And had to charge high high high for the wear and tear on his nerves as well as his tires. Almost it began to seem that the strain was just too much for him, until suddenly with no warning the cab escaped from its orbit and pursued a low plane straight and true to the airport. Here their driver, not to waste one of the valuable minutes he had saved them, reached back to open their door, shake his head with relief, wipe fresh perspiration. He'd got them here, he'd made it. He handed Mrs. Childs' little bag out to Child with one finger, when Child had paid him, but still he remained starting out from the shade of his cap as if to remind them of something forgotten. Had Child's tip been too small, too large, was he offended, what more could he want of them? Child looked to his mother.

"Thank you, driver!" she called, and tipping cap their driver raced back toward the city.

All the glass was out here. They had it hung in great panes, some stuck, some swinging, all highly polished, that you might see every move made by the agents, each generous smile, each solicitous facial expression, until they had you firmly strapped in your seat with the little door locked behind you. Even the big ashtrays had nothing but sand in them, pure rich sand which a lady in white had just finished panning. Child buried his cigarette deeply, but it soon erected itself, lay stuck there like the bleached armbone of a prospector who had expired digging for water. Turning his back on the sight, leaving his mother in the shade of some vultures on the cool pliant back of a lizard, he struck out alone for the trading post. He made it, and approaching the counter selected a youngish agent in blue, blonde and soft headed, with dimples that had not yet turned vicious. Now he had to wait a short while for her attention, in deference to applicants with briefcases, but she did see him at last. Not a minute too soon either, it seemed. He had almost missed his plane, due to depart on the hour, where where had he been, she had looked for him sooner, had had no last-minute stay from the governor, but he was in luck, for all his tardiness, she could do it, she could squeeze him in, and his mother.

"Have you luggage?"

"Yes, there on the scales," Child said pointing.

She peered over the edge of the counter, then banged his claim stub onto his ticket with three staples, the better to skid it at him. "You'll depart at Gate 90."

Thanking her, tactfully turning away from her pimples, he was made to feel that his hair was too long although not quite long enough to hide the fray of his collar. Yet he received a big smile from his mother, who seemed much impressed by his speed. He handed her her change all in a bundle, uncounted.

"No no, Child, you keep it. You'll need some."

"I have some."

"Well then, wait here a minute," she told him. "I'll go shopping."

"Mother, our plane leaves on the hour. . ."

"This will take only a minute."

"Mother, can't it wai. . .?" he asked, flopping onto the lizard still cool in spite of her sitting. He sat on his hands with his head turned shaggyside to the counter while he waited, and soon understood how he had come by his speed: she was back in what seemed half the time promised, with a hat in her hand, a brown fedora. "Mother, what the hell?"

"Look, Child, I've brought you a present!" She waved it.

"Mother, I don't wear them. . ."

She held it up before him, two-handed. "You can't travel without a hat, Child."

"I haven't had one on my head since the Army. . ."

"You can't travel without a hat. Besides you'll catch your death of cold if you go bareheaded. Here, put it on, put it on! Let's see how

it fits. Come now, Child, bend down for Mother. . ." Laughing she set
it up on the top of his head, and stood high on her toes to adjust its
position, a little more squarely. Now she stepped back, cocked, playfully,
her head for inspection. "There, that's much better," she said, offering
him her arm, allowing him to escort her past the long, long counter to
Gate 90.

Their plane could be seen through the gate at the distant other
edge of the apron, early, but an attendant, tiny replica of a pilot, bright
black eyed, delicate featured, life like, with grommet, held them off
with a chain until the hour. When that time came he faced about
smartly. Laying his chain across Child's chest he fluttered his lashes and
murmured something to Child's mother, who thanked him. Now he
nodded at Child man-to-man: lucky son, he could follow. Child had
almost to sprint to catch up with his mother on her eager way to the
airplane, where a lady in blue waited cowering just inside the low
door, her bowed head mostly hidden in shadow. But she sprang out
at sight of Child's mother, to smile cheerfully. "Watch those steps,
please."

"Thank you."

"There are seats up in front."

"Thank you."

His mother found a good pair of seats with a good wide view of the
motors, but was up at once to exchange them, preferring to look out
on the wing. Settled she asked Child if he wanted the window.

"No no, you keep it."

Patting his hand, "We'll take turns," she promised.

He wedged his fedora into the slot overhead and sat down beside
her. Something hard banged his elbow, some armored part of the
lady in blue who made her way to the front of the plane, about-facing
just before she got to the privies. She might have been sister to
Child's agent, a few years older and larger, her high heels proportion-
ately higher. She stayed up on them pretty well as she roamed back
down the aisle smiling giddily, stooping far over, peering at laps as
though in quest of a firm one. No, she preferred the ladies: under
her gluttonous smile Child helped his mother tighten her seatbelt, and
when he was done the blue lady bent low to retrieve his mother's purse,
which had fallen. Regaining her heels she favored Child's grateful
mother with another smile, wider and softer than ever; but you would

not have wanted to hit her anywhere below the chins if you favored
your knuckles. Now she showed Child her backside as she drew herself
out of the aisle, as best she could, affording passage. For here came
the pilot, the real thing this time, larger, rosier, with his plastic raincoat folded over his arm. He strode briskly up the aisle to his easy
chair; by leaning far to the right Child could view him draping that
raincoat over the back of his chair before the co-pilot closed the door
and the blue lady continued inspection.

Almost at once the ship started shaking, not under the blue lady's
heels so much as the grinding and coughing of three of its motors.
Soon the fourth caught on with a flame borrowed from its neighbor,
roared lustily for a moment before all four quit trying. People looked
out the windows, then at one another smiling, questioning, was that the
real thing, no no, just testing. But their smiles faded again as the
lights did, everything going off at once this time while they hunched
low in their seats, gritting their teeth, gripping their chairarms with
cold fingers. All save Child's mother, who was patting his, or trying to
hold them. "Isn't this fun!"

"Wonderful!"

"This is my *first time*, Child," in his ear. "Is this like the planes
you flew in the war?"

He was preparing to tell her yes but she sissed him, for a voice
was announcing. "This is your pilot, Captain John Stevens, Jr. Your
co-pilot is John Whitman. Your stewardess is Joan Johns. After take-off
we will climb slowly to an altitude of 5000 feet and proceed above
broken clouds on a 205° course. Your pressurized cabin will assure
you a comfortable flight and descent. Our first stop will be at New
York International in approximately one hour. It's raining there, folks,"
he added, gunning his motors and tricycling out to the runway.

"5000 feet, Child. Isn't that awfully high?"

"No no," he sought to assure her, but she couldn't or wouldn't
hear him as the big three-wheeler sidled up to the end of the runway
and crouched there tensely straining, as though readying for the
hundred-yard-sprint from a standing start. Folks looked uneasily at
their schedules, for this was supposed to be the cross-country En-
durance. But no time now for queries: three or four guns sounded
and they were off and wheeling, come whatever. Their man gave it all
he had for ten seconds, broke the tape easily, faltered briefly, then on

an impulse decided to go all the way, with such a good start. Once over that first obstacle he had it all to himself, left the field standing still. Down below, several ex-champions could be seen huddled along the sidelines, their dim old eyes raised in longing.

Oh but it still wasn't easy, climbing slowly, bumping and breaking the clouds, leveling at 5000, or trying to; Child's hat fell to the floor in an air pocket, no chance to retrieve it; Child's mother sighted along her wing at a ship in Back Bay, or perhaps Buzzards, but had to look away seconds later for she had sighted the sun at meridian.

"Isn't this fun?"

"Wonderful."

At least the pilot was optimistic. He switched off both his bright messages. Folks unstrapped quickly, sought to fire up cigarettes without singeing their noses. Next they collected their hats and their briefcases. Now here came the blue lady with coffee, demitasses by the time folks got them, and still sloshing. "If it gets turbulent," she advised mothers, "just put it on the floor." They would, no doubt about it. Child's mother said thank you. All slurped quickly, yet not quickly enough for the blue lady tripping back to make her collection. She was in a hurry, sometimes had to jog elbows. That did it. "Child, are you all right?"

"Wonderful!"

Now it was time to play musical chairs with the privies, folks shouldering and butting, kneeing the children, Occupied lights blinking hysterically. The game was out of hand by the time the blue lady returned, tried to divert attention by passing out magazines. She had House and Garden all ready for Child's mother, but turning to Child she flipped her stack rather rapid, he was no reader. Look, Life, Time, Sport Afield, Sport. . .? He let her go, for someone had beat him to Big Table. "Mother?"

"Child, be nice to her."

"Sorry." Closing his eyes he could not make out his mother, although he knew she was asking. In fact he could hear nothing, perhaps he was catching a cold up here in the cool air without his hat on, even those motors seemed to be losing their voices. He turned the little overhead blowhole as far as he could until it blew on his mother. "Mother?"

"Do you want the window?"

"Not now. We'll be at New York any minute—here comes the lady with the chiclets."

"Child, *remember.* . ."

They had to hurry. The blue lady, using just any pretext, was soon bending over them, but not before Child had his mother tied down securely, himself started. His mother did not chew, as it developed, but she took her chiclet anyhow to tuck in Child's pocket with a pat and a tease. The blue lady found this charming. She even gave Child a little upperlip smile as he returned the box to her. They would perhaps have struck up a little acquaintance, had not Claude's mother just then sought his attention. "Look, Child, New York!" She pointed and nodded, and folks sighted along her wing, he along with them. "That's where you were born, Child," she said, everyone turning to see him. Now the pilot's well-pleased voice confirmed her discovery, added that it was still raining. He fluttered his motors and their pressuried cabin brought them down through unbreakable clouds just as he had promised, piercing their eardrums ever so gently. As they hit the ground Child's fedora popped from its slot into his hands and he caught it, receiving a pat from his mother. At second bounce everyone sat up to look out the windows. It was raining. Time to unfasten, while their captain peddled here and there on the apron in search of Gate 90. By the time he gave up, at some neutral distance, folks were on their feet jostling and groping, in the aisles and under the seats, for hats, briefcases, bowling balls, children. Soon joined by the pilot, buttoning raincoat, smiling, with co-smiler, all filed out the little door eyeing and thanking the blue lady, who held herself sucked in against the wall of their depressurized cabin, as though thinking to make demitasses!

"Child, let's not get off, shall we? You can't see New York in twenty minutes."

He was regaining his hearing. "My thought exactly."

So they sat watching the blue lady roam her aisle, stoop to sniff cushions, pin little Occupied signs on those which appealed to her. When she observed them observing her she was for a moment awfully surprised, but then pleasantly. "Don't you want to stretch your legs? You have twenty minutes."

"Thank you, but you can't see New York in twenty minutes. Besides it's sprinkling."

"It *is* raining, isn't it? Would you like some coffee?"

No, but they thanked her, and she went away smiling. Now they sat somewhat smugly listening to sniffs slowly receding, pins puncturing much-abused upholstery, her sedulous quest for favorites, or effigies. When they could no longer hear her Child's mother leaned close to his ear, though scarcely to whisper: "I think that girl's rather hard underneath."

"I agree with you."

Well that they had not accepted her offer of coffee. Folks were already filing back through the door, smiling and saying hello to the blue lady, who welcomed each one of them from her pinched stance at the wall. Those from the tail joined the few newcomers in launching a small-scale invasion of the front seats but were quickly repulsed by the natives, and retreated in some discomfiture muttering threats for the future. They quieted down at sight of the pilot, drew respectfully aside as he strode past them, dripping a little. For a few seconds before the co-pilot slammed the door Child could view what they were doing in the cockpit, not draping their raincoats over their chairs but stuffing them into little plastic bags which they carried in their hip pockets. After a brief silence the loud speaker clicked on and a voice announced rather curtly that they would climb to 6000 (Child's mother gave him her hand and he pressed it) where they would fly above partial clouds on a 240° course until arrival at Pittsburgh, where it was partly sunny. "Fasten your seatbelts," he added, it seemed threateningly.

There was to-do at the privies. A lady was just leaving, a gentleman was just sidling past her. The blue lady came running. "Sir! Sir! No!" she cried after him. "Not *yet*." But a little too late: the Occupied sign was already glowing intensely. Blue lady stood hands-hips until he emerged, swung to watch him slouch to his seat in blushing confusion— what, what was the matter?—and did not go off guard until they were well up in the air, over the city. Thus no chance for inspection. When they began to level at 6000 Child returned his hat to the slot, closed his eyes against the warm, fetid air of their pressurized cabin. His mother had turned the blowhole back on him, which helped some. "Airplanes smell, Child," he thought he heard her whisper loudly, not long before he dozed off nodding concord, and his dreams were of smiling.

Sooner or later he was brought to his senses by an unusual activity at belt level, a kind a prodding tickle, or prickle, which he might have ignored had it not been stealthy. Thus he held himself still with his eyes closed, his mind partially open. "We were all tied up," a man's anxious voice was describing nearby. "I had a bad split in the frame, clean down the middle, and I needed a spare. McNary was on a strike, his third in a row. (He's corky, did you know that—few people do.) Well, the interesting part is that I had just eaten a mushburger and I had a little mayonnaise on my forefinger. My partner Sally Reed (she's real Irish) had the rag at the time. She'd brought me my mushburger and she had mayonnaise too. Being on TV I couldn't wait all night for her, and not wanting to dirty my uniform I tried sucking my finger. That didn't quite do it, though—it was still sticky. By now Sal had noticed my predicament, but she was seconds too late, I was already into my movement. I gave it all the wiggle I had going into my pivot, curled my toes and talked palsy to it, but do you know what really did it was the mayonnaise, the mayonnaise gave it just a wee extra bit of dirty English at the start of my laydown that sent it reeling like a drunk frog down Pig Alley, brushing the lampposts on both sides and spilling them into the gutter. I guess you know what the mayonnaise people did with that when they got hold of it—what with TV, radio, Ripley, etc, Sal and I cleaned up more on that sticky No. 4 finger than we did by beating those corkies. But the interesting part is that that wasn't Borden I had on my mushburger, it was Kraft. Few people know that. Kraft is better, if I say so myself, even if krauts do make it. It's the albumen. But you know how it is with folklore once it gets started. . ."

The voice paused to suck air and Child could hear his mother too breathing deeply, with wonder or anguish, most likely the latter since she was prodding him harder than ever. "Are you sure your son doesn't play, Mrs. Childs?" she was asked presently. "I could swear I saw him just the other night at the Chicago Invitational."

"Oh no, I don't *think* so."

"Well, you should urge him to take up the sport. It pays well. You travel, you meet all types of people. It builds up the wrist muscle. . ."

"I'll ask him. . ."

"You should take it up yourself, Mrs. Childs. You've got the hand for it. If you'd like, I'd be happy to teach you."

"No no, I'm not active. But thank you."

"You meet all types of people," the voice mumbled, fading, and under what must have been a hard stare Child felt his eyelids flutter, so he opened them, to a great bald head hovering, its little round eyes peering somberly down on him from the dark depths of their sockets, its round nose not just retrousse but askew, its pale swirl of a mouth flashing a smile as it skipped neatly from the back of his mother's chair to Child's. It had a big hand which it swung toward Child smoothly, and proudly, exhibiting its splayed hooked, callused members. "Hi there, I'm Stick Carson. I've just been telling your mother here about the Portland Mixed Fours. Didn't we meet last week at the Miami Pro-Ami?"

"No I don't think so," Child said, twisted a little off balance by Stick's grip. "As a matter of fact I was traveling."

"Ah, you were going to the Tampa Open?"

"No." Child shook his head.

Stick rocked his. "Like I was telling your mother here, I could have sworn you're mixed up in the game someway. Where have I seen you—was it in the Buffalo Meet. . .?"

No, Child rocked.

"Not there either?" Withdrawing his hand Stick rubbed his right eye with his No. 3 finger, and Child's mother took this opportunity to pinch Claude's wrist muscle painfully: she wanted to give him her House and Garden. Child was reluctant to take it from her, until he noticed her "Page 33" scrawled across the cover in Desperate Orange. Turning toward the aisle, crossing his legs and his eyes, he thumbed the pages off-handedly until he found his place, then quickly flipped the magazine shut again. "Child *you* talk to me," read her message.

"How soon will we get to Pittsburgh, Mom?"

"Good old Pitt—that's where we have the National Ducks," Stick said overhead. "I guess you caught us on TV this year? They always give us good coverage."

Child's mother laughed, patting. "Child, you slept right through. The landing and everything. We're on our way to Indianapolis now at 8000 feet. The sun will be shining."

"That's the Indiana Bowler," Stick said, nodding confirmation. "It starts on the 5th this year. You'll be able to catch us, if you're still out West. . .if you're interested. . ."

"Child. . ."

"What time are we due there, Mom?"

"On the hour." Child's mother fastened her own seatbelt, tried to open her window: she had to content herself with pressing her perspiring brow against the stuck glass. Then, "There it is now, Child, I see it!" That was Columbus, Stick advised them, but Child's mother meanwhile had discovered the Ohio. She went on at this pace, crowning one discovery with another, ignoring as far as possible the cities (even Indianapolis, where Stick left the plane briefly to buy a paper, and St. Louis, where he offered to take her out for a mushburger) while concentrating her attention on nature's own fardown wonders, the nameless lakes, rivers, creeks, mountains, Child doing what he could to fill in the bare spaces. It was somewhere over the Ozarks, probably, that they encountered a slight turbulence which tipped Stick off his rocker, sent him moaning to his cradle, where he lay blaming Borden for everything even though other folks were similarly affected. In fact both privies were soon full to overflowing, and the blue lady was too busy toting paper sacks to give thought to her demitasses. The little folk especially were a problem, preferring as they did for the most part fedoras and briefcases. Small wonder, as it developed, she wore her heels as high as she did. Her little pussycap too was well-chosen.

But presently the pilot altered his course to a more favorable northwesterly direction, taking advantage of a fresh headwind, and everyone heaved a sigh of relief as they adjusted their blowholes. Stick was real quiet. Child's mother could look out her window now without fear of interruption while making a number of discoveries not on their schedule, including some small cities. Not many of those, however. They soon were over open prairie, unfenced, perhaps unexplored, with nothing to look at except a dark cloud up ahead, off their No. 4 motor. Their pilot headed for that, climbing a little so as not to miss it. He hit it head on, leveling as they entered. They could see the rain smearing their windows now when he turned on his winglights for a moment. Or was that lightning? No, more likely that No. 3 motor. The plane picked up speed, became frolicsome, as though to show them it had no need for so many, they ought not mind heaving a little. They heard the pilot's talker click on but had to wait several minutes before he announced his intentions. Due to conditions they would have to make an unscheduled landing at the Cornhusker air strip, but no cause for alarm, he assured them, he knew the country well, had been here often. So saying he nosed sharply into the darkness, taking them down by a shortcut he knew, through lowering clouds that squirted cold water into their blowholes, down, down, yet down, until it seemed they should have hit bottom many times over, or were on their way to Death Valley. Thus folks' great joy when suddenly they leveled, longitudinally not laterally, over the Cornhusker air strip with six or eight feet yet to go. It was a marvel, how he found it, for the mud here was no different from the rest of the prairie and the tin box to one side had TERMINAL on its roof in fairly large letters, but brown. There were to be sure a few white houses in the offing, three exactly, but no one observed those until they had slushed to a stop in front of the terminal. The pilot tooted his horn, folks looked out their windows. No answer. Now all swung to the solid wham of a door. Where where was blue lady? It was Child's mother who sighted her, staggering heel-deep in ooze toward the houses; they could see, despite the poor visibility, that she had on her raincoat, her hood up, had her overnight bag, and in her hand a steaming pot of coffee. She seemed a little off course, for her transparent plastic overnight bag read Alberta in blue elite letters. Yet she made her sure way to one of the houses, whose door was already partway open, and just before disappearing inside she turned to wave a gay goodbye to the pilot. Giving her a blast on his wolf whistle he splashed off in a hurry, without waiting to tell folks where or when he would level.

How could he? He didn't know either, it soon was obvious. His old piece had developed a severe congestion in her tubes, from that air strip most likely, that was affecting her chronic weak heart condition, and he had to lash her unmercifully up through the fog and the ice and the blowhole-choking wetness of his cloud, cruelly heedless of her pitiful conkings, counting recklessly on a will to survive that any but an aquamaniac might have known to be long since extinguished, as though history were being made here and the Almighty being an interested Party must smile on it by way of proving the divine rightness of rain—as the Almighty at last did, gloriously (though behind their backs still growled unthinkable allurements) and folks turned down their blowholes and collars. Even now their pilot did not level but started back down hill, at roughly the reverse angle, strewing over the immaculate, unasking midafternoon sky lavish wingfuls of blessed water that shriveled gradually to splashes, then sprinkles, until, finally, down on all three in dry Denver, one lone greasy drip on the apron. Hard to say whether the man was pleased or not with his trip, or with his equipment; in any case he made no further demands on the latter but simply let it lie where it landed and strode at once to the door, which he opened himself, and after the briefest glance at the blue led his motley followers, proud, miffed, wet, wistful, across the hot cement flats to a clipper.

A blue lady was waiting, cringing at the tiny back door of a monster whose distended blue belly she eyed with pity and horror, all alone in her knowledge that what was indicated here was not more sacrifices but an enema. These doctors! Yet how warm were her greetings, smiling red face and weeping blue eye shadow, her unretractable bosom fragrant with the promise of imminent spearmint and coffee. She had to *shout*, for now Clipper was gagging. But how little it mattered: no one was listening. What they wanted was seats and they sought them, plunging, bucking, shouldering, stiff-arming passage, but Child had only to follow his mother's serene advance to two good ones with a good wide view of a window. This time they did not argue about positions but sat mutely viewing the seating. It seemed their gang was being discriminated against here, not just in the matter of seats which were all to the rear but the aisle was too darn narrow for good action. Even their pilot couldn't get through without being roughed up a little, and some of the gals and guys didn't like to see that, by gum they didn't. He wasn't so bad, he'd got them through, hadn't he? Well then, no fat hurry, lots of room for everyone, everyone had a seat didn't they, and old Stick didn't mind sitting on his ball as far as Salt Lake City. . .?

No time now to ask him—someone must have taken the blue lady up on that prescription, been blown clear back to New York for his trouble—Clipper took off all in a gush to a new-style preening or keening or overweening whining that it took them half the length of the runway to outdistance. Clippers are faster than sound, smell and smog of their own farting. They have to be—men, women and children find it intolerable. Blue lady, a little stun-faced and paler, brought them coffee which everyone sullenly accepted, the Cornhusker gang receiving theirs last of all even though they were nearer the creamer, and colder and wetter. All drank rather testily, even the natives up front did not seem altogether contented. There was little small-talk, less smiling, and scarcely any use made of the privies. Perhaps, deep down, they resented

being taken home in an incubator, or a thermos? Perhaps they sensed
something was missing. They had not entirely outgrown their sense of
sound, nor smell, nor taste quite yet either: but dead level at 10,000
in a Clipper they had a numbing glimpse of the day when they would
try to outglare the sun and find themselves lost in the darkness. Who
could blame them for chewing their gum glumly, for welcoming the
sight of crusty old Salt Lake City?

In fact the pilot himself seemed not quite ready for the kerosene
age: abandoning Clipper at the far outer edge of the runway he led
his gang to a handy piece of ancient equipment. This time he took
his blue lady with him. (He had lost his co-pilot somewhere, Child's
mother noted.) The other gang all decided to stay at S.L., and Stick
followed. It was in a way pitiful, in a way funny, to watch him hobble
away dragging his ball in search of a porter. Had he turned to look
back, the gang might have waved him goodbye, but he didn't. And
the apron was clean by the time they were all strapped in and hustling
along it with all the old chatter and gumption. They made it again.
Raising his voice their pleased pilot announced that they would level
at 3000 for dinner: there were hoarse cheers as the blue lady staggered
up the aisle with the menus.

Everyone, snuffling, passed up the Frozen Daiquiris, the Dry Ice
Martinis, and Coogan's Old Style itself in favor of Hot Buttered Rum
Toddies, which their resourceful blue lady had to brew up in her
creamer. Child's mother ordered Child one, as for a special occasion,
and ordered them both another to go with their Fresh Lobstertail
Cocktail, their Croquets de Poulet a la Clipper, their Hot Rum Pudding
Tasty. She ordered them one more to wash down their after dinner
anacin, since everyone else had. By now no one was snuffling, far less
coughing. They were too busy talking, talking not only to themselves
but to one another and everyone, Child's mother especially. She was
up on her feet. She stood in the aisle and commanded attention, raised
her steamy cup high to their cheering. "To our little girl in blue!"
she proposed to wild cheers, everyone joining. "For service 10,000'
above and beyond the call of duty. Our other girl, Alberta, gave us
coffee and chiclets and then she deserted us—*this* little girl gives us
Hot Buttered Rum Toddies and anacins and stays *with* us. . .!" She had
to break off for cheering and drinking. Then, "This is no ordinary
stewardess we have here," she concluded, "she's a nightingale!" She

sat down to a deafening roar of ungoverned enthusiasm, everyone
clapping and cheering, everyone pounding and stomping, their pilot
crying "Hear, hear!" over his speaker, which their blue lady fought
her way past congratulatory hands to the creamer, drew herself a long
hot one. Her raised cup, extended toward Child's mother, created
frenzy!

"Oh Child, I'd like to be one!"

"A blue lady?"

"No no, a *nurse*. I used to be one, you know, before I married
your father."

"Well, maybe we can make arrangements in Seattle. . ."

She nodded and patted, but no telling if she had heard him, for
the gang was drinking a toast to her now, their all-time favorite
traveling companion, their little white lady, and then to their pilot,
their little astronauty, to Cornhusker air strip, to old Stick Carson, to
his ball, to just about everything in this grand rummy old world except
Clipper, until their blue lady collected their cups, barefooted, over
Walla Walla. Some said the coffee she brought them was spiked, and
not with spearmint; others swore it was her same formula, but brewed
in her urn not her creamer; all found it hilariously sobering.

"Child, I haven't had such a party in years!"

"Neither have I!"

The gang agreed, sighing. They lay back catching their breath, to
hell with their balance, while outside their windows the languid earth,
not half trying, lost a friendly race to a highly favored evening, only
making it look good, until presently all that remained out there was
the sportive old moon playing a one-sided game of tag with the disinterested stars, the capsules, the tired balloons. Below, the orderly
lights of the tourists and truckers crawled intently along at eighty
or ninety. Why not pull over, the night seemed to ask them, until
morning? No, they blinked urgently, they couldn't. Tomorrow would
come soon enough, did they doubt it? No, they were taking no chances,
they would meet it. What then if it didn't come? Well, there was
always yesterday. But never a past, never a future, never now, this
copulative moment? Furiously blinking they crept on through the
night, too busy to answer it, too feeble to cut it to ribbons. Night
moved on to the mountains, where it lay undisturbed all the way to
what Child's mother took to be Seattle.

"Not yet, Mother, that's a new dam they're building."

"At *night?*"

"They're in a hurry."

She was deceived only once more, by Tacoma, before they both saw their destination blooming below them like some radiant nighttime flower that had been lavishly sprinkled with luminous water. It was at this hour from this point of view quite beautiful. But now they saw how it folded its petals, from the outside curling them delicately inward until only a pale orange glow at the center was visible; Child could almost believe he felt the blast of warmer air that had closed it. Soon even that smoldering heart was blacked out. Their pilot buzzed darkness. Now they could hear his radio cry weakly, before he came on to announce that Century 21 was experiencing a temporary failure of power, they would have to remain aloft until repairs were made. Meanwhile he had checkpoints to guide him: to the north and south the lighthouses beckoned, overhead the heavens were loaded. No call for alarm, he had gas, he assured them. Child's mother spoke comfortingly too. She found this a stimulating experience for an old gal who didn't get around much, she would keep watch at her window, let Child know if anything happened, meanwhile she knew he was tired, urged him to sleep if he possibly could. He could almost at once, and dreamed of coming to life in big soft fat circles, having just got hot wind of tomorrow's probable examination for Lamplighter.

PAUL METCALF

THE DOLL

The big old sedan drove down the mountain, going faster than it should around the innumerable curves and turns. The road, although paved, was not only narrow and treacherous, but wet from recent rain, a little of which was still falling. The air was damp and heavy with spring fog; the young poplar and maple leaves bordering the road were limp.

Suddenly, the brakes screeched and the car swerved and came to a stop, pulling off on the narrow shoulder, on a curve. The doors opened at once, and the occupants, six in all, came pouring out. With the exception of the driver, who was a woman, they were all circus clowns, in costume and makeup. Their clothes were worn and dirty, as though lived in day and night, and the makeup in most cases was splotchy and had started to run, so that it no longer hid the hardened, middle-aged faces. One of them carried a dummy, or doll, about two feet tall, costumed and made up as an exact replica of himself. He hugged the figure close to him.

The woman, walking in long strides, moved to the front of the car, where she was met by another of the clowns, and engaged in the continuation of a bitter argument. She was tall and masculine, wearing a black dress, and a man's leather jacket, open at the front. Her hair was straight and black, and her skin, drawn tight over her skull, was almost white. Her words were loud with anger, and her black eyes lashed at the clown. As though by common impulse, the two people moved away from the car, down the edge of the road, still arguing with each other.

The remaining clowns had gathered, automatically, at the rear of the

95

car. They were stretching their limbs, talking, in some excitement, and drinking, in turn, from a half empty bottle of whiskey. One of them was urinating. The clown with the dummy was clinging to his wooden figure, as though with a paralytic arm. He was very short, almost a midget, and was beginning to get drunk.

The arguing couple had moved around the curve, and were out of the others' sight. Their argument reached its highest pitch when the clown, who was taller than the woman, gave her a shove, and she fell part way down the embankment at the edge of the road. Regaining her balance, she crouched in the soft mud, and looked up at him. He was standing with his hands on his hips, watching her. Deliberately, she reached into the pocket of her jacket, and took out a black, man-size automatic. She raised it, and fired, once. Clutching at his stomach, his face agonized with pain, the clown fell, slowly, to the ground. The woman hesitated a moment, and then scrambled up the bank, and stood over him. She fired, twice, into his chest and stomach. Still holding the pistol, she leaned over, and pushed his body to the edge. She gave it a shove, and watched, as it rolled over and over, slowly at first, and then faster, down the length of the embankment. With a thud, the corpse struck a tree, at the edge of the woods, and then slid around it, and vanished under some bushes. The woman put the auto-matic back in her pocket; she turned, and strode back to the car.

The clowns were talking excitedly, hurrying their drinks, and eye-ing the woman surreptitiously, as she approached the car. Rain was falling more heavily, and thunder rumbled overhead. When the woman reached the door, the clowns disbanded, and returned to their places in the car. The doors were closed, almost at the same instant, and the motor was started. Churning the mud, as it crept back on the pavement, the old car set out again, at high speed, around the curve, and down the mountain. The rain came down in torrents.

At the foot of the embankment, under a clump of bushes, lay the dead clown, face up. His old costume was enveloped in mud, some of which had stuck to his nose, his forehead, and his cheeks, obliterat-ing the patches of rouge and powder. His eyes were closed, and his mouth open. It was a tired face, unshaven, prematurely aged. Soft spring rain, filtering through the leaves overhead, dropped on him gently.

Near the foot of the mountain, the road at last became straight, and the car took on more speed. Inside, the clowns, and the woman, were silent. Two of them slept, while the others sat still, staring straight ahead. The little clown with the dummy sat in the back seat, his mouth grinning drunkenly, thereby spoiling his resemblance to the doll. The woman crouched over the steering wheel, reaching out, regularly, to wipe off the wind-shield, which became fogged with their breathing.

In a change characteristic of the mountains, the rain suddenly stopped, the fog lifted, and the car, moving at high speed, passed into bright sunlight. At that moment, the woman lost control. The car slipped off the road, onto long, wet grass. Skidding and twisting, it swerved back onto the road at a sharp angle, the tires screeching on the pavement, and hurtled into the embankment on the opposite side. Bouncing back onto the road, it turned over three times, in continuous motion, coming to rest, finally, on its side, directly across the road. Almost at once, smoke began to flow from the motor, penetrating rapidly to the interior of the car. Muffled, agonized groans could be heard. In the driver's window, which was now exposed, at the top, as the car lay on its side, the head of the woman slowly appeared. It seemed to flow, or ooze, upward, as though not impelled by muscular effort. The eyes were raised, the whites of them staring at the sky. The face was expressionless. Coming to a halt, the head fell, slightly, and became hung, by the chin, in the corner of the window. The pupils of the eye disappeared, and the skin became totally blanched and motionless.

In the rear of the car, the back window had been broken, from within. For a brief period, a series of high-pitched, almost continuous screams could be heard. Two faces appeared, those of the dummy, and of his original and master, the little clown. The latter was streaked with blood, pouring from a gash on the top of his head. Pushing the doll before him, the clown struggled to reach the window, pride mingling with the agony in his clear eyes. But he was unable to get through the window. With a surge, he gave the doll a push and forced it through, so that it dropped to the road. His head sank down, then, and he began to slide back. His wrists, raised over his head, became caught in the fragments of broken glass remaining in the window; they remained thus, the hands open, and white, the fingers becoming stiff.

Fire broke out in the front seat of the car, starting in the old, dirty wool of the upholstery, and spreading to the back seat, to the occupants' clothes, and finally, to their flesh. There was no human sound now, nor any sound whatsoever, except that of the flames. The sun had disappeared again, and the sky was overcast, but there was no rain. The mountains, in the background, were still shrouded in fog. The fire burned slowly, and peacefully, crackling, as though with green wood, as it ate into the flesh and bones. Through the broken windshield could be seen an agglomeration of upholstery, ripped and burned, of shattered glass and steel, of shoes, and of naked, flesh-dampened bones, singed and burned. Mixed with the smell of flesh, was the sweet odor of grass, the grass that had been ripped out of the earth, on both sides of the road, by the swerving car. The damp air magnified its pungence.

There was an explosion, as flames reached the gas tank. The car seemed to disintegrate, hurled into the air, in all directions. The fire, scattered over the road, and into the wet grass, quickly died, except for a pool of oil and gas at the center, where it continued to burn slowly. The little doll, that had been shoved through the window, escaped the force of the explosion; now, however, the wide cuff of the clown suit caught fire, at the edge of the flames. Giving up its clothing first, and then its wooden body, the doll was slowly devoured.

Rain began to fall again, and the last of the fire died.

INDIAN GAME

Will went east,
>to where red dirt turns to pluff,
>and pluff to white, finegrain
>sand,

Sand and ocean.
Sand, sun and ocean,
>and unhorizoned clouds reaching high,

High, above the water—Will looked
>into a blind horizon.

Damn the gulls!
>*damn*
>*the heron, curlew, kite and rail—*
>*marganser, grebe and gallinule!*

God damn the tern and nigger goose!

The weather turns upon the weather
—midsummer handspring—
>and the ocean bakes a fish.
The sun is fat.

Turning to the land, Will discovered, across the sweep of beach, an approaching silhouette. The figure, despite distortions of lighting, was clearly that of a girl. She was walking up the beach away from town, planning to pass him, apparently, several yards in shore, toward the dunes. She followed a straight course, moving with athletic grace. He continued to watch her as she passed out of the distorted sunlight, came into her own substance and color. Her hair, dark brown, fell loosely across her shoulders. Her legs were long, slender at the calf, filling out within proportion at the groin and hips. She was tanned, but not too much, and wore a two-piece bathing suit, white. Her eyes, as he could make them out, were the color of her hair, and she had no make-up. Her breasts were firm.

> Palmettos, rattling in a slow wind,
> draw back, back
> from winds of violence.

> Sea oats fondle the air,
> and sand,
> singing a high song,
> Stings the crust of sand.

> Will's foot
> is still,
> While water warms his toes,

> And on Will's back,
> the eastward back,
> sweat grows.

Dry sand fell from his feet and ankles as he ran across the hard beach, swinging in an arc to approach on the far side, the shore side. She kept her eyes forward and he saw only the flowing, richly curled hair on the back and sides of her head until he caught up with her and fell into her stride, his arm almost brushing against hers. Then she turned to him. She started to smile, but her face became suddenly serious and composed.

Now she knows she knows that I am an Indian not a stocky white youth burned in the sun but an Indian. This is the body these are the cheek-bones the straight nose color not of the sun but of the man the body that played Indian ball game a mixture of football soccer lacrosse boxing wrestling played with sticks a hard ball no padding no shoes on a bare enormous stony field . . .

The tide was low, and a wide hollow lay in their path, ridged by the action of earlier waves, holding at its centre a pool of ocean. At the far end, through a single outlet, the water flowed gradually outward. A jellyfish hovered near the outlet.

> *History is not made by fish,*
> *not by the bass,*
> *the mullet or the cat,*
>
> *Not by the rugged-shelled oyster, or*
> *the jellyfish,*
> *holding off the tide,*
>
> *Not by the stingeree!*

At the water's edge, a broad sand bar curled into the ocean, standing just above the wave surface. The breakers parted in approaching, and lapped at its edges. Large gray gulls were gathered on it, and some took to flight, lifting themselves ponderously, drawing their legs to their bodies as they rose watchfully above sand and water. Those remaining on the sand crowded to the edge of the ocean, flapping their wings between flight and arrest, until Will and the girl had passed. Among the dunes, the palmettos became fewer and shorter, more wind-destroyed.

Will stopped suddenly, feet spread apart, and held the girl, his right arm gripping her waist, lifting her so that her toes barely touched the sand. With his left arm, he drew her shoulders toward him; she held him back, pressing both palms against his chest, and they became motionless, locked together.

> From Will's crotch,
> apex of the sand-leg man,
> her legs descend,

a plumb line
to the white,
        white sand.

Will's arm is stone,
    and the man
    —man and girl—
        are

    carved of sand,
Old figures cut against
    salt,
        high gull,
            and wind.

Face to face, their eyes met, head on. Hers were dark and large
and sober, framed in a tan face; they held Will's gaze steadily.

I to I,

    thought of time,
            and out of time,
    of tide,
            and beyond tide,

    red, and sun-fertile white
    girl, girl, girl, girl,

    the anger of nothing.

Although Will held her gaze, the edges of his vision nevertheless
"pulled in" the surrounding landscape—the soft, dissolving curves,
north and southward, of the beach.

And if the land be a map,
or the map a terrain,

And if a man be given,
or if a man uncover

What is the land, and
What is the form of the man?

If the map, of itself,
Be a form, a plan for

the discovery of land,

What brings the land,
What brings the form of the man,

into relief?

As suddenly as he had stopped her, she broke and headed for the
dunes. For a moment, he watched her, motionless. Then he started
after her. The soft sand approaching the dunes slowed her: she leaned
forward, propelling herself from the hips, swinging her arms awkwardly, like a young gull struggling to learn flight. At the edge of the
dunes he came up to her and caught her hand in his. They were panting and sweating as they trudged over the top and made their way
among the dunes, up and down, around the patches of grass and briars.
The wind descended to a whisper, and the air became sticky. Climbing
to one of the higher points, they found a shady hollow directly behind
it, and they jumped and skidded into the lowest part. Sitting down,
facing oppositely, their hips touching, they swung their upper bodies
in front of each other, and embraced hotly.

There was no wind, and the sun was relentless.

Through grasses, snarling
the earth, and
Briars,

Comes a murmur,
        captive:
    a murmur of wind.

Sweat,
        sweat and sea air

Separating, rising, they stood back from one another. Will's trunks, and the two pieces of the girl's white bathing suit, fell to the sand. For a moment they faced each other, naked in the hot sun and dampness, in the still air. With the exposure of the parts of her body hitherto covered, the girl gave a striped appearence—tan and white and tan and white and tan.

She made a gesture as though to run, a flurry, laughing a little, and he met it, halting her by implication. Again they hesitated, watching.

The whirlpool at
        the end of each breast
Draws her life
        into heavy, unwhirling air,

And to the hardness of the man.

As they came together he held her around the waist, and she leaned back, pressing against him. Then she came forward and dropped abruptly to one knee.

He lunged upon her, grasping her shoulders as she started to rise. Her legs passed between his, her knees bending her breasts rising and spreading before him. Letting him support her, she dropped her head back so that the ends of her hair touched the sand.

Among grass,
        briars,

Sea oats,
      and salt,

The hair falls,
    entangled,

A true tangent

His hands upon her shoulders, his legs dividing across her abdomen, he leaned over her and kissed her. Panting, he lifted his head and let her down slowly to the sand. He stepped back a moment, and then lowered himself and approached.

Kissing her thigh and groin, he continued across the gentle rounding of her abdomen until he reached her breasts—as he had moved, earlier, from the water's edge across the modulated surface of the beach, to the dunes.

As I have moved every autumn since I have played baseball over the level piney loam of the low country across the gently rolling sandhill uplands the lifting cotton and peach fields of the Piedmont the foothills the sharp friendly slopes of the Blue Ridge and into the Great Smoky Mountains . . . as every invader has ever moved from the water's edge the source across the gentleness and pushed climbed fought his way into the heart of the desirable land . . .

He drew himself up the dampness of her body. Sweat poured from them both, mingling and dropping to the sand. They were breathing audibly, their lungs plunging at the bottom of each breath into collapse, to expand again suddenly, gasping.

It is without movement
    that one begins,

Without labor,
    the one searching out
      the other,

As the fish swims,
    without movement.

Blood falls from the hills,
    the quiet spear

    is a Spaniard
    or a Frenchman.

Homes are fired.

Men gather meat from
    the trees,
    and chestnuts in
       the streams,

The deer is without a mountain.

The heart of
    the little squirrel
Is wrapped in the skin of
    the bear, and

The moon falls into the river.
The little boy without feet

    runs
    to the middle of the sun.

A dead man watches fire
    burn out the sumac
    on his groin.

The river is a pumpkin.

Sweat rolled over them, their bodies were salty and wet as though they were lying at the ocean's edge among the waves. Their eyes were watering, closed.

The sun burned intensely on Will's back. Lifting himself gently, he moved to the sand. She drew his head to her side, and shielded his eyes from the sun. In a moment, he was asleep.

*   *   *

When he opened his eyes, she was leaning over him, watching him. Her head, set exactly against the sun, shielding it from his eyes, seemed darker; the whites of her eyes stood out as though from negro flesh, and her hair was almost black against the brilliant sky. Her face was intent and good-humored, the lips parted slightly as before.

Stretching himself, scarcely moving, he pushed the sleep out of his muscles, as though pushing it down his arms and legs and out of his body. He raised one knee. She leaned back, touched it, ran her fingers lightly down his thigh to his hip. Shoving his elbows behind him, he raised himself, and looked down on her. She turned, resting her other cheek on his lifted chest, and their eyes met.

Hers are still watering her face warm with love and sorrow and uncertainty and fulfillment and perhaps fear her mind is divided like the tans .and whites of her body divided because she wants to talk to me to secure herself with words but more than that she wants to remain silent . . . we are both renegades outcasts I cannot guess her reasons but she must know mine she must know why it is that I swim at this end of the beach this far from town and perhaps there is a certain justice in it perhaps it is right I have no claim to the beach perhaps a Santee a Yemassee an Edisto yes but did Cherokee ever hold sway east of the middle waters of the rivers . . .

He smiled, and laughed, and gave her a gentle slap on the back. Raising herself, laughing, she sat back on her heels, her shoulders straight, her palms spread on her forelegs, so that save for the shape of her breasts she looked like a child.

Scrambling to his feet, he started out of the hollow, stretching his arm to her. She hesitated a moment, and then took his hand. They charged into the soft, steep sand on the bank of the dune, their knees pumping until they came to the top.

Still holding hands, they headed toward the ocean, walking, half running around the grass and briars, through the hollows and over the dunes. At the head of the beach, before descending to the flatness, they paused again. There was no one in sight. They remained still, gazing at the sky, the horizon clouds, the methodic rows of low breakers creeping in from the ocean. Warm ocean wind curled around them, cooling them only with its motion. Will looked down on her, on the tan legs, midriff, shoulders, arms and face, separated by two bands of white.

For an instant, she leaned her head against his shoulder.

Stepping forward, they broke the handclasp as they plunged down the face of the dune to the level of the beach. She ran as hard as she could, and Will held his pace to hers, running a few feet apart from her. As they reached the line of high tides the sand became hard packed, and the bottoms of their feet slapped against it.

The water was warm, scarcely cooler than the air. Will approached her and they ran close together, splashing each other's legs as their feet struck the foam. They ran through the first low breakers and on out. Will moved faster now, went beyond her. At the first breaker of size, he dove in, passed through it, and swam a few feet under water, close to the sand. When he came to the surface he turned, tossed the hair from his face, to see her dive in awkwardly and sit down. Catching the crest of another breaker, he rode it in, returned to her. She was laughing helplessly, splashing the water with her hands; her hair hung in wet curls against her cheeks. With both hands Will pushed back the hair, then slipped his arms under shoulders and legs and picked her up. She laughed and kicked, holding firm to his neck as he turned and faced the ocean.

Walking steadily, he carried her away from the beach. At each breaker he paused and set himself, one foot diagonally behind the other, his knes flexed; he lifted her body and she buried her face in his as the wave broke. They became covered with foam as he carried her further and further, walking, pausing, setting himself, and walking again. Between breakers his eyes were set upon the dim horizon, where ocean melted into sky. She laughed like a child.

When he could carry her no further, he let her down. Her arms clung to his neck, and she clasped her legs around his. They kissed, and he held her tightly to him. They were beyond the area of the breakers;

as each wave approached he gave a little spring with his feet and they floated up with it together, descending slowly on the water.

Finding that she could stand, she let herself down and they faced each other, sideways to the waves, still holding hands, floating up and descending as before.

The tide was still going out they found themselves carried away from the beach. Separating, they started swimming in. They swam easily, close together, watching each other. She still laughed occasionally, and gulped water, but she kept pace with him. Among the breakers they started to ride on the crests, moving more rapidly. He was more skillful than she and came to the shallow breakers earlier; he sat among them and waited until she floated in. Coming together, they embraced, resting as the water broke over their legs and hips.

> Waters pour two ways
>   to a joining, and
> Turn the matter.
>
> Warmness, channeled,
> Streams upon them,
>
> Upon the embracing,
>
>   and old warmth,
>   old exhaustion,
> Gulfing out of endings,
>   stirs.

She kissed him, grasped him firmly by an ear, by a lock of his hair. They slipped, lost balance, went under water, and came up spluttering. Breaking suddenly, she stood up and ran from him. She was laughing, exhausted. He rose and chased her, running parallel to the beach. She cut toward the ocean and he followed her. When he caught up with her, they were in the middle breakers; the water came up to his waist, and almost to her breasts. Facing the ocean, he caught her wrist, and swung her around. He lunged upon her, his legs spreading over her, and she fell back. Her head went under the ocean.

Reaching under her shoulders, he lifted her: she came up gasping. She had swallowed deeply, and her eyes were bloodshot, the whites of them broadly exposed. Mucous and ocean poured from her nostrils. As he drew her toward him her breasts seemed to sink against her chest, and she pushed against him with real force, against his chest, neck and face. Her fingers caught in his throat; he released her suddenly and slapped her. He slapped her again.

That is an energy gathering in me without release for many years since I was a youth and lived on the reservation played the Indian ball game the energy of striking an opponent with my hand or with the stick shoving him to the ground and fighting hitting wrestling him to give up the ball then to capture it and run an energy nowhere opened in the later game . . .

Her knees wavered and she reached toward his shoulders for support, gasping.

This is the decision the void the place where time stops the choice before an act enters the deadmarch . . .

Stepping back, he caught her hands in his. Facing the ocean, the eastern horizon, he watched her cough, struggling to approach, and held her off. They were between breakers.

The ocean,
foaming,

voided by clean land . . .

Stepping back again, he let her fall, and she went down on one knee, her face dipping in and out of the water. He lunged upon her like a dog, and turned her body under his. She struggled, her knees striking his back, her fingernails digging into his arms and chest; but he discovered her throat and pressed it with both hands, under the water. Letting her do to him what damage she could, he drew his fingers tighter and tighter.

Her motion grew slower, more lethargic. Her legs were almost floating. Gradually her body became taut, her hips pushing upward against the arch of his legs, her head turned back so that it almost touched the sand.

As the head turned before,

To the earth,
    a tangent,

Formed by her hair:

This was the beginning.

    and with this
I reclaim myself,

Recover what is
    in the conch,
    the gull and tern,
    the long coastal sky,

Draw back from horizons,
    from back breeze
    over marsh grass,

Come up from sand and briars,
Down from wing of curlew,

Out of mullet,
    clam shell, and
    frond of palmetto.

My parts fly back to my limbs.

Lifting himself, he jumped back from her.

It is as though she were a fish a porpoise a white whale belly-upward
and dead . . .

Her body turned over and over in the breakers, always at the surface. Her hair, following the motion, encircled her head so that her face was largely hidden; her breast and stomach and hips pushed forward on the thrust of each wave.

Jumping back further, he moved backward toward the beach, not taking his eyes from her. The tide was still retreating, slowly pulling her away from him, and there was a cross tide, carrying her up the beach.

Turning away for the first time, Will surveyed the land. After only a moment, he turned again to the ocean, and had to look more than once to find her. The body turned up, white and tan, in the foaming of a breaker, and then disappeared under the surface.

Facing the beach, the land, the continent, Will ran out of the ocean, to the hard sand. Bending forward, he ran hard, as he had not run in years, never in baseball; as he had not run since his youth. He ran toward the dunes, and the land beyond.

JOHN RECHY

EL PASO DEL NORTE

This is about El Paso (and Juarez: the Southwest), which so long was just a hometown to me and which now is different from any other section in America.

El Paso and Juarez are in the middle of the Texas, New Mexico, and Mexico white, white desert surrounded by that range of mountains jutting unevenly along the border. At sundown the fat sun squats on the horizon like a Mexican lady grandly on her frontporch. Appropriately.

Because only geographically the Rio Grande, which in the Southwest is a river only part of the time and usually just a strait of sand along the banks of which sick spiders weave their webs, divides the United States from Mexico. Only geographically. The Mexican people of El Paso, more than half the population—and practically all of Smeltertown, Canutillo, Ysleta—are all and always and completely Mexican, and will be. They speak only Spanish to each other and when they say the Capital they mean Mexico DF.

Oh, but, once it was not so. When the War came, Christ, the Mexicans were American as hell. The youngmen went to war wearing everything that was authorized, sometimes even more. Huge stars appeared on the southside tenements and government-project windows. OUR SON IS SERVING AMERICA. My mother wore my brother's Purple Heart to Mass and held it up when the Priest gave his blessing.

Outside El Paso City, giant machines dig into the mountains for ores (Smeltertown), and beyond that (where I used to climb poetic as hell) is a tall beautiful mountain.

The Mountain of Cristo Rey.

113

Huge processions go up this holy mountain. The people of El Paso, Ysleta, Canutillo, of Smeltertown and of Juarez march up climbing for hours, chanting prayers. The procession starts downtown in El Paso, outside the churches, and the groups join each other in the streets, kneeling at intervals on inspiration, carrying placards of the Virgin, Saints in colors. Small bands jazz solemnly, crying dissonant sounds. The shawled ladies of the Order of Saint Something grip rosaries and mumble and feel—as rightly so as anyone in the world—Holy. The priests in bright drag lead them up. They carry sadfaced saints. The small bands stay behind at the foot of the mountain, the musicians wiping the sweat off their dark faces, and drinking cool limonada and mingling with the sellers of coca-cola, religious medals. The procession winds up the mountain slowly past the crude weatherbeaten stations of the cross along the path. And at the top, finally—where they say Mass, the people kneeling on the rocks in the blazing white sun—is The Statue.

It is primitive Christ.

Fifty-feet tall. And it looks like a Mexican peasant. Mr. Soler made it. I think he was a kind of semi-atheist who didn't believe in God but believed in the Virgin Mary.

But the poor Mexican Christ, what it has to look down on—the line of desperate ants, as the Magazine (I think it was *Time*, or if it wasn't they would have) called it, of mustached, strawhatted men, braceros invading America.

Because the Rio Grande, no matter what you think, is usually dry, as I said, just sand and scrawny spiders and fingery indentations where water should be or was. Sometimes it is very full, though, and beautiful, and then the Rio Grande is like a dirty young black animal full of life rushing along the sand, swallowing the bushy dry banks. And I would walk along its bank, to the mountains. But usually it is so dry that the wetbacks can enter Sacred Country by merely walking across the River.

On their way to Georgia?

Well, Ive heard that from I dont know how many people. They say, for some strange reason, that Georgia is a kind of heaven where all good spiks go—some crossing into the country illegally, others standing at the Santa Fe Bridge lined up all rags and cloth bags and wooden and cardboard boxes and holy amulets, whiskers, waiting to be inspected by the Customs-gods. The Magazine also said, well,

wasn't it natural, those wetbacks wanting to come into America?—
Christ, they heard about sweet-tasting toothpaste. It really said that.
And if sweet-tasting American toothpaste aint enough to make a man
face the Border Patrol (as Bad as L.A. fuzz) and the excellent labor
conditions in progressive Georgia, well, man, what is? The Magazine
said it was sad, all those displaced wetbacks, but all that happened
though was that they were sent back, but they tried to come across
again and again and again.

(I remember a dead bracero near the bank of the Rio Grande,
face down drowned in the shallow water, the water around him red,
red, red. Officially he had drowned and was found, of course, by the
Border Patrol. And his wife will go on thinking forever he made it
with a beautiful blonde Georgia woman—loaded with toothpaste—and
so, therefore, never came back to her and the even-dozen kids.)

Which brings me to this—

The hatred in much of Texas for Mexicans. It's fierce. (They used
to yell, Mexicangreaser, Mexicangreaser, when I went to Lamar Gram-
mar School, and I thought, well, yes, my mother did do an awful lot
of frying but we never put any grease on our hair, and so it bothered
me—if God was Mexican, as my mother said, why did He allow this?)
Many of them really hate us pathologically, like they hate the Negroes,
say, in Arkansas. Here, it's the bragging, blustering bony-framed
Texan rangers/farmers/ranchers with the Cadillacs and the attitude of
Me-and-god on My ranch. It has nothing to do with the Alamo any
more. It's just the full-scale really huge (consistent with everything
Big in Texas—and Alaska wont change anything) Texan inferiority
complex. Dig: the Texas rancher strutting across San Jacinto Plaza,
all bones and legs, getting kicks from sitting, later, booted- feet propped
getting a shine from the barefoot spik kid, tipping him 50 cents—not
just sitting like you and I would get a shine but sitting Grandly, and
strutting across the Border owning the streets, I hope he gets rolled.
They dont really dislike Mexicans in Texas if theyre maids and laborers.

So the Mexicans live concentrated on the Southside of El Paso
largely, crowded into tenements, with the walls outside plastered with
old Vote-for signs from years back and advertisements of Mexican
movies at the Colon—the torn clothes just laundered waving on rickety
balconies along Paisano Drive held up God knows how. Or if not, in the
Government projects, which are clean tenements—a section for the

Mexicans, a section for the Negroes. Politely. Row after row of identical boxhouses speckled with dozens and dozens of children.

So this, the Southside, is of course the area of the Mean gangs. The ones on the other side are not as dangerous, of course, because they are mostly Blond and mostly normal Anglo-American kiddies growing up naturally and what can you expect? Like the ones from Kern Place —all pretty clean houses at the foot of Mount Franklin—and if those kiddies carry switchblade knives, at least they keep them clean, and when they wear boots, they are Cowboy Boots.

The southside gangs—that's a different thing. Theyre blackhaired. And tense. Mean and bad, with Conflict seething. El Paso's southside (the Second Ward) gave birth to the internationally famous Pachucos. (Paso—Pacho.) They used to call them boogies, marijuanos, the zoot-suits—and the baggy pants with the pegged ankles were boogiepants, and, man, those tigers walked cool, long graceful bad strides, rhythmic as hell, hands deep into pockets, shoulders hunched. Much heart. They really did wear and still sometimes do those hats that Al Capp draws —and the chains, too, from the belt to the pocket in a long loop.

And sitting talking Mexican jive, *mano,* under the El Paso street-lamps along Hill and Magoffin and Seventh, around Bowie High School and next to the Palace Theater digging Presley and Chuck Berry and Fats Domino, outside the dingy 40-watt-bulb-lighted Southside grocery stores, avoiding *la jura,* the neo-Pachucos with dreamy junk eyes and their chicks in tight skirts and giant pompadours and revealing 1940-style sweaters hang in the steamy El Paso nights, hunched, mean and bad, plotting protest, unconscious of, though they carry it, the burden of the world, and additionally, the burden of Big Texas.

Well, look. In East Texas. In Balmorhea, say. In Balmorhea, with its giant outdoor swimming pool (where that summer the two blond tigers and I went swimming, climbed over the wall and into the rancid-looking night water) there were signs in the two-bit restaurant, in Balmorhea-town then, that said WE DO NOT SERVE MEXICANS, NIGGERS OR DOGS. That night we went to the hick movie, and the man taking the tickets said, You boys be sure and sit on the right side, the left is for spiks. So I said I was on the wrong side and walked out. Later at Kit's aunt's ranch, the aunt waited until the Mexican servant walked out and then said, miserably, Ah jaist caint even eat when they are around. And because earlier had made me feel suddenly a Crusader and it was easy now, I walked out of the diningroom and said well then I shouldnt be here to louse up your dinner, lady.

And you never know it—to look at that magnificent Texas sky.

And something quite something else. . .

Once upon a time in El Paso there was a band of fairies—yes, really, in El Paso, Texas—and this city became a crossroads between the hot Eastcoast and the cool Westcoast (fuzzwise, vice-wise) or the hot Westcoast and the cool Eastcoast, depending on where oh where the birls had got Caught Jay-Walking. And soon San Jacinto Plaza (or Alligator Plaza—sleepy crocodiles in a round pond, so tired and sleepy they dont even wake up when little kids grab them by their tails and flip them into the water) was a fairy paradise, rebel. The birls would camp there in that little park—the queens with pinched-in waists, lisps, painted eyes, digging the soldiers from Fort Bliss, proclaiming Too Much. Alas, they went the way of all fairies. The Inevitable Clean-Up came, and the fuzz swooped on them jealously and to jail they went, all fluttering eyelashes justifying gay mother love.

Now it is not the same passing through the park not seeing the queens, not hearing their delighted squeals of approbation floating into the clean summer Texas air. Not the same at all.

At Christmas is when Mexican El Paso is magnificent. I dont mean the jazz at San Jacinto Plaza (trees and lights and Christmas carols and Santa Claus). I mean the Southside Christmas. A lot of them— most of them, in fact—put up trees, of course, but many of them put up nacimientos. My father used to start putting ours up almost a month before Chirstmas when we lived on Wyoming Street. It's a large box-like thing—ours was, anyway—about six-feet wide, six-feet tall, eight-feet deep, like a room minus the front wall (the minus faces the windows, which are cleaned to sparkle), and inside is a Christmas scene. Ours had the manger and the Virgin of course and St. Joseph, and angels hanging from strings floating on angelhair clouds. To the sides of the manger were modern-looking California miniature houses, with real lights in them—some had swimming pools. And stone mountains. On one was the Devil, red, with a wired neck so that the slightest movement made it twitch, drinking out of a bottle. Christ was coming, and naturally the Devil would be feeling low. My father painted an elaborate Texas-like sky behind the manger, with clouds, giant moon, the works—lights all over, and he enclosed the boxlike nacimiento

with Christmas-tree branches, and then, one year, he had a real lake—
that is, real water which we changed daily. The wisemen on their
way. Christmas lights, bulbs, on top. He moved the wise men each
night, closer to the manager. The Christchild wasnt there yet—he wasnt
born. Then on Christmas Eve everyone came over. My mother led the
rosary. We all knelt. Someone had been chosen to be the padrino—the
godfather—of the Christchild to be born that night. He carried the
Child in his hands, everyone kissed it ("adored" it), and then finally
He was put into the manger, in the hay. We prayed some more. *Dios
te salve, Maria, llena eres de Gracia.* . . . At the stroke of midnight,
the Child was born. Then there was a party—tamales, buñuelos, liquor.

Most Mexicans are Catholic, of course. My friend Sherman is an
intelligent Catholic from Evanston and he said it was bad when Catholics substitute, like the Mexican people he loves so much (Sherman
in Chihuahua City that time trying so hard to look like a Mexican
peasant, with Indian sandals and muslin shirt—him, six-feet-two and
Scandinavian curly blond!—and people staring at him thinking he
came probably from the American moon), the image of the Virgin
for that of Christ. He loves the Virgin himself, a lot, but still he says
Christianity should mean Christ. (He says he would rather see the
Mexicans worship the Sun, incidentally, like their Indian ancestors,
then become protestants, because for a while the Baptists especially had
a full-scale campaign going, and pretty soon, on the doors of the
broken-down southside houses they tried to invade with irresistible
chocolate American candy and bright colors for the shoeless children
living in cardboard houses along the Border appeared signs THIS IS A
CHRISTIAN HOME PROTESTANT PROPAGANDA WILL NOT BE ALLOWED.)

But that's not what I started to say, which was this—

The Patron of Mexico is the Virgin of Guadalupe. The story says
She appeared to Juan Diego, one day, and in order to make the
incredulous know that he had indeed seen Her, She stamped Herself
on his shawl, and that is the one you see in Mexican churches, all stars
and blue robe. Oh, how tenderly they believe in the Virgin of Guadalupe
(*even the Priests!*), and how they love Her, the Mother of all Mexico.

How they Respect mothers because of it. Mothers are a Grand
Mexican thing. They belong sacredly in Mexico and the Mexican
Southwest.

Dig: a serious Mexican movie. The favorite theme. The son goes away. The little Old Mexican Mother stands at the dingy door with her black shawl sheltering her from the drizzling rain. Christ. The son goes away, and forgets about her. He becomes a Great Matador, lured by women like Maria Bonita before the President's wife—and this is only gossip—chased her out. Wow! The Little Mother in the Black Shawl wanders over Mexico, working for harsh people—like sewing in a factory where, she's so old, poor thing, she cant keep up with the heftier ladies. She comes at last into a very rich home in Mexico City. Of course. It's her son's home. But he doesnt recognize her, and she decides not to tell him who she is so he wont be ashamed of her. She'll just be satisfied to be near him. He is gruff. "Old woman, look how much dust has accumulated on this my favorite table." "Yes, sir." She wipes it. He is cruel, yells at her despite the pitiful black shawl. She takes it, and this is true. Mexican mothers and wives do take it— not Americans, and this is what grips a Mexican audience. Loyalty. One day the Big Corrida comes on. The wife is digging it on television (she cant bear to go it live). The matador is gored. The shawled Mother screams, MI HIJO!!!! The wife knows now, and being Mexican herself and on the way to becoming a Mexican Mother, she hugs the Old Lady. They run out, get a cab, go to the bullring. There he is. Unconscious. Dying. The beautifully dressed wife pulls the shawl off the the little old Mother and proclaims to the dying matador, "Die if God wills it—but not without knowing that—This—Is—Your—Mother!!!!" Everyone is crying, the unnatural son repents (as he must), and all three live happily ever after.

This is real. Mexicans really love Mothers. Americans dont. I dont have a single American acquaintance whose mother faints everytime he comes home and again when he leaves. Mine does. The Mexican mother-love has nothing to do with sex, either. You can imagine an American wanting to make it with his mother. She is slick. She looks almost as young and bad as he does. But can you imagine making it with your mother if she wears a Black Shawl, and even if she doesnt, if she acts all the time like she is wearing One?

How does it follow, then, that a little Mexican kid (as I will tell you later) can say to an ugly big Texan tourist, HEY MEESTER YOU WANT MY MOTHER SHE IS CHERRY? I'll explain it by describing something else. Someone related to me lived with a woman for 25 years. Suddenly they decided to make it permanent. Get married. After 25

years, remember. Not silently, you believe it. They had a real Mexican
bash, with canterers and mariachies, and the bride's 26-year-old daughter (from another engagement) crying all over the place—and the bride
dressed in WHITE, and the Priest that married them and had been
invited over saying well, God was certainly smiling in pleasure to see
His laws being obeyed.

There's a Mexican Saint you make bets with. San Calletano, patron
of gamblers . . .

Mexican religion is a very real thing, not lukewarm at all, nor
forbidding and awesome. Mexican Catholics (and this, again, includes
the Priests) believe in a God with two hands, two feet, eyes—the
works. The Devil has horns, a tail, and he is most certainly red. Each
church in the Mexican sections of the Southwest, and all of them in
Juarez have Real patron saints, who guard them. On their days, they
have kermesses—this is like a fair. On the really big days (for example,
in May, the month of the Virgin Mary), the Indians (who are Catholics
although their religion is still magnificently pagan, having room in it
for Mayan, Aztec, other legends—witchcraft—right along with the story
of Jesus) come into the City. The matachines (they used to scare me,
like the beggars I will tell you about later) are Indians dressed in all
kinds of feathers, painted all over, making dance marathons, dancing
for hours. Some Indians—I think the Tarahumaras—run all the way
from somewhere like Chihuahua City to Juarez, offering I suppose
that amount of exerted energy to the Virgin. In religious frenzy, they
burn an effigy of Satan—a kind of man-shaped catherine wheel. They
light him up, and the bastard burns shooting fire straight from hell.
The people yell up a storm, and the Politicians and Gangsters shoot
real bullets into the air in this tribute to the Virgin Mary.

Juarez!

Time and time they try to clean it up. But Juarez is Dirty. And will
be dirty long after we are gone.

The same close acquaintance I mentioned before is a gangster in
Juarez. They really have bigtimers there, like they used to have in
Chicago. You can always tell them by the way they wear Western-type
gabardine clothes *a-la-mejicana*, and hand-tailored boots (NOT square
cowboy-type), and always, always, but ALWAYS, sun-glasses, especially

blue ones. My relation in question belongs to a very respected Mexican class—the gamblers, the gangsters, the pimps, the politicians.

At night, Juarez is all lights and neon signs. Clip-joints. Cab-drivers pouncing on tourists. This is your chance to find out If It Is True What They Say About Oriental Girls (i.e., does their Snatch slant?). Find out, they say, from Chinese Movie Stars. Get dirty postcards made to order. Peepshows. Men, women, dogs—sometimes a horse. And the little urchin barefoot Mexican boys saying, HEY MEESTER and they really do say meester YOU WANT MY MOTHER SHE IS CHERRY. Bars and cabarets, Exotic entertainment. The Chinese Palace. The Stork. The 1-2-3. Girls, girls, girls. The thickly painted prostitutes stand in a line openly soliciting at bars—big fat red lips, narrow-waved long hair falling over great big dangling earrings.

At the Taxco they had this magnificent woman who looked like Mopsy of the cartoon. A genius. To wit: She dyed her hair *bright green*. And her costume was a large green powder-puff, same shade, right on her snatch. That started one of the many clean-ups. So she had to get decent. She added two tiny green powderpuffs, the color of her dyed hair, to her nipples. . . .

In the early clear-blue Texas-Mexico mornings, the whores, the pimps, the politicians, the gangsters, the gamblers—that is, the upper classes—are all asleep, the rich ones in their grand mosaic houses (sometimes the roof leaks, but, oh, rebel, the luxury of them pads!). And then another group of people takes over the City—the vendors and the invalids and the beggars.

You've never seen anything like it—never so many people lacking legs, eyes, hands—the legless rushing around in their homemade wagons on skate wheels, with padded cloth knuckles rolling themselves along. At almost every corner, outside the market, along the park in front of the Church of Guadalupe, you see the gaunt women sitting draped in black shawls. You cant tell if there is anything wrong with their eyes or if they are just rolling them in a kind of poverty-frenzy. They used to frighten the hell out of me, they reminded me of Death when I used to think of Death as ugly. Around these women there are two or three or more kids, all filthy, mud caking on their legs, and inevitably a baby suckling their withered breasts, where Im sure nothing is coming. *Madre de Misericordia*, they chant, *virjen sagrada de los dolores, una caridad.* And kids without legs, hobbling along on tree branches. And so much damned ugly poverty.

The market is all sounds and colors—and of course odors and smoke. All along the streets. *Aqui, marchante,* says a seller luring the buyer from a competitor. Prices fall fantastically, and a kind of haywire auction in which the buyer has no part goes on fiercely. Stands of cheap jewelry like broken kaleidoscopes, medallions of Christ and the Virgin, Indian masks, limeade and orchata (drunk by everyone out of the same two glasses), leather whips, hasaderos (like cheese), tacos in roalroadcar-like restaurants outside, tortillas pounded by the squatting women. And flies all around, always, lord, yes, always flies—especially around the red watermelon slices or pineapple slices where the little girl stands absently with a stick with thin strips of paper tied to it to shoo the flies unsuccessfully to the next stand and fans herself instead. And Mexican toys (always with strings to be pulled and someone kicks someone, or a chicken bites a woman, or a rock falls on an Indian). Paper flowers—different colors, from one stalk, covered with wax to make them look velvety—skirts with gaudy pictures of the Virgin of Guadalupe, of Catholic churches in the City. Boots (purple, yellow, green)—and everyone calling at the same time. Hot "rubies" for a dollar—"emeralds," "diamonds" for pennies. And the flies buzzing.

Outside, in the streets, especially outside the market, the kids in empty parking lots offer to watch tourists' and American shoppers' cars while theyre gone—or offer to carry groceries to the streetcar (sometimes running away with them to hungry brothers and sisters—I hope), or offer to show you the City, or take you to a whorehouse.

I forget exactly on what day it is—the 16th of September or the 5th of May—both are important dates in Mexican history, like the 4th of July—the population of the Mexican cities gathers outside the City Hall, the Courthouse, etc., waiting for the President, the Governor, or the Mayor, depending, to give *El Grito*—The Yell. At midnight, it comes. VIVA MEXICO! And they echo, QUE VIVA!!!!

And cockfights!

And witches—lots of them.

They hold a position in the Mexican Southwest almost as respected as that of the priests. There's a kind of hierarchy among them, headed by Don Ben (the Pope of El Paso's witches). A problem too big for an ordinary witch is referred finally to Don Ben, a root-twisted old, old man. (He wont die—he'll shrink.) I remember when I was a kid, an *espiritu maligno* kept bugging us, misplacing my father's glasses. We ended up going to Don Ben. He fell into a dramatic trance, and when he woke, he said, My *tata Dios* (daddy God) is so busy right now He suggests we call Him later. We called later, and *tata Dios* said to leave the *espiritu* alone and it would go away.

My second-aunt ("she of the blue hair and the deer eyes—ahhh!" —Don Ben's description of her) has had a picture of her husband, inverted in a glass of strange liquid, behind her bedroom door, for years. About 40 years ago, he left her—and this will bring him back some day.

And why should devout Mexican Catholics (as they are) consult witches (as they do)? For the same reason that a man with a sick ear goes to an ear specialist. . . .

And bullfights.

But they dont get the best bullfighters at the Juarez arena, although sometimes they do. The real sight—when the bullfight aint good—are the American in huge Mexican hats being so Mexican, and the inevitable cluster of Mexicans around them, the fawning ones glorifying the grand American—these are the sick ones—and then the opportunists, hoping the money will rub off and willing to see to it that it does.

At dawn, on a lady's birthday—even now and in El Paso—five or six men gather outside her window, singing and playing their guitars. The sun is about to come out. They sing softly,

> *Estas son las mañanitas*
> *Que cantaca el Rey David.*
> *A las muchachas bonitas*
> *Se las contava el asi. . . .*

Now the lady comes coyly to the window, standing there until they have finished the soft dawn singing. Now all the neighbors' windows are up and everyone is listening. (No one thinks of calling the police.) Then the lady invites the serenaders inside, and they all have early-morning coffee, *pan de dulce, menudo.* Then the sun is up in the sky.

The Southwest sky. Beautiful and horrifying. And therefore Wonderful.

Because in all the blunder and bluster of Texas about the wrong things, one thing is really so. The sky.

When it is beautiful it is depthless blue. The sky in other places is like an inverted cup, this shade of blue or gray or black or another shade, with limits, like a painted room. Not in the Southwest. The sky is really millions and millions of miles deep of blue—and in summer, clear magic electric blue.

(How many stars are there in the sky? was our favorite six-year-old children riddle. The answer: *cincuenta*. Which means fifty, but also: countless. And it's true, so true.)

Before the summer storms, the clouds mass and roll twisting in the sky clashing fiercely, sweeping grandly across the sky. Then giant mushrooms explode. The sky groans, opens, it pours rain.

But before the windstorms, everything is calm, and then a strange ominous mass of gray gathers in the horizon. Then swiftly, in a moment it seems, blowing with the wind, the steel clouds cover the sky, and youre locked down here, so lonesome suddenly youre cold. The wind comes. The tumbleweeds rush with it.

And always there's the fearful wailing.

THE CITY OF LOST ANGELS

Southern California, which is shaped somewhat like a coffin, is a giant sanitorium with flowers where people come to be cured of life itself in whatever way. The sign on Crenshaw, surrounded by roses, said: WE TREAT THE SOLES OF YOUR FEET FOR INNER PEACE. . . . This is the last stop before the sun gives up and sinks into the black, black ocean, and night—usually starless here—comes.

You came here to find the wish fulfilled in 3-D among the flowers— the evasive childworld (some figurative something to hold hands with like you used to with Mommie until you discovered Masturbation), the makebelieve among the palmtrees that the legend of the Movies (soda-fountains and stardom and the thousand realized dreams which that alone implies), of perpetual sun (never the lonesomeness of gray . . . lost . . . winter, say, or of the shrieking wind), the legend of The Last Frontier of Glorious Liberty (go barefoot and shirtless along Hollywood Boulevard) have promised us longdistance for oh so long.

You shut the windows, drew the blinds, bolted the doors. Still, life came screaming at you. So you came to Southern California to dash yourself against it.

Like inmates in other sanitoriums, of course, those who came to be cured sometimes die prematurely—but among the roses and the sun: in a swinging haven. So this is why you stay if you stay or come back if you come back: *You can rot here without feeling it* . . . and what more have you been led to expect if youve lived this long? And although youre still separated from the Sky, trapped down here by the blanket of smog and haze locking you from Heaven, still theres the sun almost all year round, enough—importantly—to tan you healthy Gold . . . and palmtrees . . . greengrass . . . roses, roses! . . . the cool, cool blessed evenings even when the afternoons are fierce. . . . And the newspaper in its "Forecast of the Stars" omits The Sign of . . . Cancer and replaces it politely with The Sign of the Moonchildren in its gentle Zodiac. . . .

And what you came hoping to be cured with (which is what some-one else came to be cured *of*— your sickness being someone else's cure)

is certainly here, all here, among the flowers and the grass, the palmtrees, the blessed evenings: sex and religion and cops and nymphs and
cults and sex and religion and junk—and these, along with Hollywood
Boulevard and Main Street downtown, Laguna Beach, Laurel Canyon,
La Jolla in the sun, etc., flowers, palmtrees, smog, Sunset Strip, greengrass all year round, roses, Strip City, all-night movies, fairies, religion,
roses, sex, manufactured dreams (and the doctor that can create clouds
and stars) . . . and sex and flowers and junk and religion, fairies
and sick, sick cops make Southern California The City of Lost Angels
as I would like to tell you about it now.

It's dainty blue flowers you think how phony, theyre paper—but
theyre truly real this time, outside the bank on Hill Street off 8th downtown (with the poetic street-names: Hope, Flower, Grand, Spring)
where the man put up a sign: WE WILL BE OPEN SUNDAY YOU
BUY FLOWERS FOR MOTHER—flowers like white Easter, plants
and vines inside the buildings when you go see your attorney—flowers
illuminated outside by lights hidden beneath the green tropical-leafed
plants across the street, among other places, from The Church of the
Open Door over which like in the old college cartoon the sign flashes
neonbrightly JESUS SAVES like an advertisement for the bank around
the corner. . . .

Oh, yes, flowers . . . flowers from the Garden of the Roses by
Exposition Park next to the Dodgers, flowers into the hills—orange and
yellow poppies like just-lit matches sputtering in the breeze—carpets
of flowers even at places bordering the frenetic freeways where cars
race madly in semicircles—the Harbor Freeway crashes into the Santa
Ana Freeway, into the Hollywood Freeway, and when the traffic is
clear, cars in long rows in opposite lanes, like two armies out for
blood, create a *whooooosh!* that repeating itself is like the sound of
the windswept ocean, and the cars wind in and out dashing nowhere,
somewhere, anywhere. . . .

Where?

To for example the golden beaches; Laguna and the Artists and
Mamma Gabor; La Jolla and the Elite, set like a jewel in a ring of
gleaming sand, next to the mysterious cave—and the sailors nearby
flooding San Diego with make-it; Santa Monica and everyone, where
pretty girls and boys turn brown in the hazy sun lazily rotting like

mangoes but they dont know it, beside the frenzy of Pacific Ocean Park (dig: POP)—"Crystal" Beach—Jack's and the Girls and the would-be kept boys . . . the waves lapping at the sand like frothing tongues— and Long Beach—and the rollercoaster that went hurtling like a rocket and sent the youngman plunging into the ground like a bullet while his girl laughed convulsed at the impossible absurdity . . . the now-ghost of Muscle Beach where the men with the balloons for muscles posed for each other, until The Authorities of Santa Monica (Aghast and Indignant) Found Three of Them Shacked with Two Negro Girls, One Twelve, the Other Thirteen, and the city council of Santa Monica, why, it proclaimed: like this is The End. . . . To Venice and the beat generation in stores where the man like a slightly smaller slightly less hairy gorilla encouraged his urine-scented little girl to play in the traffic while he read a swinging Ode to Allen Ginsberg, amid the beat odor of urine and beer, while away along the Long Beach Pike, teenage girls with painted lips hustled sailors in the park and tough merchant mariners looked for Negro women in San Pedro.

It's more flowers: birds of paradise with long pointed tongues; blue and purple lupin; joshua trees with incredible bunches of flowers held high like torches—along long, long rows of phallic palmtrees everywhere with sunbleached pubic hair. Even downtown if you stand at 9th Street looking up at San-Francisco-like-ascending Grand Avenue (do this on one of those rare Los Angeles mornings that come suddenly like a miracle, when the sky is clear of smog and haze, truly Blue, depthless Blue like a Texas Sky, and youre liberated into it as it were Heaven), you see—magic!—a row of palmtrees! They lead you out, farther, out along Wilshire Boulevard, into Beverly Hills and the jacaranda trees—more flowers (flame-red hibiscus for the rich, rich people—Palm Springs, especially: resort, USA . . .), Amarillo lilies— and Bel Air and Laurel Canyon, Mulholland Drive and Marlon Brando's wife, and into: . . . houses hiding in the trees crouched low (the witch-house out of Hansel and Gretel—and I have to tell you the lady in slacks, shades and calypso hat walking her pink poodle)—houses hiding snobbish or embarrassed, others brazenly shooting up, or trying for clean air, desperately piercing the smog; stooped over like vultures in the hills, wings spread in imitation of Flight.

And I like to think Valentino's falconhouse will make it, soaring away—away . . . to tango-swinging angels.

Los Angeles is Clifton's Cafeteria.

On Olive.

Next to Pershing Square.

And it's draped in verdure outside somehow like a demented Southern plantation in a movie.

But inside!

Inside, to the tune of "Anniversary Waltz" palmtrees burst into lush neonlife! erupt into fourth-of-July-sky-rocket pink! and blue! and green!—phony trees and flowers outlined with neon tubes all over, and the walls of the cafeteria simulate rocks. All around are rainhuts—but surprisingly no rain—draped with lonesome yellow thatch. As you walk upstairs, balancing your all-you-can-eat $1.25 tray—passing the of course American flag, theres the organ, and the man playing (against the sound of waterfalls gushing over phonyrocks and sometimes into your tray) "Anniversary Waltz" for the couple from Kansas here to celebrate their anniversary, wholl write the Cafeteria Folks expressing their Sincere Gratitude (and their letter, thurrillingly, will be printed in the Food for Thot, which is the brochure published weekly by the Cafeteria, full of Inspirational Poetry (Walking, for example, Through the Dark Holding Hands With Thee) and Friendly Thots for the Miseries of the Day). And if youre out and out, you can get for a nickel (or nothing if you aint got that) a pint of multipurpose food containing every swinging vitamin and necessary mineral to get you through the infernal day, and the Citizens of Skidsville stand hands extended for their box of vitamins and minerals before the lush counters of meats and fruity desserts and gaudy salads that look like they'll bite back—all neonlighted among the simulated caverns and the waterfalls, the thatched huts, strains of "Anniversary Waltz," the American Flag, the tough chick with the camera and the leis about her neck: "Can I take your picture honey for The Folks Back Home?"—and a neonlighted Cross.

Suddenly, that junked-up day, along the serviceline, the cat from New York rubs his pupiled eyes like he cant place the scene: dig the woman in the long flowing drag, man. She was dressed in a kind of robe, with like a turban, green and blue and purple, and sandals, and bright-gleaming anachronistic bifocals which reflected the neonlighted flowers like miniature searchlights.

She had the air about her usually reserved for someone who has just enjoyed A Death In The Family.

Well, she glides through the serviceline with a truly virginal air, sits down, smoothing the folds of her drag—away from the crowd— but benignly, all hushed words and Virginity. Finally she gets up—she ascends. We followed her, like hypnotized, to a place to the right of the entrance—still, remember in the neon cafeteria—where a sign says:

THE GARDEN.

Down the narrow panel of stairs directly under the toilet with many mirrors and Hawaiian scenes in the Lounge. Past the picture of The Founder. Into The Room—where the lady in drag replaces another lady as virginal as herself—like holy sentinels changing the guard.

Now The Room—

And here is The Loom, and the lady is suddenly explaining to us, standing like that picture of Ruth St Denis, that this is a replica of a loom used in the time of Mary. Dig, she drones on like a holy record (we turning her youll pardon me on), the tables, all genuine replicas, dig the benches; the beautiful parchment books with the Holy words.

Soon, she will allow us to pass into The Garden.

And when we passed into The Garden, through a replica of a wooden door, the bifocaled lady stayed behind like a dream when you wake and it's gone—and we stooped into a kind of cave and sat in the dim murky gray light. I could detect the faintly stagnant odor of probably a phony brook somewhere.

Then a voice booms out from somewhere:

"MILLIONS HAVE PERISHED IN WAR AND TERROR. We survive. . . ."

It tells us how lucky we are. Then The Voice tells us about Christ. It tells us about Sacrifice. Then leading to it I forget just how (the tune of Anniversary Waltz kept running persistently through my mind, though you cant really hear the organ down here), The Voice ends with: WHAT SHALL I DO???? Maybe this is not what The Voice had in mind, but what we did was what the bifocaled lady had told us to do—why, we passed into—*lo and behold!*—The Grotto of Medita-tion. . . .

Under the lush neon jungle erupting upstairs, beyond the tough chick taking pictures with leis around her good-looking neck, under the gushing fountains and the multipurpose vitamin food—under the sad yellow thatch rainhuts and the American flag, and the organ now playing Happy Birthday, directly beneath the head and the mirrors and the South Seas scenes:

Theres Christ.

A giant white statute, kneeling before a rock, hands clenched. And then the lights hidden somewhere behind the cavelike rocks (like the lights hidden all over the city to illuminate flowers, or a statute, or a cannon) become brighter, slightly, slowly, then dim—slightly, slightly.

And in the weird light, Christ seems to shift uncomfortably. . . .

As we came out for air like submarines, the lady in blue and green drag and the crazy-gleaming searchlight bifocals, still basking in the radiance of someone whose Dear has just Recently Departed, standing behind the Things For Sale, her wrists touching each other delicately, palms creating a U before her face, said:

O boys why dont you buy some colored slides of our Beautiful Garden—they make Lovely gifts to send home—or just plain old Souvenirs? . . .

Motionpicture theaters downtown featuring three movies and hard floors for sleeping when you dont dont care—strung along Broadway and Main Street like a cheap glass necklace—Main Street between say 4th and 6th with jukeboxes rattling rock and roll sexsounds, blinking manycolored, and the Main Street is mean looks and the arcade and magazine stores with hundreds of photographs for sale of chesty far-away nevertobetouched women in black stocking and spiked heels, and the vagrant youngmen trying to score no matter how—along the arcade and the stripmovies, the live New Follies and the flesh-show where the young boy with his hands in his pockets pled with the nymph bumping brutally before him, please, please, *please* honey do it some more, *right here!!* while she Did It on the apron of the stage, snatch crowning the inaccessible V of her spread legs, and he sighed and sank into the seat . . . and even on Main Street: it's Dreamland—Dreamland where the girls in tight reddresses dance for hire in the speckled light and crowded Marty lonesomeness extending to Roseland on Spring Street (a title for, say, a musical play by Tennessee Williams), while at the

Greyhound station leading everywhere the Vice squad vengefully haunts the head and you cant tell them from the real-life fruits; move to the Waldorf or Harold's on Main Street with the long accusing mirrors where you can hustle the lonely fairies for anywhere from a fin to whatever you can clinch or clip—even, expediently, in the head—very, very quickly—for say a deuce standing before, once, the scrawled message: IN THE BEGINNING GOD CREATED FAIRIES & THEY MADE MEN . . . or Chi-Chi's with the femme queens, the sad young-men with sallow painted faces—shadow of the 3-2-6, now closed, downtown on Spring, where outside, the junkie who looked like Christ asked you right out did you want him to turn you on?

And moved to East Los Angeles where the spade after-hours club seethes with conflict, swings with junk and jazz—black-gleaming faces crying hate the fayboys, not so much in the other largely spade bar farther away on Broadway where outcasts from everything hang, and in the head sweat-gleaming fay and spade faces focus intensely on the dice, cramped bodies in the tiny room exploding with the odor of maryjane smoke more powerful than at Gloria's downstairs when the heat is Off—while the spade chicks with the classic butts squeezed into gold and orange hugging dresses wait outside, and on the dancefloor the bulldikes and the femme-queens dance with each other—the roles of course reversed but legal—broadshouldered women and waist-squeezed youngmen.

The dikes are leading the queens. . . .

Main Street again and the surrounding area to Skid Row: sweaty apartment houses squeezed tightly against each other (but not far from the green ebony trees, the carnations . . .), Spring Street, Los Angeles Street—Skid Row: squeezed hotly protesting against each other, walls greasily containing food from days' cheap cooking, cob-webbed lightbulbs feebly hiding from sweaty plaster peeling in horren-dous childhood-nightmare leper shapes snapping at you, windowscreens if any, smooth as velvet with grime—rooms squashed in by lonesome-ness where for a buck a night you die that night easily until checkout time—and you can face the day again in that endless Resurrection—among the roses nearby somewhere—the flowered trees before the courthouse on Wall Street, and you step out having paid a fine and see them—lavender and yellow flowers—and a short, short palmtree, with arched leaves shrugging what the hell.

And the Skid-rowers (now talking about them at night without pad), flying on Thunderbird in this sunny rosy haven— past the owl-faces of the Salvation Army fighting evil with no help from God or the cops, wonder, these citizens of the country of Skids, shall they go to the Mission (and surrender to the owlfaces and the empty uplifting words before the lambstew) or just give up right here, now, on this corner, now on this doorstep, surrender for the night into the pool of their own urine—a surprise to discover—until the heat patrol comes by and makes up their minds, and they wake up hung over in the drunk tank: then out—into the green, green grass, the flowers. . . .

Oh, Pershing Square. They tell me it used to be a jungle of Expression as opposed to now (relative) Repression.

They cut down the bushes.

Gay fountains gush in the midst of the wellkept grass—a stream of colored water, amber, blue. Once, on Christmas (when the Vice squad couple, a woman and a man, fatherly-motherly spoke to the young vagrants about why dont you go home and get a job—before the bulls took them, the young vags, for a ride in the wagon to the fingerprinting glasshouse)—once, as I say, oh, on Christmas, they had The Dancing Waters on Pershing Square. The bums and the studhustlers and the queens and the vagchicks and the preachers and The Visitors stood on the grass in the middle of the park before the fiercely perspiring man manipulating a set of keys which caused like spurts of water to change colors as it gushed into the air, swaying to the rhythm of the corn-music. . . . Very pretty . . . very, very pretty.

And on Easter, the cops roll eggs for the lonesome children, future, probably, delinquents, whom later theyll spreadeagle against the black and white car with red searchlights like science-fiction eyes—rousting them for mean kicks.

Pershing Square.

It's bordered on the Hill Street corner, at 5th, by a statue of a general, and on the 6th Street side theres a statue of a soldier. They love soldiers and generals in queer parks. On the Olive Street Side, at the corner of 6th, is a tough cannon pointing at Clifton's Cafeteria. And on the 5th Street corner is a statue of—really—Beethoven with a stick, and he is glowering, I mean to tell you, at the Pershing Square menagerie: at, say, Ollie talking sometimes sense, mostly not, mostly rot, and once they threw a firecracker at him which landed on the flowers and sputtered. Ollie was then going to make a Citizen's Arrest, like he says Officer Temple, the fat cop, told him he could—but Ollie, oh, he didnt figuring, rightly, the Lord couldnt be on the side of the bulls.

Talking about Citizen's Arrests—whereby anyone can come up to you and say I saw you do such-and-such you are under arrest—once this chick clipped a fat looking score trying to make it with her sweet-boy, and a square caught the scene and marches to the clipping chick and says she is under arrest, he is making a Citizen's Arrest because he pinned her clipping the score. All the swinging hustlers from Pershing Square, oh, they gathered round, while the chick, checking the mean-it faces all with her, said to the square, Like youre going to make a what arrest, man? The Square naturally walks away, leaving the chick with the clipped wallet: a Fine example of Togetherness.

And the statue of Beethoven (getting back) glowers fiercely at the studhustlers coming, coming, and the lonesome fruits coming after them; hears, daily—brutally—Holy Moses strumming a soulful guitar, sees the hungry nymph who haunts the park around the men's head, search-ing the homeless youngmen, so used to being clipped she leaves her bread on the dresser of the rented room to make it easy; and Beethoven glares at the bucktoothed Jenny Lu, singing spirituals; at the Negro woman sweating quivering in coming-lord-type ecstasy, for sometimes hours, bumping and grinding (lord-*uh!* . . . mercy-*uh!* . . . hallelu-j-*uh!*) at each *uh!* in a long religious orgasm; at the tough stray teenage chicks making it from night to night with the studhustlers at Cooper's coffee-and-donuts-for-a-dime; at the epileptic youngman thanking God for his infirmity among the roses and the warm sun; and the five white Angel sisters, standing like white candles while their old man preaches, and they hold in turns a picture of Christ crucified. The blood is wax. It gleams in the sun. And the cutest of the angel sisters, my of course favorite, with paradoxically alive freckles snapping orange in the sun, and alive red sparkling hair, is always giggling in the warm Los Angeles smog-afternoon among the palmtrees—but the oldest is quivering and wailing, and one day, why, the little angel sister, she will see theres nothing to giggle about, her old man having come across at last with the rough Message, and of course she will start to quiver and wail where once she smiled, freckles popping in the sun.

All this to the piped paradox of the Welkian-Lombardian school of corn. . . .

Downstairs, in a little tool hut, hidden in typical sneak-cop fashion, is the baby-joint, like, where the fat bull daily interrogates the new butch-hustlers in the park—and downstairs, like a swollen toad, the bull sits before the pictures of the wanted angels. . . . And Miss Trudi, the swinging queen whose stud husband got busted by this bull, periodically starts rumors about Officer Temple and how she saw him in the mensroom doing you-know-what. . . .

But when the heat is On in Pershing Square, watch out. Like not long ago. The studhustler who used to hang in the park snapping a whip around the water fountain killed the chick like 17 years, who was having such a great time, wheeeeee, and he killed her with an iron. Then he strangled her. Vengefully—vengefully for not having spotted the psyched-up stud before the papers implicated them— the bulls stormed the park. And everyone, hiding out on Main or Spring or Miramar, said, that lousy psycho, man, screwing up for everyone, had to go and kill that chick.

And didnt recognize that the greatwinged bird had merely chosen the guise of Murder to swoop ridiculously upon him.

Longing for a Texas Sky . . .

The sky here is usually a scrambled jigsaw puzzle—allindefinable smears of grayish-blue.

And longing for a Texas Sky, I went to Griffith Park Observatory, made famous by James Dean in "Rebel Without A Cause" (and the Lord, oh, He took him away to save the pardon me go-mankind, and left us Marlon Brando in a suit).

It's circular, the planetarium where they reproduce the Sky— shaped like half a womb—like the Hollywood Bowl—and in back of your seat there are headrests so you can look up comfortably. In a moment, they will simulate the most beautiful Sky youll see in the City of Lost Angels—an imitation Texas Sky. Here it comes! A skyline . . . hint of clouds . . . the black night creeping up . . . the stars appear. . . . Youre truly gone—as if the half-womb had opened magically and carried you into the real Sky. But now a Voice announces this is such a planet, such a star, drones on, shattering the illusion—and then there appear Walt-Disney-like cartoons of the figures of the Zodiac on the simulated sky. The illusion is over. Youre sitting in a slick shell-shaped auditorium with a voice telling you about distances, etc. They play "Afternoon of a Faun." Now the shellsky turns, spinning, churning you out of the dream. The lights come up. You walk into the smoggy day. . . .

To Forest Lawn, to gloat at the tombs. See the hills all green, the tasteful stones—the marble Depiction of Life (or Love?) in a garden, with benches. Sit in as a fourteenth guest on the duplication of The Last Supper. A super mosaic. Then you go to the actual Crucifixion. A cinemascopic painting presented first in sections, then you see at all—and the sick voice of the ubiquitous announcer (is it the same Voice?. . .) tells you again about Christ like talking about the local boy made good—in such a way I thought this cat's flipped—hes a sadist digging the Crucifixion.

You came to find the dream fulfilled, the evasive childworld.

You go to Disneyland, and you walk through an umbilical tunnel (dig) and you enter the mouth of a whale (Dig) and (Dig!) pass through replicas of nursery dreams! and I dont wonder that when you came out you looked for Mommie and you were stooped over, like curling up. And went to Santa's Village later—and believed in Santa Clause—because there he is, with all his helpers, before your longing eyes. . . . And Knott's Berry Farm, tribute to live TV Westerns (I wanna be a cowboy when I grow up), and they held up the stagecoach, and the chorus girls did a Can-Can, flinging out their garters coyly at the adult tourists shouting with naughty delight. (Their wives thus have an anecdote for The Folks, how the Can-Can girl looked straight at Harry All Through The Show.)

Remembering the swallows, to the Chapel of Capistrano with the giant bell and the sunken gardens where the fruit that day later going to Laguna Beach the long, long way said to hell with the swallows, wheres the monks? . . .

And I with my time-obsession stand longingly before the Hollywood Ranch Market watching the clock move backwards. . . .

Dash like a crazy somekind animal on the Hollywood Freeway, into Sunset Boulevard (and remember Gloria Swanson going mad thinking shes playing Salome for Cecil B DeMille in knickers but the flick was shot on Wilshire Boulevard where the slick building now commands attention— a modern act of faith—and Erich Von Stroheim, said Mr.

Brackett at USC, insisted there should be a scene of him ironing her panties), to Vine and the recordstore and the TV studio where the visiting ladies in the live studio say oh hes much handsomer on television, and at home say oh hes much handsomer in person—to Hollywood Boulevard, most disappointing street in America—expecting to see The Stars in limousines, and extras in costumes— and see instead the long rows on either side of stores and counter-restaurants and B-girled bars and moviehouses—and, happily, that day, a giant picture of Susan Hayward, the swingingest star in the movies—in a sexpose screaming out against the railroading LA cops I WANT TO LIVE!!!!

Toward the end of the stretch of more-or-less activity, before the street turns into softlawned houses and apartment units where starlets live lonesomely wondering will they make it, finding no substitute for stardom in the carefully rationed joints of maryjane for manufactured dreams—there (before the soft-lawned swimmingpooled houses) is a coffeehouses for teenage queers. Inside the mosaicked windows like a church, the dike with pencil and pad, stocked up on bees, writes love poems to the femmetype teenage fairies. After 2 in the morning, they wait in line to come in.

Now heres the Chinese Theater. Your own big foot can rest where The Great Star's tiny one rested, impressed in the cement—though sometimes, tough to say, not quite so tiny, and youre disappointed to find that Marilyn Monroe (sigh) and Jane Russell are represented by their hands, and on premiere days at the Pantages the unenchanted crowd forms early to glimpse the enchanted men and women—and the searchlights screw the sky—while the lady from say Iowa sighs ahhhhh . . . writing mental postcards, and the twin Boswells of the Golden Cinema World—the screeching ladies with the hats and the weird—one of them—personal grudges against *Lolita*—record the phony fable of the Stars, from the dim nightclubs on the Strip—and Chasen's.

While the cafeteria in Beverly Hills serves caviar hors d'oeuvres . . .

Off Las Palmas, along—but on the opposite side—the outdoor newsstand where professional existentialists with or without sandals leaf through a paperback Sartre and the horse-o-manes (going tomorrow to the races where theyll see Lucille Ball) leaf through the racing forms, and the fairies cruise each other by the physique books and the same lady from Iowa staying at the Biltmore for a convention of the PTA buys a moviebook—off Las Palmas on Saturday nights the oldman graduate of Pershing Square writes Bible inscriptions on the street, in chalk, neat, incredibly beautiful letters. The young highschool delinquents with flattops proclaiming their youth heckle him cruelly in merciless teenage fashion while he dashes out his prophecies of notunlikely doom, and the fairies having crossed the street on their way to the Ivy (where Miss Ana Mae plays her organ coyly) say my dear she is Too Much why doesnt she get a Man and swish on giggling wondering nervously does it show (which ruins a birl) and will they make it tonight and if so will it be someone Nice and early please God so they wont have to add to the shadows on Selma—while the queen who left her telephone number in the toilet at Coffee Dan's waits—this is only conjecture—nervously by her telephone wondering will someone call?

The palmtrees look down apathetically—but green—from the surrounding hills.

Mmmmmrrrrrrumph! The motorcycles dash by on the Boulevard—ghosts of the Cinema Bar where the sadists and the masochists, now scattered, used to hang, rubbing leather-jackets and staring at belts and boots and exchanging notes with sketched whips across the bar now slowly transferring far out (intentional) to the Satellite and the Jupiter. . . .

Away . . .

Away, beyond the house hidden in the hills where the Doctor of Something Divine stood on the balcony like a fairytale wizard—highpriest of a cult—making clouds and stars appear where there were none—blessing the world from the balcony—and later, inside, preaching love and fraternity, serenity and subsequent contentment, while he padded our legs fraternally, serenely, contentedly—away, away, outside, beyond the spiritualists and the Holy Ghost Services, the maps of Life, dividing life into tiny blocks like beehives—far from the fat Negro woman sprawled like chocolate pudding on Main Street, snoring, the copies of "The Watchtower" falling from her lap to her fat tired feet—beyond MacArthur Park and the little boats where if you aint got a pad but got a willing fish you rent a boat and screw her on the pond, surrounded by grass, dark-green in the light night, under the stars—the odor of, of course, flowers, and justmown greengrass—beyond the other side of the park where hot mouths lurk in the bushes and the spade cat killed a cop while the ducks shivering out of the water made a noise like laughter—beyond the miles of flowers and greengrass, plants in the downtown buildings, away from the fruit Y where the fairies sunbathe naked with semihardons—beyond the signs on the sidewalks that say LAWD and you think of a religious Negro but it stands for Los Angeles Water Department—far from Strip City on Western and the nymphs with the tantalizing G-strings feeding on hungry yearning eyes— beyond the gossip at Schwab's on the Strip in the afternoons where the beautiful girls and boys go to be Discovered in one way or another (and one of them put a doublepage inside-spread ad in the daily variety film journal, with an almost naked sexpicture of herself, a man's shirt clinging wet to her nipples, open in a V almost revealing her own—and the ad said shes available to Furnish New Blood To Hollywood—she is The Challenge to the movies—call her up and see, and soon after, another ad—another sex picture. HOLLYWOOD HAS ANSWERED!!!! And very soon after, why, a young cowboy without shirt, he does the same thing, and he says he too is available to furnish, this time, New Masculine Blood To Hollywood—he also is A Challenge to the movies—and soon, why, Hollywood has answered him too, the ad says, and it shows another picture of the cowboy—and a new phone number) (and the starlet who advertised two months ago now advertises shes back in town again)—and, oh, away, still moving away, from existentialists who used to grace the Unicorn and Cosmo Alley until they became famous as "beats" and now the tourists pay 75 cents for a cup of coffee and stare at each other wondering is he one? beyond Coffee Dan's and the young punks, the bars on the Boulevard and the B-girls looking at their watches, the bar on Cahuenga and the B-boys looking at *their* watches where the maleprostitute walked into the women's toilet and the flashy woman followed him . . . far from Chinatown . . . as real as a "hot" Juarez ruby . . . beyond the Men's glamorshop on Sunset, where in a penthouse lavishly decorated the select clientele of gentlemen change the color of their hair subtly, gossiping about the Stars over a cup of Italian coffee in the natural light from the windows overlooking the trees and the flowers—beyond the sirens incessantly screaming—away, beyond the miles of geraniums and grass, past in the summer the stands of youngmen and oldmen selling strawberries and corn at bargain prices—beyond all, all this . . . up there on a hill, threatening heaven, piercing the sky brazenly, all glass and vines, the ocean thrashing beneath it, is The Church of the Wayfarer designed by Frank Lloyd Wright's son.

I am glad to tell you that now at last it has been properly immortalized by Jayne Mansfield when she wed there in kewpiedoll I think pink.

To Southern California everyone comes: to be Discovered and get in the movies, to be loved by the world, to find out if indeed your Brother is your keeper, to find the evasive child-world, or to find God in fruit or vegetables or in the sun or ghosts—or standing on a balcony creating stars and clouds . . . or to bask in the sun—to rot without really knowing it . . . to think youll be cured, with sex, religion, junk, cool nights, etc. . . . or to cater to personal grudges by joining the Los Angeles Police Force' and so attain to holydom and omnipotence and wear the stick like a mighty scepter and the badge like a sort of misplaced halo—and become merely another gang in a many-gang rumble—and brag about it, like the one who said he could keep me 72 hours, for nothing, merely because I was "wise." I had been playing a schizie game' to myself, pretending I was a Pachuco, walking cool, past the May Co., on Hope Street, incidentally—walking with long bad strides, shoulders forward, hands outward—a harmless schizie game, youll agree—and as Badge No. 4118 frisked me on the street, in the afternoon—on the Lord's Day, too—running his hands down my thighs, I asked him was he getting his kicks.

Later, at the station, why, he say I give him a fuck-you finger as he pass me (not true) and it sound so funny even the detective break up and let me go. And when the tough bull go out, with me, I ask him will he give me a ride back where he pick me up, and this, it put him on bad—but he still have his Badge, boy. (And guess what happen now automatically to my middle finger each time a bull car pass? . . .)

And if youre a head or a hype, well it's heaven for you in the LA jails. Outside, sometimes, it's not too cool to get. But inside, you take your choice like buying candy bars. Hard or soft. And the junky in the joint died from an overdose.

Dig. Significantly.

Walking along Hollywood Boulevard the other afternoon thinking about how I would end this, I thought I would say:

R.

I.

P.

or maybe say that rats in a maze possibly wouldnt know theyre lost if they had roses and poppies and sun grass and palmtrees swaying in the cool, cool breeze—and childhood dreams in 3-D: a maze shaped at the same time conveniently like a coffin. And I was thinking about this when I saw her, coming out of Kress's on the Boulevard: a wild gypsy-looking old woman, like a fugitive from a movie set—she was dark, screamingly painted . . . kaleidoscopic earrings . . . a red and orange scarf about her long black hair . . . wide blue skirt, lowcut blouse—an old frantic woman with demented burning eyes, and as she stepped into the bright Hollywood street, almost running into the suntanned platinum blonde getting into a Cadillac, this old flashy woman began a series of the same gestures: her right hand would rise frantically over her eyes, as if tearing some horrible spectacle from her sight. But halfway down toward her breast, the gesture of her hand mellowed, slowed, lost its franticness.

And she seemed now instead to be blessing the terrible spectacle she had first tried to tear from her sight.

I heard a siren scream, dashing along the palmtrees.

CHICAGO, SAVAGE CITY

You get the impression that once Chicago was like a constantly pregnant woman, uneasy in her pregnancy because she has miscarried so often. After its rise as a frontier town, plush bigtime madams, adventurers, and soon the titanic rise of the millionaires, the city's subsequent soaring population—all gave more than a hint that Chicago might easily become America's First City. But that title went unquestionably to New York. Brazenly, its skyscrapers, twice as tall as any in the Midwest city, symbolically invaded the sky. Chicago, in squat self-consciousness, bowed out. It became The Second City. . . . The movies started here. But after the industry's initial growing pains, the exodus began to palmtreed Hollywood. Chicago waved goodbye to the movies. . . . And once, too, along 57th and Stoney Island, the important writers gathered, and the American literary renaissance began. Jazz musicians came up the long, long river, bringing American jazzmoans, converting them to Chicago Jazz. But soon this wave of creators drifted away restlessly. Once again, Chicago had miscarried.

But now, like the slightly less pretty, less accomplished sister in the family of America's foremost cities, Chicago seems to proclaim: "What the hell?" And saying what-the-hell, in each smoky breath it takes every morning when it uncovers itself of the night, Chicago concentrates now on its own personality, to become a city on its own terms—and sometimes with a vengeance.

Chicago, actually, is two main cities: north and south, divided by the river and the great medieval-like drawbridges that separate to let the giant barges pass. And within north and south, east and west, Chicago appears at times like a cluster of villages and ghettos: the former displaying quiet small-town scenes duplicated by every "clean" American city; the latter teeming with the sights and sins of the Great American Cities.

It is the monstrosities of a city that largely give it its personality.

And the most monstrous of Chicago's sights is the Madison Street jungle.

The enormous Kemper Insurance Building, built by one of Chicago's titans, Samuel Insull, to house the Civic Opera, is a huge gray ugly building a block square along the river. Looming darkly more than 40 stories high, it gives the impression of a great bulwark, a great fortress. Almost symbolically (with a large square area windowless, blind), it turns its back arrogantly to the west side of Madison.

And West Madison stretches in shabby tatters for blocks of leprous buildings. Networks of fire escapes cling to the crumpling walls like steel spiderwebs. Intertwined among the transient hotels and the harsh yellow-lighted bars with the ironic names (The Kings Paradise, The House of Rothschild) are the missions, each presenting its scrubbed face to the stained desperate faces of the doomed tramps, waiting for the sermon and whatever else they'll get.

In one, a deacon-type athletic man, radiating health, shouts: "I got a friend in Jesus"—while an old tramp, doubled over in a wrecked heap, experiences a religious (drunken, hungry) fit, howling: "Lord, Lord, Lord!" . . . And after the services, shaggy old and young men get a pamphlet which shows the wellfed face of TV star Ty Hardin, grinning. "LIFE HAD NO MEANING," says the smiling Mr. Hardin. And the tramps, before they begin to pace the streets again funereally, can learn how The Star had "Two big cars, money in the bank, a new home, world-wide fame, and over a thousand fan letters a week. Yet," he is quoted, "I was miserable and dissatisfied."

Miserable and dissatisfied, with no cars, no money in our out of the bank, no fame, and no address to receive even one letter, men along Madison sleep under parked cars, trucks. One man rolls onto the street, groaning, while the parade of wined-up zombies passes ignoring him. Men stand like displaced sentinels. Dismal mask-faces hang outside doorways. Shadows huddle sinisterly, drinking. And from the street, you look up into the apartment buildings, through the naked windows of the tiny cubicle rooms. They reveal more haggard faces peering blankly, skinny bodies of uncaring women in slips, men without shirts. All have the same look: the look of no-longer-questioning, resigned doom.

A beat-up old man chases a wine bottle along its course into the gutter. He yells at it: "Go on, damya—into the gutter where ya belong. I ain gonna touchya no more!" Instantly, three men jump out of the shadows to retrieve the bottle. Discovering it empty, one smashes it on the filthy street.

The beach in Chicago is not so much a beach as a stretch of concrete along the lake. To get to it you walk through a subway tunnel. Lights slanted on one side of the wall flash on you like interrogation lights. Guiltily, you come out on the concrete beach. Through cracks in the cement, weeds and patches of grass struggle desperately for life. . . . Look back, and you see the outline of the Gold Coast, a stretch of luxurious apartments, glistening. Somehow, for all their plush elegance, they resemble clean hospital wards. Rows of giant apartment buildings like monsters ready to march snobbishly into the lake turn their backs on the rest of the city. They huddle close to each other as if for protection. Some of the buildings are squat, others slender—all somehow healthy and muscular. I saw no faces peering dismally out of *these* windows.

Walking along the Gold Coast, at night, past the signs of 10-room suites for rent, I was stopped by a cop. He said I looked suspicious. "When you walk around the Gold Coast," he told me haughtily, "you oughtta wear a suit. Otherwise, you stick out suspicious."

On the beach at night, ghostly waves seek out life, dashing against the shore. Teenagers swim, men fish, young couples make love. The lake is a wide expanse of black.

Negro and white tramps sleep along the fringe of the lake, against a cement wall, huddled tightly in blankets.

Chicago is a city in which the old fuses with the new. It's a city haunted by memories of once-elegance. . . . South Prairie, once the street of mansions, is now a series of office buildings. Fashionable synagogues, abandoned, along West Douglas Boulevard in the Lawndale area, are now Negro Baptist churches, revivalist centers. The New Michigan Hotel, once the headquarters of Al Capone (echoes of big-time gangsters, mass murders that doubly immortalized St. Valentine) is now surrounded by public housing developments. And the University of Chicago holds on courageously to its accolade of Liberal

School, America—yet the first nuclear reaction took place here. . . .
Even Chicago's famous stockyards seem on the verge of becoming
haunted with memories of once-greatness. Still much alive, continuing
to belch their rancid odors, they feel nevertheless the threat from
Kansas City and Omaha.

Like picture postcards, clean, neat, new neighborhoods dot the city's
jungles prettily.

Beyond the five-and-tens and the big department stores (Sears &
Roebuck, democratically, crosses the tangle of the elevated into the
wrong side of the tracks), State Street becomes carnival street. . . .
Tattoo joints; novelty shops (horror masks leering among rubber
cobra snakes); arcades ("Parisian Movies," "Chauffeur Photos," "Art
Films"). Tough girls shoot pool. Sailors stand in corners. Burlesque
bars coax you with NO COVER, NO MINIMUM. The Gayety Burlesque
features Teddy Bare and Borden's Ice Cream.

As I entered a burlesque theater, a tall gaunt man handed me a
pamphlet that asked me: ARE YOU BORN AGAIN?

Inside the Rialto Burlesque on State Street, there is the usual awed,
almost-religious restlessness of burlesque audiences before the show
starts, as a man like a mortician announces he is making an "unparal-
leled offer of thrills." Double-talking—telling us this offer is made
possible only because of "advertising" and because they sell "Borden's
Products," he offers us a veritable Kit of Kicks for just 50c—"not ten
bucks like it would costya at any stagshow," he tells us, as he removes
from an envelope a familiar-looking booklet, familiar from high-school
days of self-conscious, groin-throbbing sexnaughtiness. "In this kit,"
the mortician-announcer tells us, winking suggestively, "is a new edition
of Big Dick Tracy . . . Learn how the lady got his gun." Also included
in the bargain kit is a set of dice "from Czechoslovakia . . . Look
through one—and, boys, I guaranteeya—ya wont believe wotyasee.
Then hold the other one up—and wow! Put the two together—and
youll see a real E-motion Pictures." In addition to these two sex-
treasures, "you get a picture of one of our most popular strip queens,"
he tells us, explaining that this is no ordinary photograph, because:
"It's been specially treated with a chemical. When you get home,
boys, locate The Spot; sprinkle The Spot with water—and just watch

what happens—you won't believe it." As he walks up and down selling the sealed envelopes, the anxious audience digs breathlessly into its pockets for the sexmagic 50c.

What you *really* get is a booklet of cartoons, not especially naughty —right out of any drugstore-stand magazine—and not about Big Dick Tracy. When you look through the "dice from Czechoslovakia," following the directions carefully to get that "E-motion Picture"—you can't, indeed, believe your eyes. You see . . . nothing—except the dice themselves. As for the "specially treated photograph," you can sprinkle it with water, rub it with a wet towel, submerge it in a tub, and it remains the same: the leggy photograph of an almost modestly clothed girl.

Two questions still obsess me: How do "advertising" and "Borden's Products" make this possible? And how *did* the lady get Big Dick Tracy's gun?

As if in rebellion from nearby Evanston—the home of the militant-Victorian Women's Christian Temperance Union (the current president is Mrs. Tooze, whose name so strangely rhymes with "booze"), Chicago is an open town in many ways—and because of that, redfaced conventioners, wife-free for a few days, invade the city—with printed tags on their lapels.

One result of this has been that street-walkers have graduated into the relative safety of "call girls," working out of fancy hotels, bars in the area of Brush Street. Occasionally, you see one of the studiedly pretty girls walking along hurriedly. From a car a man calls to her. "Can't tonight, honey," she answers unequivocally, "I already got a date—call me some other time, okay?" . . . Restaurants and bars keep up signs that merely say: WELCOME CONVENTIONERS.

On weekend evenings—time out for play—conventioners flood the burlesque shows.

Chicago's stripshows have grown up with Las Vegas'. The young barker at the door assures you you'll witness AS MUCH AS YOUR EYES CAN SEE. In this case, he's almost right.

Blondes! redheads! brunettes!—lips liver-colored in the changing light shouting Ah-haaaa like cowboys; hands edge toward hypnotic spot between the legs, rest there caressingly; hips momentarily mag-

netized, suddenly released, swinging sex around; now kneeling—fingers
teasingly on the breasts, playfully pinching them, coyly affecting looks
of mock pain. . . . Now here's a tawny girl, a Negro Brigitte Bardot.
Tiny, like a sextoy, she squirms her butt cutely, the G-string, blue,
like a phosphorescent badge etched across her slim thighs. Spread legs
radiate their unfulfilled invitation. . . . And now a woman with breasts
like round searchlights appears. Teasingly, she removes one patch from
one breast, covers that breast with her hand. Now the other patch comes
off, covered quickly again by a hand. Suddenly she drops her hands
to her sides—apocalyptically revealing completely naked full-grown
breasts crowned by pink nipples. She presents these cupped in her
hands like an offering to the hungry audience. At the apron of the stage,
she bounces her breasts playfully, they jiggle temptingly like white-
jelly. The music blares "Night Train" from the jungle of sex. Her
hands at the back of her neck, her naked breasts pointing toward
heaven, she tenses her stomach into a tight "8," legs arched open.
She slides her finger into her G-string, untying one side, slowly—letting
that side dangle. . . . And she groans now, thrusting out her thighs,
simulating orgasm.

Chicago has its touches of Contemporary California Eccentric—
slick Big-City America. (We can disregard the Worsham College of
Mortuary Science as purely functional.) But more difficult to disregard
are the artificial flowers along State: futile ugly splashes of paper
imitations clustered in shabby baskets. . . . Chicago has its Poodle
Parlor, its Quid Restaurant (swim show! girls! mirrors!), its French
Village—a painted conglomeration of pseudo-New Orleans, neo-Cali-
fornia decor. And, too, there is The Space Age Club of Chicago, Inc.
Its window displays a cotton sun, tinseled gold sheet at the bottom. No
surprise to read that there will be a "lecturer from Palm Spring, California" talking to The Group.

And along the streets, pedestrians bullfight with cars. Vic Tanny
hawkers call out sinisterly, threateningly: "Good evening". . . . Teenage
gangs plot vengeance. . . . Shunning the Los Angeles influence, North
Michigan Avenue decks itself out elaborately in Fifth Avenue
finery. . . .

Chicago also has its big-city share of homosexuals. At the Front
Page on Rush, men dance intimately with each other. And along the

beach at night, homosexuals lean along the shadows of the wall lining the concrete beach, waiting. . . .

Almost every big American city has a park which reveals a large aspect of its personality. In Chicago it is Washington Square, sometimes known as Newberry Park—but primarily referred to as "Bug House Square."

In the afternoons, the city's old and young vagrants, serving their novitiate before Madison Street, gather drearily. A couple—"just in from L.A."—drink wine to celebrate "two years on the wagon." Behind them, a lame squirrel looks on quizzically, hobbles now among the pigeons on the grass. A shabby, fat middle-aged woman says to her crony: "What good is a beautiful body?—it ain got me nothin," as she shifts the hills of her spent flesh. . . . Romances sprout, in tatters. An oldman calls to an oldwoman: "Hey, hon, cummon over—I got somethin forya." She sits, he produces a bottle of cheap wine. They invade heaven together momentarily. . . . One harpie in an overcoat grits her teeth and says to no one: "Moody woulda killed him—I mean to tell you, he woulduv." A young man lies on a bench, asleep. And throughout the park, bunched like birds, young vagrants play "rummy" —which means dice or poker, their eyes trained to remain on the dice while still watching out for the cops. Nearby, as the dice tumble to the walk, a woman, huddled over in wined-up terror, whines from the wasteland of her memories: "My daddee was—. . . My daddee was— . . ."

At night, new faces alter the park's makeup. A street socialist stands on a can, shouting ferverishly: "Jesus Christ—not Karl Marx— was the first socialist!" Cowardly teenagers from high schools and colleges, secure in groups, heckle him: "Go home!" He answers: "If I go, where will you go?—watch television?" . . . The tourist bus parks by him, only momentarily, and the awed middle-aged middle-classed ladies make a mental note, I'm sure, to tell the folks-back-home about the crazy park, God Save Us!

Now through the park—a queen—a slim young fairy—all coy swish-gestures—completely painted like a woman, wearing a woman's blouse and slacks—parades languidly, thinking "she's" fooling everyone. . . . Homosexuals outline the ledges. Male hustlers, assuming the necessary tough veneer of hoods, openly offer themselves for money, sometimes stopping the cars that go around and around the block to choose a partner from the stagline.

There are always the threats of muggings, rollings—among the sinister night shadows—an atmosphere of muted violence, sometimes erupting.

Three Negroes dash through the trees, scattering. Two whites follow. Police appear. They spreadeagle a Negro against their car, speed him away. Later, cops at each corner clear the park of all young people. "There's gonna be a rumble," one said, "a race fight cause we arrested a spook."

A man in the park says to me: "Bullshit about a race tumble. They just need a work pack for the city. They tell you to move out, they come back, find you still here—and they got an excuse to bust you for the work pack."

An old tramp, sitting on the ledge nearby, sighs: "Sure be glad when the snow comes. Only time this dam city looks clean."

A block away, on Dearborn, *Opportunity* Magazine has its office.

Recently, a ring of robberies was uncovered. Thieves named cops as their accomplices, and Chicagoans knowingly blamed it on "The Syndicate," a quasi-political organization that, for the worse, controls the city. There are even mutterings of "Mafia." Everything— from tenements to poor restaurant service—is linked by Chicagoans to The Syndicate.

In most bars they play a game called "26." It's played with nine dice. You choose a number from one to six; you shoot the dice 13 times. If your chosen number comes out 26 times or more, you get one dollar's worth of free drinks at the bar. Usually, the game is run by a woman, sitting behind a small square booth. Tell her it's the first time you've played the game—and you'll always win—the first time. The following times you lose, lose, lose.

The damn Syndicate, I thought.

There is a story that in some parts of the South, Negroes arrested for certain breaches are given a choice: Go to jail, or get a one-way ticket to Chicago. If this is true, they are sentenced to one of the many Negro ghettos about the city. (The few lucky ones will live in middle-class splendor about the area surrounding the University of Chicago.)

Under the elevated at 63rd and Cottage Grove is the Temple of

Brotherly Love. On a cross are the words: GOD'S CORNER. And GOD'S CORNER is a tangled glob of steel tracks, thundering with the roar and screech of trains. You see only Negro faces for blocks in that area. Jukeboxes blare jungle sounds. Vainly, the sun tries to pierce the tracks.

And along Wells, Oak, Franklin, 35th, at night, you walk, ignoring warnings of muggings and murders and you see the black faces staring through curtainless windows into the dark street, where—everywhere—young Negro hipsters hold bottles to each other, stalk sinisterly cool, are swallowed by the dark. Into the streets—even if only to their torn porches—Negro families escape out of the tiny crammed rooms, the dark stairways like tunnels. You don't see the cops. A little girl asks you derisively: "Hey, mister, ain I seen you on TV?" In the hot night air you feel the resentful stares. The silence explodes into laughter coming from somewhere within the crushed darkness.

Walk faster. Night is sinister where oppression is thick.

Along Maxwell—with one end of the street being typically torn down—street vendors call out insistently: "Don't run away—I Got Bargains!" It's a street of tent-shops—$3 watches, boots ("at special prices"), rings, wallets—stolen items. . . .

And the gypsies with stamped smiles sit slyly on the steps of murky rooms and call out as you pass: "Tell your fortune?"—trying to make their own.

Clark Street is another of Chicago's monsters. It is a panorama of ripped sights along the rows of loan shops, poolrooms, "bargain centers," billiard halls, cheap moviehouses. Zombies go through a ritualistic hung-over imitation of life. Men stare dumbly at nothing. A body lies in a heap at a doorway. An epileptic woman totters along the block with staring startled eyes. Mutilated harpies wobble along the street— past crippled bodies. A man beats a woman cruelly. You don't interfere. The man's two husky friends stand guard over the scene.

NO DOGS OR OTHER ANIMALS—a sign warns outside a bar.

Inside the Shamrock—a mangled bar with tables—tough outcast faces hang. One woman passes out on the floor with a long, desperate sigh. Three men pounce on her viciously, pulling at her, while another harpie beats them with her hands. Another woman passes out on a table, unmoving as if dead. A man slides a glass of beer toward her.

Instantly, she awakens—reaches for the beer, guzzles it, passes out again.

Skeletons peer through apartment windows into the street.

If there is such a thing as Fun in Hell, it is the Kings Palace on Clark Street on a weekend night.

A huge bar, with a skeleton awning (no canvas) and a drawing outside of what could be a mangled clown, the Kings Palace is a square hall with two oval bars. On the walls are faded paintings hinting of faraway escape: sailboats, palmtrees, cactus plants, leis. A sign advertises: "Fish Sandwich—35c & Up" . . . . And the people are a hybrid of all the tarnished outcasts of America.

A woman who looks like Mrs. Haversham of *Great Expectations* sits woodenly as if dead. A drunk man shoves a woman through a door with a sign that says PRIVATE KEEP OUT. She doesn't come out. A skinny old woman sits at the bar sticking out her tongue at everyone, to the world. A Negro fairy goes through the motions of a strip. A harpie hops to the rock-n-roll moans of the jukebox—a badge across her emaciated breast proclaiming her name pitifully: "Beatrice." A sadfaced man, surprisingly welldressed, guilty buys drinks for all the derelicts around him. An old sullen woman huddles against a cubicle, menacing with a bony fist anyone who approaches her. An old fat homosexual stares longingly after a young man and bursts uncontrollably into tears. A brown-faced man howls like an Indian. A huge woman calls out to a man across the bar: "Wottayalookinat?" "You, honey, I wanna kiss you." "Kiss my ass!" she roars. "Okay," he says, getting up, "where?" She shakes her giant butt. "Can't miss it, baby," she says, "I'm ALL ass." . . . A fastidious man, in elegant tatters, sends back his beer because the glass is dirty. The waiter stares incredulously at him. A Negro woman perches like a crow on a stool next to a tattooed sailor. She feels suddenly beautiful at his attentions (she smiles, rolls her round eyes in pleasure)—his attentions being stroking her butt, which she squirms to the rhythm of the juke-music.

Against a wall a faded blonde woman—an exiled angel, the hints of beauty still lingering on her pale-white face—sits with her black-outlined eyes burning into the bar. A young tramp, drunk—the mark of premature doom stamped on his face which resembles James Dean's— offers her a beer. She takes it wordlessly, her gaze relentlessly nailed beyond the bar. The boy touches her intimately between her thighs. She turns in demented blazing fury, ready to slap him. He hurls the beer at her in a stream. "Dirty whoor," he yells, "huccome you don wanna screw with me?" He slaps her. She smashes the beer bottle on the counter, threatens him with the sharp glassy teeth. He runs out. Someone calls: "You wanna fight? Join the army. . ."

And now the man on the small stage announces The Amateur Talent Show. First Prize: $5. It can buy much wine. . . . A man with a harsh voice tries to sing: "Enjoy yourself, it's later than you think." The wasp-woman who had been sticking out her tongue says imperiously: "Git him off! *Off!*" Next comes Mrs. Haversham strumming a guitar, producing an anarchy of pitiful sounds. . . . Now on the stage is a giant of a man, introduced as "The Growling Bear." In a cracked, beer-slurred voice, he begins to sing. Noticing the lack of response, in desperation he gets on all fours, pretends to be an animal, howling, while the master of ceremonies, trying to inject something of comedy into the tragic moment, hops on him, and, now, the man groans like a wounded animal. . . . A fleshy woman tries to do a belly-dance, inspired by the wine. Someone hoots: "TAKE HER OFF!" And misinterpreting the harsh command, she begins to do a strip. . . .

I didn't wait to find out who had won the prize.

As I stepped into Clark Street, I saw a fat, fat whore talking to a mousy man. "Five bucks," she said. He started to walk away, toward a skinny woman waiting only a few feet away. "Don't go away mad," the fat woman called after him, "I'll go for less." I saw them disappear.

Whoever has said that Chicago has no skyline has not viewed it from the lake at night.

Move northward along the impassive lake—beyond the huddled couples under the silhouettes of trees—beyond the alcove sheltering quiet chessplayers—move northward along the lake. Look back. And you see the magnificent Chicago skyline: a magic cyclorama embracing the water. Buildings which earlier seemed like giants marching snobbishly into the lake now blend into a glittering network of lights, a lighted checkerboard. (Black and mysterious, the water trembles toward the shore uncertainly. A distant light shatters the black water in a shimmering streak.) Along the drive, cars move as if in slow motion along street lights strung blue-white in a curve. And dominating the skyline, at the top of the Palmolive Building, a giant searchlight scans the city. It glides eerily, swirls over the black water. It floats above the skyline, encircles the city at night.

And suddenly you wonder if perhaps, in this ingrown city—Chicago! —that spotlight swirling nightly about the city is not trying somehow to embrace it all—its jungles, Gold Coast, ghettos, postcard villages: that fusion of contradictions within the legend called America.

MICHAEL RUMAKER

8 DREAMS

1

1ST NIGHT

A wide field of bright green grass over which I run, alone. Overhead the sky is gray and there is the constant crackling and roar of thunder—as tho it would split the earth open.

2ND NIGHT

The same wide field of green grass. I am running over it again but this time there is a man running with me. His body and features are not clear but he is running almost beside me. The sky is again gray and there is the same crackle and roar of thunder. I look up as I run and see the dark clouds fuming and boiling as tho churned by the thunder.

3RD NIGHT

The green field. The sky is quiet. I come, alone, to a deep well and, walking up to it, peer over the edge. It is dark and deep. Standing at the bottom is a negress. I see just a part of her face and her shoulders. Her coarse hair is streaked with gray and parted precisely over the middle of her skull. Suddenly, from above, I hear a faint crackling noise and, looking up, the lips of the sky open and a smooth brown oval stone drops down slowly. I watch it as it comes down, descends into the well and strikes the head of the negress exactly at the part in her hair.

2

Walking down a city street, my body straining into a white wind: snow that was not snow plastered against the sidewalk, embedded in the walls of the buildings. A fierce powerful wind driving the breath out of me. I could not breathe, was strangling, and yet walked into it, bucking the force of it, cold that was not cold. As I passed the doorways of shops I saw from the corner of my eye dark shapes huddled out of the wind, faceless and anonymous. They were watching me.

3

A dark night. A deserted sidestreet. A truck-load of pigs pulls up to the curb, stops before the round door of a thick-walled oriental shop, the long shutters closed. The driver and his helper jump out and let down the back flap. From the dim doorway a chinese in a coarse brown coverall emerges. He has a long knife in his hand. He leaps up on the truck and begins rooting amongst the pigs. The driver and his helper watch. The chinese picks up a black pig by the scruff of the neck. I watch from the shadows across the street. The pig is going to be killed now and doesn't know it, I think. The chinese lifts the knife and slowly slices the animal's throat—a smooth, rocking movement of the blade—in the movement the feel of the thick tough skin as the edge saws into it. The pig hangs quietly in the man's fist as his throat is being slit—as tho it did not know what was happening. The blood will come and then he'll cry, I thought. And, sure enough, black blood spurted from the slash, the pig began to cry in thin, high squeals— terrible to hear. Then he knew that he was going to die. I turned into the darkness, weeping.

4

A door opens and an aged negro woman ushers me into a long dingy corridor. She motions for me to follow her and leads me down the hall to a flight of steps. We climbed the stairs and at the top, standing before a dark door, he stood, tall and large. He wore a long voluminous black robe and on his head was a black turban with a gold crescent moon. He stood solemn and erect, a quiet dignity. He did not speak. The negress bowed to him, then, backing away, nodded to me, motioning that I should approach him.

5

I take his yellow bird on my finger. I will make it fly, I say. I wave the bird thru the air and its wings beat. My arm moves the bird in an arc before my breast. The bird flies, responding delicately. I made it fly circles, then figure 8's. Fluttering and gold, I push it close to his face, try to show him how to put it in flight.

He motions that he wants the bird.

I struggle to release it, so tight are its little feet wrapped around the flesh. I pry them off—purple, as beveled rings, the print of its claws left in the knuckle.

In his hand the bird won't fly, hangs head down from his finger, its wings spread loose. He moves it every which way. It hangs as if dead. He looks at me perplexed. Then, abruptly, the bird darts up, jerking his hand to his face, its claws hook onto his nose, its wings fan rapidly against his cheeks as the yellow bird pecks fiercely at the eyes of my friend.

6

My friend and I were working at a Woolworth 5 & 10. We were in the back of the store stacking lampshades on shelves. Suddenly my friend shouted an explosive obscenity. A whitehaired floorwalker came back and motioned to us.

'You must be judged now,' she said.

We followed her to the front of the store. There, sitting just inside the door, was a negro woman. Her coarse gray hair was combed out in loose pointed strands at either side of her head. She wore a cheap black dress. At her side hung a large ring of keys. She was reading the No. 5 issue of *The Black Mountain Review*. As we came up she stopped reading and rested the book on her thigh. We stood facing her, the matronly floorwalker a little to the rear, watching.

'Nigger! You can't judge me!' I shouted.

A confident, serene smile spread over the negro's face, subtly impish and playful. One of her front teeth was edged in gold. In the smile it was tho she knew everything, that she could tell me everything.

7

The tall one had come home from the city full of ideas and concern. In the darkness he had clutched the slim dry body to him, thinking it was the other brother, the sailor, who had flown thru the skies from the West. But it was his younger brother, fair-skinned and blond, and this one had responded clumsily. So that, reclining back on the pillow (the other crumpled at the foot of the bed), the tall brother crooked his finger at him, speaking softly—so as not to wake the working brother in the bed across. 'How long have you done this thing?' he asked. 'Known it?' (Speaking as tho to impart wisdom) And the heavy arm of the working brother fell on his shoulder—the blond one crying hssssst! in warning. But the city brother did not heed, saying, 'So he was awake and not asleep, but he will not mind what he has seen and heard, he will not reprove us.'

The bearded father spoke, hidden behind the shoulder of the working son. And the city son knew and was shocked. A cold fear paralysed him, seeing the father there. He fled from the house, carrying his blond brother under his arm. The father would give them a few minutes start. Then they would pursue, he and the other sons.

He fled thru the dark wood, the ground moist underfoot, and black, the city brother crying in himself, Mother, Mother—but not daring to cry it aloud.

It was the sailor who caught up to them first. Turning, the blond brother riding on his hip, the city brother saw the house thru the trees, the windows aflame with light.

'Every one is up,' he said. Then shouted, 'Brother of the seas, do not slay us! Give us clothes so that we can escape!'

The sailor drew from behind him a net and flung it at them. But as it flew thru the air it turned into two pairs of new khaki trousers and the city brothers grabbed them, thanking the sailor.

Now the working brother came down the path, chasing them, and the city brother shouted, 'Brother, do not kill us! Give us some money so that we can take the bus on the highway and make our escape!' This brother flung at them a bomb. But as it flew thru the air it turned into paper money and the city brother snatched at it with his free hand and crumpled it in his fist as he carried his blond brother under one arm.

They came out onto the highway.

'The father will be coming!' shouted the sailor. 'Hurry!'

He and the working brother stood at the edge of the wood but would come no further. The father would come further so the city brother hurried along over the damp shoulder of the road, thinking, 'It must have just rained.'

Now, on the opposite side of the road waiting for them to pass was the ancient mother and the daughter. He could barely recognize them, they stood in dark shadow amongst low hanging trees. The mother, dressed in queen's burial robes, was dumb with grief, lifting her arms to them. The daughter stood quietly beside her.

Suddenly there came the crashings of the father's footsteps thru the woods. The air went cold. A damp wind blew.

'Mother, I cannot stop!' cried the city son. 'We must hurry to get away. I will take care of my brother!' And he ran on down the road, still carrying his brother on his hip, as the mother lifted her arms amongst the dark trees.

Now they got to where the bus passed, near an old hut. He could see the lights of the bus coming down the road. He put his brother on his feet and cried, 'Quick! Put on these clothes before the bus comes. Now we must make our escape to the city!'

He handed him trousers the sailor brother had given them and started putting the other pair on himself. They were twice as big as needed and bagged at the waist. The blond brother was struggling into his and they, too, were big around the waist so that he bunched them at his belly with his fist.

The bus was coming on, they could hear the motor.

Now dark figures began to collect around the hut, watching the two brothers. The blond one fell into a stupor. He began to fall asleep, nodding on his feet.

'What will I do with him?' thought the tall one. 'He will not be happy in the city.'

The bus drew near and roared past them. The city brother waved his fists and shouted. The bus stopped some yards on. He ran to it and got on, handing the driver the bill. But his brother did not follow him and he asked the driver to wait, apologizing.

He went back to where he had left him but he was not there. An old woman, her face hidden in a dark shawl, her hands folded at her breast, came forward from the group of dark figures. She bowed to him and said, 'Your brother has fallen on a heap of glass. His hands are almost cut off at the wrists. There is much blood. He said: "Tell the son of the king, the prince, for whom I have long waited, that I am tortured that I cannot go with him." ' She melted into the shadow and the city brother, stunned, his breath gone out, looked into the darkness and saw the mother, her gray arms thrashing the air.

The bus horn blew. He returned and, climbing on, saw the bill in the driver's hand a five where he had expected to see a one.

8

A jagged rock in the midst of a dark, storm-torn ocean. The rock has a peak at either end, the center of it worn flat. And it is there I stand while tall waves crash all around. A fierce wind howls and it carries me first one way and then the other over the rock. I'm afraid of the wind pushing me in the sea.

There is no land in sight. The sky is dark green, around the horizons it is yellow. A sharp rain slashes at me and the wind continues to buffet me over the rock, forcing me closer and closer to the edge. I hug the slippery rock, pry at it with my fingers. I hear voices and think they are voices in the wind, for there is no one. Over the wind's roar the voices grow more clamorous. Looking down into the sea I see dark heads bobbing in the waves. They are black, without eyes or mouths, but they are calling to me. I strain to hear but I can't make out what they are saying. The wind rises in fury. The rain beats down harder, it's cutting me. I creep down the edge of the rock on my hands and knees, my fingers digging into the rock. I'm deeply afraid but I must hear what the voices say. I creep close to the edge. I sense that the dark heads are calling me into the water—but I still can't make out their words. My fingers ache and I am cold and paralysed with fear, exhausted from trying to stay on the rock. I think: Why not fall in? Why not give this up? The wind rises to an even more terrible roaring, drowning out the voices of the heads, Suddenly the sky goes black. There is an abrupt burst of lightning over all the sky. Then darkness.

THE TEDDY BEAR

Ben sat in the dayroom in a big chair drawn up to the window. He sat very still, holding onto the arms of the chair. He tried not to move because he was afraid that if he moved he might fall, or maybe break.

On the other side of the room several other patients were playing pingpong. He had tried to play pingpong once but it had made him dizzy. And he had held the paddle so stiffly he could hardly hit the ball. He didn't like to go to gym either. When he played basketball he felt that he was going to fall down.

It was better to sit still, he thought, and not move. It was better to have everything still around you, and not talk to anyone or have anyone touch you.

The ward was very noisy this morning. Some of the slower patients were still doing their chores, listlessly pushing brooms over the mustard-colored linoleum. Ben hoped the one moving nearer and nearer to him would not want to sweep under his chair. Dust motes raised by the brooms sparkled in the shafts of light. He concentrated on looking out the window, his long thin body sitting almost primly, and tried to shut out the noise of the pingpong players.

Outside the window the sun was shining. Far down below the highway was filled with cars flashing in the sun. They were moving to and from the bridge over the river. In his dreams were always broken bridges and the river was always the one that flowed past the town in which he grew up. The waters were black and fuming and he had to get to the other side but there were only the broken bridges and he didn't know how to go over the river. It was as though he had not been able to build a bridge to go upon into his early manliness.

I'm out there, he thought. Under the water.

He watched the river moving grayly, peacefully by in the morning sun.

The leaves on the trees were changing color and on the bluff across the river the trees were brilliant now. There was blue smoke over the water.

He watched the cars. He thought in one of them might be his

mother and father coming to take him home. But he knew they would never come. Sometimes when he spotted a car that looked like theirs, he would try to figure how long it would take the car to get from the highway to the entrance of the hospital. Then he would wait. It was a game he played sometimes, pretending.

A slim colored patient approached him and bumped into his elbow. Ben looked up, startled, then an expression of annoyance came into his face. He put his elbow very carefully back on the armrest of the chair.

"I beg your pardon," said the Negro, his eyes lifeless and not looking at Jim, as though he couldn't see. "You do believe it was an accident?" he asked in a soft serious voice.

Ben turned back to the window. "Go away, Harold," he said. "You're always doing that."

Harold moved off, bowing and apologizing, still unseeing.

He always bumps into me on purpose, Ben thought.

He became intent again upon looking out the window. Gulls wheeled down the sheer face of the bluffs across the way, starkly white against the jagged rock. The sweeper swept his little mound of dust up to Ben's chair, paused a moment as though undecided, the long broom clutched in his hand like a sentry asleep at his post, then he laboriously turned and began sweeping in the opposite direction.

Ben felt a sense of relief that quickly disappeared as a big broad-shouldered boy now wandered over near his chair. Ben tensed, seeing him. He was a boy no older than himself, perhaps twenty-one, with large heavy limbs—a clumsy, ungainly build, bulky and ill-proportioned. He let himself drop in a chair close to Ben and the chair groaned and sagged under his weight. Ben couldn't stand for him to sit across from him, smacking his heavy lips as though he were eating. His eyes were always glazed and dull, made more so by the heavy dose of tranquilizers they poured into him. Some days he would be restless, as now, and his eyes would go more glazed and lifeless than usual and he would begin to whine and slowly rock his big body back and forth. Gradually the whining would build up to a steady groaning, becoming louder and louder, and he would continue to rock in his chair, looking like some enormous beast stuck in the mud of a swamp, or in quicksand, who was going down and down slowly to his death and trumpeted out in fear and hopelessness.

Sometimes he was different and would sit down at the piano in the corner of the dayroom, his enormous bottom covering the entire piano seat as he played. Strangely, his hands were long and delicate and his touch was light, his fingers moving swiftly as though they barely touched the keys—high, light music, like the brushing of crystals.

But now he began to rock slowly and Ben was frightened, not looking, but knowing, hearing the springs of the chair squeak. Finally, Ben stole a glace, hoping he would not see it, but there it was. The deadness had come into his eyes, stupid and dense. The eyes did not seem to cry for help—as though they knew no help could come, had never come, that no one would ever touch the fat and ugly thing he was, smelling of stale sweat. It was the dead scrutiny of his eyes watching him, watching him as though for some sign, something—Ben did not know what—that made him nervous, frightened.

He began to make a racket, now screaming like an elephant, sending a cold shiver down Ben's spine. Ben wanted to move away but felt as though paralysed. His legs would not move. The other patients looked, then looked away. Several moved off to the far end of the dayroom.

As though in his misery he was sentitive to this, the boy lumbered, still heaving to and fro, to the office door and asked the nurse on duty to put him in seclusion. She led him to a room off the dayroom, around the corner, and unlocked the door. Ben could look into the room from where he was sitting and the room was bare and stark except for heavy screening over the window and a big padlock on the window and nothing in the room except a thin rubber mattress in one corner. The seclusion room smelled of stale urine and there were fingernail clawings scratched deep in the plaster of the walls.

He flopped down on the mattress and began his moaning again, the roars growing louder, then dropping to a sing-song whining, then rising again. To Ben's ears the screams had in them something dying and lost and he tried to shut out the sound but couldn't, put his fingers in his ears but still heard his crying. And now above the bellowing he heard the slap of the leather belt as the boy began to beat himself, lacerating himself as though the way to kill his pain was to inflict upon himself more pain.

The dayroom grew suddenly quiet. No one moved or spoke. A sullen heaviness seemed to hang in the air and, although the sun was still shining, it was as though, in the dayroom, the sky outside had quickly clouded over.

I'm going to fall, Ben thought in a panic, holding on more tightly to the armrests of the chair.

The nurse, moving swiftly, went back and stood in the door of the seclusion room. She was thin and had her thin hands on her hips. She stared in at the ungainly creature lashing himself ferociously. There was a faint look of annoyance on her face.

"Give me the belt," she said patiently.

But he seemed not to hear and went on striking at himself, squatting now on the rubber mattress, his big arms batting himself awkwardly about the head and shoulders with the strap.

"If you're in seclusion you have to give me your belt," the nurse insisted, in a louder voice, the look of annoyance growing intense on her face.

Out of the heaviness and depth of his grief, the boy seemed to hear her. He stopped abruptly for a moment, staring up at her with lost eyes. In his face was a pleading, as though to tell her he could not stop and he went on slapping himself, now hard about the face and arms so that red welts began to appear. He seemed to be in the grip of some power over which he had no control and continued inflicting pain to kill pain.

The nurse called to one of a group of attendants who had been standing close by, waiting. Then she stepped into the room. She stood quickly over the boy and spoke firmly, but there was a softness in her voice.

"Come now. Give me the belt."

Then, as though the torment in him had spent itself, he dropped his flabby arms and looked up into her face. A tear fell down one of his heavy cheeks, and another. Soon his eyes were red with crying. He handed her the belt. With his other hand he snuffled at his wet nose like a small boy who had been naughty. He was quiet now, crying quietly, and the attendant who had been called stood looking in at the doorway. The nurse motioned him away and stepped out of the room, drawing the door closed after her.

"It's all over this time," she said, and winding the boy's belt up into a neat compact roll, went back into the office.

The tack-tack of the pingpong ball was heard suddenly in the still dayroom. It came as a relief to the others and seemed to bring them back. There were low murmurs of conversation now and a card game was started at one of the corner tables. Ben let himself relax a little. He felt numb and cold, as though there were no heat in him.

A young nurse walked into the dayroom. She looked around brightly and smiled and said hello to several of the patients. She went over to the cardplayers who all gazed up momentarily from their hands to smile at her. She went around the table looking over each shoulder and with a knowing grin, winked, putting a finger to her mouth as much as to say, I won't breathe a word. Then going to a box of plants in one of the windows she fluffed up the withered leaves, saying, "Poor things, you don't get enough sunlight," and walked over to where Ben was sitting. She squatted down next to him, balancing herself with one hand resting lightly on the arm of his chair. Ben quickly withdrew his arm and looked at her with an expression of surprise.

"I'm not going to bite you," she said, a teasingly radiant smile on her face. "How's it going with you, Ben?"

"I'm looking at the river," he said, turning from her and staring out the window again.

"It really is a lovely day, isn't it?"

Ben was silent.

The nurse hunched there quickly, gazing out the window with him. She was very thin, like the other nurse, only she had a grace and softness in her long limbs and an almost luminous quality to her complexion. Full-faced she was almost beautiful, but in profile her nose was too large and not shaped well. Her eyes were very large and soft, nice soft brown eyes. And her hair was brown, very fine loosely hanging hair. She overflowed with vitality and warmth and yet all about her was a quietness, as of fragility and softness, as though the slightest harsh movement would break her, like fine porcelain.

An image leapt up in Ben's mind of him kicking her in the face. And, yet, how badly he wanted to cry, to put his face in her shoulder and cry out all the misery that was in him. But something stopped him, as though a wall existed between himself and the nurse—as

though his fingers were leaden weights he could not lift to touch her
—as though his voice had gone dumb and had forgotten how to speak
of all the ache and torment in him.

How old he felt, and sick. Sicker than he had ever felt. And it
would not go away. Neither pills nor attempted solace made it better.
It was as if he were something unfeeling and dead, frozen in the
midst of ice. It was as though all the warmth of his blood had left him.
Only his mind, his reason, remained, tormenting him with memories
of feeling and warmth which seemed no longer in him. The coldness
and emptiness of his bleak sickness held him silent, unmoving, as
though he were paralysed against his will.

He forced himself to pretend she was not there. And, yet, he could
smell her perfume. But it seemed he was smelling it from a far place.
And she, too, seemed far away, unreachable, although he had only to
slide his fingers over a few inches and he would touch her slim white
arm. A heavy despair hung over him. It was better when he was
left alone. He no longer wanted to look out the window. He wanted
her to go away, to leave him, not speak to him like a bright, chirpy
bird when he could not feel the same. He hated her for her aliveness.
She was walking up on the grass in sunlight and he felt himself buried
below in darkness, stifling, lost.

"Don't you see Doctor Cornelius today?" he heard her asking, and
he pulled himself back, unwilling, hearing her words. "I think I
saw it on the appointment chart in the office."

Was it today? Ben asked himself, confused. He had forgotten. He
didn't want to see Doctor Cornelius. At their last meeting the doctor
had promised to bring him something. Had he told him what it was?
He tried hard to remember, but he only felt frozen, unable to recall.
What could he possibly say to him?

"Look! There's a ship going by on the river," cried the nurse,
pointing out the window. Down on the water a robin's egg blue oil
tanker moved slowly downstream heading out to sea, so heavily laden
its bulkheads bearly lifted above the water.

"Wouldn't it be nice to go on a boat trip?" said the nurse cheerfully, her eyes shining as she watched the slow-moving tanker. "It's
such fine weather. It must be Indian Summer, the air's so blue."

To be out on the moving waters, to be going. For an instant the bright image of a ship on a vast sea arose in Ben's mind, then quickly vanished. A grayness entered. The ship had been like an old memory, a long dead dream.

"I don't think I want to," he said quietly.

"Ben!" an attendant called from the doorway. "The doctor's here to see you."

"I'll walk down the hall with you," said the nurse, getting up and smoothing her uniform down over her hips.

Ben got up slowly from the chair. He felt unsteady and began to sway so that the nurse reached out to take his arm. He stood a moment to get his balance.

"Are you all right?" she asked.

He nodded and they went out of the dayroom and down the corridor together. I can walk, Ben thought. My legs are always playing tricks on me. They don't always take me where I want to go.

At the far end of the hall they stopped before the consultation room. The door was ajar. "I'll leave you here," said the nurse, squeezing his arm gently. "Have a good session."

She waved to him over her shoulder as she went back to the dayroom, the rubber soles of her shoes squeaking on the waxed tiles. Ben wanted to go with her, to go back. He stood a few seconds before the door, watching her move up the hall, and when she had disappeared around the corner, he hesitantly pushed open the door and went in.

Doctor Cornelius sat behind the desk. He glanced up from a sheath of papers spread out before him and smiled as Ben entered. He was a short, pudgy man. His face was pale and flabby but there was a warmth and intelligence in his eyes. He had a slight cast in one eye so that Ben was never sure if he was looking at him or off in another direction.

"Sit down," he said, waving his arm toward a chair. Ben sat down. There was little else in the room beside the desk and a few chairs. Several water colors done by patients in Occupational Therapy hung on the walls.

Ben didn't look at Doctor Cornelius. Instead his gaze rested on a large red box that sat on the desk near the doctor's elbow.

"And how are you today?" the doctor asked, collecting his papers and tamping them into a neat stack. "Have you been going to gym?"

Ben shook his head.

"Have you tried the pingpong again, or talked to the other patients?"

Ben remained motionless, making no sign, as though he had not heard, his eyes fixed on the red box. The doctor looked at the box and smiled. He tapped the side of it lightly with his fingers. "I suppose you're wondering what's in here?"

Ben turned his head into his shoulder as though he did not want to see. Doctor Cornelius opened the lid of the box and brought out a small toy teddy bear.

"You told me last time that you never had a teddy bear," said the doctor. "I've brought you one. I hope you like it."

He waited, expectant. Ben looked at it dumbly. He got up quickly. "I want to go back to the ward," he said.

Doctor Cornelius came around the side of the desk and held the teddy bear out to him, but Ben put his hands behind his back and looked away.

"I'll put him here," said the doctor. "I think he wants a little fresh air after being stuffed in that box such a long time."

He sat the teddy bear on the window sill. Ben stood staring at the floor, twisting his fingers behind his back, prying at the joints as though he were trying to snap them off.

"Look," said Doctor Cornelius, "He seems to feel better already." And he laughed. "Look, Ben."

But Ben remained silent, his eyes fixed on a waxy spot of dirt on the floor between the toes of his shoes.

The doctor lifted his cuff and glanced at his watch.

"There's an important call I have to make," he said. "I'll be back in a minute."

He gathered up his papers and his notebook and went out of the room, closing the door quietly after him.

Ben stood in silence for some moments, then, slowly, he lifted his head and looked at the door, as though to make certain the doctor had gone. Assured, his gaze moved cautiously to the teddy bear, glancing sideways, as though the stuffed creature was a blinding light that might hurt his eyes if he looked at it too quickly and directly.

It was a small brown teddy bear with yellow ears and a yellow chest, and the pads of its feet yellow. Around its neck was a green ribbon. A little red cloth tongue lolled out one side of its mouth. It sat lopsided, its small paws outstretched, its brown glass eyes gazing out at him warmly over the little fur snout.

Ben went to it and touched it, gingerly, as though it might be a hot stove. The teddy bear was soft and he stroked it for a moment, then picked it up and cradled it close in the hollow of his shoulder. He closed his eyes. It fitted the shape of his shoulder perfectly and it seemed to cling to him, like an alive and cuddly animal. He stood for a long while, kissing the soft fur.

The door opened quietly and Doctor Cornelius stepped into the office again. Ben was so absorbed in fondling and whispering softly to the teddy bear he didn't hear the doctor enter. Doctor Cornelius stood, his back resting against the door, watching Ben with the teddy bear. The papers in his hand shook. He waited a moment, then pushed the door shut firmly and, clearing his throat, stepped into the room. He didn't look at Ben but went to the chair in the corner and sat down, pretending to study some of the papers in his hand.

Ben started, seeing him, and then, as though slowly coming out of a dream, his body stiffened. With a rigid arm, he let the bear slide from his shoulder to rest on his hip where he held it squeezed between his fingers, bunching the toy animal out of shape.

"What are you going to call him?" asked the doctor, conversationally, still studying his papers, as though he didn't really care what Ben named the bear.

"Nothing," Ben said, almost inaudibly. And then, as though the doctor had accused him, "I was only looking at it."

He began pulling at one of the stubby arms of the bear, then he started winding it around and around with an agitated gesture.

"You can rip it apart if you want," said the doctor, looking up at him. "I gave it to you. It's yours to do with what you want."

Ben stopped pulling at the teddy bear's arm. His left eye began to flick and the blood semed to drain from his face. Then, heaving back his arm, he threw the teddy bear hard at the doctor. The doctor flinched and lifted his arm too late as the stuffed animal struck the side of his head. It bounced off harmlessly and lay face down on the floor, its little rump and rag of a tail pointed toward the ceiling.

"You can call the attendant now," Ben said in a choked voice, his fists closed tight at his sides. "You can have me locked up now."

The doctor said nothing. He got up and put the papers and note-book in his pocket. Then he turned to Ben and said, "I'm going to leave now. I'll drop in on the ward tomorrow and see how you're getting on."

Ben didn't look at him. He couldn't bear to look into his eyes. He wanted to call him Cross-eyes, scream it at him.

Doctor Cornelius went to the door, opened it and went out.

Ben stood for a long while without moving. He tried hard to feel numb, to feel nothing. But this time it wouldn't work. He started for the door, moving quickly, his heart pounding, and as he placed his hand on the knob to jerk it open, he stopped. His mouth was trembling. He turned and stared down at the upended teddy bear still lying on the floor. He went and stood over it for a moment, drawing back his foot as though to kick it. Then he slowly sank to his knees and taking the bear in his hands turned it over and held it cradled in the cup of his hands a moment, gazing down at it, a wistfulness in his eyes, before moving it up to his cheek and nestling the head of the bear there.

"I'm sorry," he whispered, over and over, and he began to cry, his tears wetting and staining the small brown head of the teddy bear.

After awhile he got up and went out of the room, holding the bear in one hand. When he got out in the hall he was worried that the other patients might laugh at him, seeing him, at his age, carrying about with him a child's toy. Then he decided what he would do. He put the bear carefully in his side pocket, stuffing it down deep with only the tip of its nose showing.

Now, he can breathe, he thought, and walked off in the direction of the dayroom.

THE PUPPY

Bill stood on the porch of the cabin, the boards of its floor worn silvery and smooth with the weather and years, curling warped at the edges. He gazed down the path leading away from the cabin. The pine trees thrust up darkly on the steep slopes as far as the eye could see. Amongst the trees craggy boulders jutted out here and there on the sides of the mountains. Far down in the valley was a rise of smoke from the town. Down there all seemed so far away. He himself felt so far away from everything.

A puppy lay stretched in the sunlight in a patch of grass a little distance from the cabin. His mother had sent it to him a few months before. It was a Russian Wolfhound puppy, "a borzoi" his mother had called it. It was a fine sleek animal with long slender muzzle and legs. In the brilliant sunlight it was the color of light cream. Bill looked at it admiringly. It really was a lovely animal, a fine quivering dog, highstrung and nervous.

His mother had had it shipped to him by train from the East— "So you won't be lonely," the accompanying letter had said. "And so that you will remember me."

He turned from the animal with a feeling of disgust.

His mother.

Her voice so complaining, so martyred. Her hands which fluttered so, which never seemed able to grasp firmly, to hold on. And the way she cracked eggs, such a simple thing, he thought guiltily, scraping one boot along the porch, but why had it always set his teeth on edge? He had hated to hear her crack eggs in the morning—the hesitant, yet precise tapping of the edge of the fork on the shell. When she had scrambled them—always scrambled—he had had to force them down, gulping, smiling and saying they were good.

He sat down on the edge of the porch and smoothed the rough boards under his fingers. He liked the feel of the wood, like bone, and slightly warm now in the late afternoon sun. He tried hard not to think of his mother, not to think of anything, except to feel, to take pleasure in stroking the velvety warm wood.

The puppy stirred and got up slowly from the grass. It stretched its long lithe body, extending the thin neck and opening its jaw wide in a softly howling yawn. It looked from right to left, sniffed the air nervously, then, turning, trotted across the yard. It loped up the steps and taking a position, on the other side of the porch began to paw nimbly at the flooring.

Bill swung his body around slightly and looked at the dog. The puppy turned its head aside and scratched at the boards again, the front paws going in a little prancing movement.

It's hungry, Bill thought, and wants to be fed and this is the way it tells me. He looked across at the puppy with an expression of disappointment in his face. Doesn't even scratch at my feet or legs, he said to himself disconsolately, like any other dog.

Since he had got it, the puppy had never come near him. He had longed to pat it, to stroke its throat, play with it, rolling over and over on the floor. But the wolfhound never gave back to him the affection, the spontaneous animal love he had hoped for, had expected.

He continued to stare at the animal's lean, waiting face, the slightly curved eyes averted from him. After his first realization that the dog would be forever alien to him, he had not bothered to give it a name.

He had the feeling if he could somehow get the dog to be friendly with him, well, then everything would be all right. He had tried everything. Talking kindly, patiently, to the animal. Smiling at it a lot. Even to the point of feeding it two cans of dog food a day—in spite of his mother's advice.

That had been in the beginning. And nothing had worked. Gradually he began to detest the bribery. The pup remained as aloof as ever. It did not want to be touched, did not seem to want him near it. He left off talking to the dog altogether. And never again smiled at it. Sometimes he would forget to feed it.

Now, he did not want to feed the pup. He felt no need to do it. Pangs of guilt stirred in him. The animal was hungry. And yet it hurt him to know that the only thing he could do for it, and that the only thing the animal itself wanted him to do for it, was to feed it. A can of dog food, once a day—"No more, no less," as his mother had strictly warned him in her letter.

He leapt up and hurried past the dog into the cabin, slapping his boots down hard. It angered him that the dog would not again show him a sign that it wanted food.

The cabin was one room, dusty and shadowy. Soiled clothes were strewn about the floor and there was a heap of more soiled laundry in one corner. In another corner was an unmade bunk, the grimy sheets the shade of coffee. A wood stove stood out from the wall between two small square windows in the rear. There was one other window, near the door, and each let in only a little light. In the middle of the room was a table with two chairs drawn up to it, one with its back broken. The table was stacked with dirty dishes, in the midst of which stood an oil lamp, its chimney blackened with soot. Most of the plates on the table were caked with the hard yolk of eggs. On one wall, propped on two wooden pegs, hung a gleaming, well-oiled rifle.

He kicked away several pieces of dirty clothes, booting them toward the corner pile, as he strode across the room. Out of the corner of his eye he could see that the wolfhound had come to the doorway and was standing there looking in silently, stood simply like a statue, still and slender, watching him.

Bill pretended to ignore the dog and looked at himself in the piece of mirror propped on the slanting shelf over the wash basin.

His face stared out at him with a heavy bloodedness. He ran the flats of his hands slowly down either cheek. Shave? The question flitted through his mind, hardly a question, so struck was he by the sudden realization of lifelessness in his eyes, as though his gray eyes were a closedness, revealing nothing. What stared out at him was a lean red face, the slender cheeks stubbled with auburn beard, a neatly trimmed drooping mustache, also auburn, of which he was proud and which gave to his face, he felt, a somewhat distinguished look. A light shudder ran through him as he realized, in spite of his patiently grown mustache, the anonymity, a certain unlivedness, of his face. Smooth, in a bland red way, as if it had not been touched by life.

It reminded him of those early photographs before the turn of the century of rows of stiff, carefully posed men in rumpled dark coats and baggy trousers standing in front of clapboard notion stores or saloons in the early mining and frontier towns—each face slightly blurred and looking like the others, the same mustaches and grim empty eyes—the rigidity of the standing men, as though they were facing a firing squad, there was a strained look of darkness and death in the face of each, and in the feel of the rough places in which they stood, the feel of impermanence amidst the dry insistent terrains: Craggy hills, like those beyond his cabin, showing between the quickly constructed stores and hotels of tar paper and newly-sawn, unpainted boards. The very dust at the feet of the men had in it more of a feel of substance and lastingness than they themselves— as though they were, darkly and frightenedly, hurrying away soon, would leave no mark upon the landscape, no more than the hastily thrust up shelters that would fall and crumble quickly, made to last only as long as they had use for them—a short time, a very short time, and then a hurrying on—to the sea—as though in each strained white face was a darkness of running—Wings of blackness seemed hovering always, invisible, yet palpable, in the endless light alkaline skies overhead.

He heard a light rustle of fur on wood and without turning his head could feel the shape of the dog sitting motionless now, sitting almost, he sensed, in heavy judgment upon him. He felt embarrassed as though afraid the dog, with its thin intelligent face, could also see what the mirror had revealed to him. He wanted the dog to go away, he had only to speak one word, but he dared not turn around.

Instead, he gazed steadily into the glass, forcing himself back, remembering how he had come to this place, aimlessly, with his vague ideas of simply finding something, his rag-ends of feeling leading him. He felt so purposeless, without any concrete shape or meaning to his life.

Like an amoeba, he thought, with a keen intake of breath. I push this way and that way and split myself and begin again, and never change.

He had come so far to this place seeking something and, at first, everything had gone well, had even been exhilarating. He had worked the night shift at the paper box factory at the edge of town and hating the job had saved up some money and quit. Thereafter, he spent his days roaming the hills and once in awhile going in to town to get drunk on beer and, after, would walk the unfamiliar streets endlessly, block after empty block, until he came to the end of it and saw the steep wall of the canyon rising before him.

An emptiness and dullness had come upon him. As it had always come. He had come seeking, and he had not found what he had hoped to find. There were the mountains outside the door and the clear sharp blue of the sky above him—He thought, You can only look at the mountains and sky so long and they begin to lose something.

He felt a profound loneliness in the neatness, the uncomplicatedness of his inner life—a sterile and empty satisfaction in his solitude instead of the richness, the fullness he had hoped to find.

He had run here, too, like those nameless and unknown men, now all long dead, in the photographs. He laughed to himself. For gold? For cattle? Land? Not even to learn to ride a horse!

You run, he thought, and wherever you run it's always the same. As though things—the terrain itself, doesn't give back anything. The rocks, the boulders seemed to sleep inanimate and voiceless, the pine trees—each a total and slumbering life into themselves.

This is what you wanted, he thought, and he tried to find comfort in the thought of the solitude of the pine-dotted hills and, breathing in deeply, in the crisp thin air which no longer made him giddy, vitalized, he had become so used to it.

In the mirror, he saw his hands still resting on his cheeks, saw that his hands were red like his face, the fingers tapering and long, the blunt flat nails set deeply into the tips of flesh, the nails pale blue.

Hands like my father, he thought. Long hands like him.

He heard a bark outside. He turned from the mirror, his body tense, listening. The wolfhound was gone. He went to the doorway and looked out into the fading light.

A stray dog had wandered up to the cabin and was sniffing and pawing around the porch. The wolfhound pup, having sensed its presence, had bolted out and stood stiff, almost shyly, on the edge of the porch gazing at the strange dog. Bill leaned against the door jamb watching as the pup went down off the porch and each dog approached the other cautiously, sniffing at each other. The stray leapt, yelping away, inviting the puppy to play with him. The wolfhound looked at him puzzled a moment, his long head cocked to one side, then, barking, chased after the other dog.

Jim watched the two animals leaping and barking in the slanting sunlight of the yard. Their short yaps and low, half threatening growls filled the empty stillness of the canyon as they frisked and leapt in the high grass. A slow inexplicable feeling of sadness came over him. He sprang off the porch.

"Go on, get outa here!" he shouted at the strange dog.

The dogs stood stock still as he continued to shout and come at them in long strides, and stared uncomprehending at him. He ran at the stray dog and began kicking at it. The dog bolted off down the trail and stopped a little further on and looked back, its shoulders hunched, its tail between its legs. Bill picked up a couple of rocks and threw them at the stray. The rocks danced around the dog and clattered echoing down the sloping path. The dog ran off howling, scurried around the bend in the trail and was gone.

Bill stood with his hands on his hips for several moments, his eyes fixed on the empty trail. He could see the wolfhound slinking quietly up the steps and into the cabin. His cheeks began to burn and a quick feeling of shame came over him. His body sagged and biting his lip he swung around and kicked hard at the ground with the heel of his boot.

I'll make it up to the pup, he thought, and could not understand why he would think this because he did not know what he could do.

He let out a long sigh and tucking his hands in his back pockets walked slowly to the cabin, his head lifted, looking at the sky. The light was going out of it, the sun having now sunk beyond the hills. In the darker blue of the eastern sky the first faint stars began to show through gathering heavy clouds.

He walked quietly, almost shyly, up the steps of the cabin, as though the weight of his body would make the boards creak and somehow disturb the pup. He paused at the door, reaching up and gently resting one arm against the sill, and gazed in.

In the dark dusty room he could see the long shadowy form of the animal stretched near the stove, its thin head slunk between its paw.

How much, he thought, the dog seemed out of place in the ruggedness of these surroundings, too fine bred and thinly blooded a creature to exist happily in the strong light and rough craggedness of the place.

He felt a catch in his throat as he entered. Strangely, the old hopefulness appeared again and he found himself brooding once more on the strange aloofness of the animal, its queer, and maddening, unacceptance of him.

Going to the table he lifted the chimney of the oil lamp and striking a kitchen match on the seat of his trousers, lit the wick. He watched the flame leap up, turned it down, and replaced the chimney. The room felt brighter, more cheerful. Now that the sun had gone down the place was growing cold. As Bill closed the door there was a smell of snow in the air outside. He went to the stove and poked at the ashes and putting in kindling and heavy pieces soon had a fire going.

Then he sat down in a chair and leaning forward stared down at the dog. The room was still except for the crackling of burning wood in the stove.

"I'm sorry," he said, and was startled at the sound of his voice in the silence of the room.

The dog cocked one eye up from between its paws for the fraction of an instant then let it drop. It lay inert as though dead.

Bill reached out, a slight shy smile on his face, his fingers trembling awkwardly to touch the puppy. The wolfhound swung its head away. Bill went down slowly on his knees, his hand still extended, and moving on his knees over the floor, crept to the dog. Abruptly, the dog leapt up and pranced a few steps sideways as Bill crawled to him, his lips still parted in an expectant smile. Again the dog neatly sidestepped further away until it bumped against the corner wall, shuddering as its fur brushed against the rough boards.

"Please," Bill whispered, his voice coaxing and low as he reached again to touch the dog. The wolfhound's eyes darted frantically, as though searching for some means to get away, then, ducking its head, it swung about and with a fierce light in its eyes shot its jaws forward and, snapping with a low desparate whine, bit the outstretched hand.

Bill sucked in breath, a look of astonishment on his face, as he stared at his hand, seeing the fine and deep rake of the teeth over his knuckles and the furrows of bright blood oozing up. The image of a freshly plowed field leaped into his mind, subsided, and a darkness swam into his eyes. He straightened up and kicked out at the dog. The dog shivered and moaned as the boot struck at its flanks and it curled itself, as though trying to make itself small, turning its face into the wall.

With stiff steps Bill walked across the floor, took down his rifle from over the fireplace, pulled back the breech as he recrossed the room and standing directly over the dog, his legs spread, pumped a shot into the animal's throat. The dog's head snapped around at him, the eyes startled. With a slight lift of its jaws it emitted a high keen bark before the body hurtled against the wall with a thud. The dog tried to rise but could only manage to fling itself forward a little, the head hanging to one side as though broken, before it slumped to the floor.

Bill stared down at the dying creature, the rifle held tensely in his hand.

He grabbed the dog by the tail and dragged it across the floor, the inert body leaving a swath of moist blood on the dusty boards. He kicked open the door and pulled the puppy out behind the cabin. Big wet flakes of snow were falling noiselessly amongst the pines. It was dark now. He staggered several yards into the brush, away from the cabin, stumbling like a drunken man. Taking the dead puppy by its two hind legs he flung it as far as he could into the brush. There was a faint crackle of dried leaves as the carcass fell, then silence. Bill stood still, staring off into the darkness of trees. His body began to tremble uncontrollably. Lifting a hand, he wiped at his lips with the back of it and, for the first time conscious of pain in the hand, winced and taking out his handkerchief, rubbed his knuckles gently.

The flakes, falling heavily now, felt stinging on his hot cheeks. As he stood, staring dazedly, a wind rose and the sudden noise of it through the pines frightened him. He spun around and began to run. As he hurried back to the cabin he saw the voluminous black trees bending in the night wind.

Once inside, he slammed the door behind him and leaned against it, breathing heavily. He was sick, a sickness he had never felt before. Not a good sickness that you could crawl into bed and feel warm and doze and have stray patches of dreams you didn't remember and in the morning felt better. It was a pain and a nausea that was not in his body and yet was there. He wanted more than anything to throw up. There was a stiffness in his arms, a growing powerlessness, and a blindness in his eyes as though what he looked at was not real, that nothing his gaze lit upon had familiar shape or recognition.

He peered around the room and there was a cold dumbness in his mind. The lamp still glowed and there was the warm steady hum of heat from the stove. He felt as though the warmth of his blood had left his body, that he was some thing, inanimate, dying, being slowly divested of blood and bone, of the ability to think and feel as he had, just a few moments before, been able to think and feel.

He walked to the stove and spread his hands over its warmth and rubbed briskly at his hands but they felt as though frozen, as though he could never get them warm again.

It would not go away. And the feeling that he was not himself, was another person suddenly stepped out of himself who was watching coldly and lifelessly a young man he no longer knew, no longer recognized.

I need a drink, he thought, and the thought almost cheered him. Calm me down, he said aloud, as though to hear his voice would make him feel himself again.

He went to the cupboard in the corner and took out a bottle of whiskey and pulled out the cork stopper, his hand shaking, and poured himself a long drink into a tumbler. He drank it down in one gulp, then let the bottle rest against his thigh, clenching the empty glass in the other hand. He waited, hopefully, for the whiskey to run through his veins, warm him and bring him back to life.

Outside, the wind was rising. He could hear the soft and mournful whistle of wind through the pine boughs. The snow had now turned to sleet and the hard frosty pellets struck against the window panes like handfuls of buckshot fiung violently against the glass out of the blackness of the night.

He trembled. The liquor did not seem to be working. He poured himself another, stiffer, drink and swallowed it down. He sat down at the table, one tense fist closed around the bottle's neck, a woodenness in his face. He continued to drink and when the bottle was empty, flung off his clothes, tossing them about the room, and nauseous and sodden-headed, crawled beneath the blankets and fell instantly asleep.

Next morning was a world of whiteness. Even the green of the pine trees was smothered in snow. His head ached and his mouth had a dry dead taste.

Sitting naked on the edge of the bunk he could smell an acrid smell, as though he were steeped in the stale liquor of the night before, the odor oozing out through every pore, musty, sour. He loathed the smell of himself and wondered vaguely if he should heat up water on the woodstove for a bath. The room was cold with a dry thin chill. He pulled the blanket up around his shoulders. His eyes felt glued together and his mouth full of cobwebs. He scratched his hair roughly and wondered why the cabin was so still. The windows were squares of luminous whiteness. The cabin was so still and he continued to wonder why and it was as he was slowly lifting his head to look around that he remembered.

Nothing was changed, and everything was changed. There was an emptiness in the room. Too much of a stillness, he thought, sickly, as the memory of the night before crept over him. He held up a hand, instinctively, as though the memory were a quick blow he must protect himself against. He sat slumped, his shoulders and belly sagging. Forlornly, he stared down at his long toes and wriggled them in the cold ashen dust of the floor.

After a few moments he flung off the blanket and gathering up his clothes, got dressed. He put on his sheepskin jacket and gloves and going to the door took down a yellow poncho hanging on a nail there. He shoved open the door, shuddering in the biting cold air, and stepping off the porch, sank almost knee-deep in a drift of snow. Rolling the poncho in a ball, he trudged around behind the cabin to where sere tips of sedge stood up from the rolling drifts. In the blinding whiteness, his eyes searched the surface of the snow. There was a slight rise between two cottonwoods several yards from where he stood. He plodded over to the trees and laying the poncho over the low bough of one of them, squatted down and began digging into the snow.

After scooping snow away for several minutes his hands touched something rough and hard and he pushed away the snow on either side and soon uncovered the stiff frozen body of the wolfhound. He stood up slowly and gazed down at it, breathing heavily from the exertion, his face red.

There were tiny balls of ice coating the thin hair behind its legs. Its slender black eyes were upcurving slits and the hairbreadth dark line of the mouth was rigid in a tight grin. Cautiously, he reached down and touched the puppy. It felt stiff and strangely heavy.

He wrapped the animal in the poncho and kicked away more snow with the heel of his boot. Then, going into the cabin, he brought back a pickaxe and straddling the cleared area, began hitting hard at the frozen ground. The earth was unyielding and after a half an hour of digging he had been only able to scrape out a shallow grave. He threw the pickaxe aside and taking the yellow bundle into his arms laid it in the hole, then kicked the dirt back over it again.

He stepped back. The crude grave stood out starkly like a black scar amidst the white unruffled smoothness of the snow. He thought of covering it over with fresh snow, then looked around him quickly, as though fearful that someone had been watching him. He was alone and the air was still. Snow slid noiselessly from the bough of a nearby pine.

He ran the back of his hand over his brow, wiping away the sweat, and turning reached for the pickaxe and headed back to the cabin.

Maybe it will snow again, he thought as he walked along. He gazed up at the silent leaden sky with a feeling of hopefulness.

When he got back to the cabin he stood the pickaxe in a corner and took off his gloves and jacket and tossed them on a chair. He felt sluggish and tired. His face burned. He went over to the bunk and dropped down on it. After being outside in the glare, the room seemed very dark. He could not make out objects in the room. The bright light in the window hurt his eyes. He rolled over on the bed, turning from the windows.

Tired, tired, he thought, and closed his eyes. As in a dream he saw an old seed buried under layers of dust. An old seed encased in its dry, weather-silvered pod, waiting, yearning with unutterable pain —an ache of a dream of a far-remembered sun, of sky, of a vanished life, lost. And yet, as in a delirium of fever, half waking, half sleeping, he lay inert in the darkness of its ache and sorrow and he was touched by a dream of its blossoming, a dream not yet come into being.

As though waking from troubled sleep, he rolled restlessly in the bunk, flinging his arms about. He saw, through half-closed eyes, the dead animal as a warm seed of himself, a tiny light at its black core, buried now in cold earth.

He could not rest. He swung his legs around and sat up on the edge of the bed and stared across the ashen light of the room. There were small tics of emotion about his mouth and his eyes twitched almost imperceptibly. Then he lowered his eyes and stared quietly down at his hands in his lap, seeing the hardened crust of blood across one and covering it gently with the other.

A stiff freezing wind whistled around the cabin. The walls shuddered under the impact of it.

He put his head in his hands. How foolish, foolish, he cried within himself, and slipping to his knees at the side of the bunk, buried his face in the coarse blanket and was surprised to hear himself crying because he did not remember crying for such a very long time.

ROBERT CREELEY

MR BLUE

I don't want to give you only the grotesqueness, not only what it then seemed. It is useless enough to remember but to remember only what is unpleasant seems particularly foolish. I suspect that you have troubles of your own, and, since you have, why bother you with more. Mine against yours. That seems a waste of time. But perhaps mine are also yours. And if that's so, you'll find me a sympathetic listener.

A few nights ago I wrote down some of this, thinking, trying to think, of what had happened. What had really happened like they say. It seemed, then, that some such effort might get me closer to an understanding of the thing than I was. So much that was not directly related had got in and I thought a little noting of what was basic to the problem might be in order. That is, I wanted to analyze it, to try to see where things stood. I'm not at all sure that it got to anything, this attempt, because I'm not very good at it. But you can look for yourselves.

1) That dwarfs, gnomes, midgets are, by the fact of their SIZE, intense.

2) that dwarfs, gnomes, midgets cause people LARGER than themselves to appear wispy, insubstantial, cardboard;

3) that all SIZE tends toward BIG but in the case of dwarfs, gnomes, midgets.

But perhaps best to begin at the beginning. And, to begin, there are two things that you must know. The first of these is that I am, myself, a tall man, somewhat muscular though not unpleasantly so.

I have brown hair and brown eyes though that is not altogether to the point here. What you should remember is that I am a big man, as it happens, one of the biggest in the town.

My wife is also large. This is the second. But she is not so much large as large-boned. A big frame. I sound as though I were selling her, but I'm not. I mean, I don't want to sound like that, as though I were trying to impress you that way. It is just that that I don't want to do. That is, make you think that I am defending her or whatever it is that I may sound like to you. In short, she is an attractive woman and I don't think I am the only one who would find her so. She has, like myself, brown hair but it is softer, very soft, and she wears it long, almost to her waist, in heavy braids. But it is like her eyes, I mean, there is that lightness in it, the way it brushes against her back when she is walking. It makes me feel rather blundering, heavy, to look at her. It seems to me my step jars the house when I walk through a room where she is. We have been married five years.

Five years doesn't seem, in itself, a very long time. So much goes so quickly, so many things that I can think of now that then, when they were happening, I could hardly take hold of. And where she comes into it, those things that had to do with her, I find I missed, perhaps, a lot that I should have held to. At least I should have tried. But like it or not, it's done with. Little good to think of it now.

I did try, though, to do what I could. She never seemed unhappy, and doesn't even now. Perhaps upset when the baby was sick, but, generally speaking, she's a level woman, calm, good-sense.

But perhaps that's where I'm wrong, that I have that assumption, that I think I know what she is like. Strange that a man shouldn't know his wife but I suppose it could be so, that even having her around him him for five years, short as they are, he could still be strange to her and she to him. I think I know, I think I know about what she'd do if this or that happened, if I were to say this to her, or something about something, or what people usually talk about. It's not pleasant doubting your own knowing, since that seems all you have. If you lose that, or take it as somehow wrong, the whole thing goes to pieces. Not much use trying to hold it together after that.

Still I can't take seriously what's happened. I can't but still I do. I wish it were different, that in some way, I were out of it, shaken but at least out. But here I am. The same place.

It was raining, a bad night for anything. Not hard, but enough to soak you if you were out in it for very long. We thought it would probably be closed but when we got there, all the lights were going and I could see some people up in the ferris-wheel, probably wet to the skin. Still they looked as if they were having fun and some of their shouts reached us as we went through the gate and into the main grounds. It was fairly late, about ten or so, another reason why I had thought it would be closed. Another day and the whole works would be gone and that's why she had insisted.

I feel, usually, uncomfortable in such places. I don't like the crowds, at least not the noise of them. They never seem to stop, always jumping, moving, and the noise. Any one of them, alone, or two or three, that's fine. As it happened, we went by a number of our friends, who yelled at us, fine night, or some such thing. I can't remember exactly what the words were. But I didn't like them, or didn't like them then, with that around them, the noise, and their excitement.

No reason, perhaps, to think she knew where she was going. I didn't. I think we followed only the general movement of the people, where they were going. It was packed and very difficult to go anywhere but where you were pushed. So we were landed in front of the tent without much choice and stood, listening to the barker, to see what might be happening.

I can say, and this is part of it, that I didn't want to go in. For several reasons. The main one is that I don't like freaks, I don't like to look at them or to be near them. They seem to have a particular feeling around them, which is against me, altogether. A good many times I've seen others staring, without the slightest embarrassment, at some hunchback, or some man with a deformity that puts him apart from the rest. I don't see how they can do it, how they can look without any reaction but curiosity. For myself, I want only to get away.

But this time she decided. It seemed that not very much could be inside the tent. They had advertised a midget, a knife-thrower, a man with some snakes, and one or two other things. Nothing like the large circuses and none of the more horrible things such might offer. So I got the tickets and we followed a few of the others in.

They were just finishing a performance. It was so packed at the front, that we stood at the back, waiting until the first crowd was ready to leave. I felt tired myself. It must have been close to eleven at that point. It seemed an effort there was no reason for. But she enjoyed it, looked all around, at everyone, smiled at those she knew, waved to some, kept talking to me, and I would say something or other to hide my own feeling. Perhaps I should have been straight with her, told her I was tired, and ducked out. It would have saved it, or at least got me free. But I kept standing there, with her, waiting for the show to finish and another to start.

It did soon, the first crowd moving out, and our own coming up to take its place. The man on the platform had got down at the end and now we waited for him to come back and the new show to begin. There was talking around us, sounding a little nervous the way most will at those times when something is being waited for, though what one can't say with exactness. At this point, I was almost as expectant as the others. Nothing else to be, perhaps. In any event, I had got over my other feeling.

The first act was a cowboy with a lariat, rope tricks. Not.much but he was good with it, could make it spin all kinds of loops, shrinking them, making them grow right while we watched him. It was good fun, I thought, not much but enough. At the end he started stamping with one foot and at the same time, he slipped his loop off and on it, brought it up around both feet at the end, jumping and grinning. I think there may have been some music with it, something for the beat, but it doesn't matter. The man told us he was deaf, couldn't hear a thing. There didn't seem to be much point in telling us that but I guess we're apt to like that adding of what we don't expect.

We enjoyed it, the both of us. It's not often that we can get out, like that, to see anything. And after the first I forgot about being tired and liked it as much as she did. The next act was the knife-thrower. He could put them all in a circle no bigger than my hand, eight of them, so that they shivered there with a force which surprised me, each time one hit, she gripped my arm, and I laughed at her nervousness, but it was a funny thing, even so.

Then came the snake act, which wasn't up to the others, or simply that dullness in it, the snakes much the same, doped, I expect, though perhaps I was wrong to think so. Then sort of a juggling act, a man with a number of colored balls and odd-shaped sticks, which he set into a strange kind of movement, tossing them, one after the other, until he must have had ten somehow, going and all this with an intentness that made us almost clap then, as they did move, through his hands. Altogether a wonder it seemed, his precision, and how it kept him away from us, even though some stood no more than a few feet away. Until at last he stopped them one by one, and then, the last, smiled at us, and we all gave him a good hand.

It's here that I leave, or as I go back to it, this time; or this way, that is, now that I make my way out, through the rest of them, my hand on her arm with just that much pressure to guide her, or that is my intention. Perhaps the lights that make my eyes ache, begin to, or simply, that it's now, this point, that I am happy, that it's ourselves, the two of us, have come to some sort of feel of it, that makes us so. Just that I am, now, running, that it is just that I do.

What she had been doing, or going to that, it was a cigarette she asked me for, and I reached into my pocket for them, had got out the pack, and given her one, and then lit a match for her. She bent a little, got it lit, then looked back to the platform where the juggler had been.

But the trick, that it's him who's there, the midget, as such he is named, but the size, it's that which hits me, at first, that he isn't small, or looking, he must be five feet, or perhaps, a little smaller. Four feet. But not small.

The eyes, catch, get me so into it, that they are so, void, in the head, shaded, the shades like changing shadows, colors, coming in to want, to want to be filled. Seem huge. He looks at all of us, moves over us so, to bite, to have something to be there to bite.

But nothing, certainly, to make of it more or more than what I could see, would be, that is, the barker introduced him, and we stood, as we had, in that group in front of him, the boards which made the platform, that roughness, and the poles on which the lights were strung, the wires sagging between them. That is, what is it had come in, as this was, to be not or to make it not as it had been, if it were, as it was, the same place, which I couldn't say or put my finger on, then, but waited like any of the rest.

I could see the muscle of his arm, where the sleeve had been pulled up, rolled, above it, and with his movement, that slightness of tension made him lift it, slightly, from time to time, the muscle tightened and it looked hard, big, below the roll of the sleeve. As my own would. He was smiling, the face somewhat broad, well-shaped, the smile somewhat dreamy, or like sleep, that vagueness, which couldn't be understood.

The barker had laughed, the pitch of it rolled out, on us, and I wondered if he was as drunk as he looked. He was calling the midget, cute, saying, a cute little fellow. He made a joke of it, looking at the women and laughing. Saying, who would like to take him home. There was laughing, they liked the joke, and he carried it further, sensing their tolerance, and played it up. It was the joke he seemed intent on making us remember, the cuteness, the idea of the women.

Taking the cigarettes out of my pocket, the pack crumpled, I held it out to her, but she was intent on what was before us, and I expect that I was myself, and only did what I did, took them out, to somehow break it, to make it break down. It seemed that, that is, that gesture or an act, an action, so meant to serve double, to be a break, but what was it, that is, more than the taking, just that, of the cigarettes, which I didn't want to smoke, had even just put one out. I looked, then, around me at the rest of them and they were looking at him, the midget, and I couldn't see one that noticed I looked, or gave the least sign.

The midget stood still, beside the barker, who staggered a little, under the lights, moved from one side to the other, his face to us, that drunkenness. He was still on the joke, fumbling, and it wore down on us, that weight of it, kept at us, and I wanted to get out. There seemed breaks, lengths of silence, hung there, made the other, the midget, the whole of it, in his own silence, which he kept as a distance around him, that the eyes made actual.

I would have gone, or as I think, I should have in spite of it, simply slipped out, when the others weren't looking, just left and waited for her outside. I can't see that she would have been hurt. That is, I would think, or think I would have that right to, that it would make no difference to her, that is, that she would understand my going, seeing that it had begun to tire me, even became painful to stay. I think of it so, being such, that no difference could be in it, since she was enjoying it, or so it seemed.

I tried to, but the people around pressed too tight, pushed me from the back, all forward, to the one on the platform in front of us. Not the barker, I knew that much, but the other, who pulled them, kept them all, because the barker had somehow fallen altogether to pieces, had just the joke he hung on to, and that was played out. But then he switched it, perhaps feeling it had, and turned to the midget, and said, but you should have some say in this. Which one would you like.

The midget turned, then seemed to pull himself out of it, the distance, out of nothing, the eyes pulled in, to focus, to grow, somehow, smaller, larger. The eyes went over us, the voice, when it came, was breath, a breathing but way back in, wire, tight, taut, the scream and I couldn't hear it, saw only his finger move to point at her, beside me, and wanted to say, he's looking at you, but she was turned away from me, as though laughing, but struck, hit. I looked, a flash, sideways, as it then happened. Looked, he looked at me, cut, the hate jagged, and I had gone, then, into it and that was almost that. But she said, then, she had seen him, earlier, that same day, as he was standing by a store, near the door, I think, as it had opened, and she, there, across the street, saw him motion, the gesture, then, a dance, shuffle, the feet crooked, and the arms, as now, loose, and it was before, as before, but not because of this, that made it, or I thought, so made it, was it, or it was that thing I hung to, when, the show over, they motioned us out, and I pushed a way for her out through the crowd.

THE GRACE

From somewhere else he could hear it, but the crying at least had stopped, and turning, he saw her at the door, shutting it quietly, and putting a finger to her lips.

Quiet, she said, and came in, then, to sit down in the chair opposite him, sinking down there and letting her legs go out, slack, in front of her. Behind him he had put the candle and it burned, flickering, but a light, and as soft as any he might hope for.

Otherwise, there was a moon, and this rose, very gently, somewhere back of the house. The road looked a liquid, or water there, translucent. He felt it as pleasant, perhaps, but was too tired to get up and at her suggestion, that they might walk, said, no, and slumped back.

There was no time, he said, but knew she had another sense of it. Something, he said, makes a mess of it.

She got up to light another candle and put it on the table behind him, but bitterly, he thought, and watched her sit down again.

We can hope for another place, he added. This is just for the time-being. Call it a vacation, or anything like that.

But the house, or the rooms, something bothered, and she had little peace, accepting nothing of it, and moving with a kind of rigidness through it all. Now she got up again, impatient, and lighting the stove, began to heat water for the dishes.

Can I help, he said, when she looked at him, but she turned away again, and he relaxed.

Outside it grew light, or seemed to, almost like day, but whiter, again that translucence, and he wondered if out there one might not be another thing altogether, even though it should seem otherwise. To the west were some small lights, single, each a small brightness, and separate from the rest. He imagined gayety, or even singing, the tables of some place packed and people altogether without malice. He thought it might be like that, and felt, too, the moon was the sign.

She had cleared the table, taking the dishes to the sink, to put them at the side, and then filled the sink with the water she had heated.

Meticulous, in some sense, she washed them one by one, to put them down again, again at the side, until they were done. Then left them there, to dry by themselves.

Sitting down, she looked up at him, and waiting, she reached over to pick up her knitting, and then began, the needles very bright, and quick, in her hands.

But he had started, and spoke, now, of what he had thought himself to have forgotten, a picnic so long ago it seemed inconsequential, though he could not have said, then, why. Somewhere his grandmother had carried out the lemonade, or he remembered it, in a bright tin pitcher, to place it on the long table, under the trees.

It should be like that, he said. What do we give of that, or what do we try to. Tell me one thing we do that is as nice as that.

She hadn't answered, but anyhow he assumed her attention, and wanted to make it clear.

A fine old lady, he said. I mean, really. She knew what work was, though I suppose she minded, certainly. That it couldn't have been very pleasant for her.

I don't suppose it was, she said, and looked at him.

Or that other, the one the old man told us about, his mother, who died by the window there, took three drags on her pipe and then slipped out. How about that!

She laughed, herself, and found it simpler, the time less persistent, and had gone back again, with him, and sat in the old room, as she supposed the old lady had, lifeless, and in the dark.

That was in our house, she said. In the living-room, by the back window. He said she used to knit there too, in the moonlight.

One would like to go back, he had said. One would rather not move away ever, or go anywhere but where one was.

Even so, the moon rose, higher, and now came clear through the door they had left open, and came across the floor very softly, to touch the back of his chair. He grew quiet, sinking down, and pushed out his legs, reaching her, one foot against her own.

From somewhere above the boy cried, whimpering, and putting down the knitting, she got up, to cross to the stairs, and then he heard her go up, the crying continuing, and growing louder. He started to get up himself, but sat down, annoyed, and wondered what the matter was, calling to her, to hear her answer, nothing.

Echoes, he thought. But the crying grew less, then stopped, and soon she was back, and sat down again across from him.

He was frightened, she said, and seeing him angry, added, he isn't settled yet.

The anger went, and left him lost in some other thought, of the house, and where they had been, call it, in another place.

He must miss it, he said. But there it is, I mean, one moves anyhow? And stopped, to say, isn't it? Isn't that what has to happen?

I don't know, he said, insistent. I don't know why it is so much place with them. Not that I don't get it, that is, don't get what moving does to a kid, but what else? We've been here close to two months.

She let him go on, and sat only there, silent, and not with any malice. Hard to believe it otherwise, or he wondered, then, if it could be otherwise. Something he thought of as impenetrable, but getting up, he asked her to come out, saying he felt like a walk now, if she still wanted to.

She followed after him, and they started off down the road, past the other houses, close, and then off through the fields, the moon there very much a whiteness and lying on the ground with grace. He said he could not really believe it. That it was, then, a world so very close to their own.

But it is here, he insisted, and took her arm to hold it. It has to be?

They went on, following the edge of the field, the ground rough and uneven under their feet. Now and again she stumbled, and he held her up, and at last they sat down there on the grass, and lay back.

Straight up, above them, the moon was beginning to slip, and sink down, but shone with a fierceness, and made them seem bluish to each other, hands looking pale and unreal.

She had raised herself, a little, then leaned on him, over, and her hands took his own, lightly, as she kissed him. But he had not stopped, or only for that instant, and looked up at the distance above him, saying, he didn't know, and felt the ground hard under both of them.

It's all right, she said, and moved to stroke him, hoping to help, to ease it. One knows that it will be.

He rested, and felt her fingers very careful, finding him with a certain gentleness, or that sure. He said, thanks, and laughed a little, lifting to take hold of her, but they heard the faint crying, from the house, coming after them, and got up.

She went ahead, running, and he called to her to be careful, then saw her reach the road. From somewhere another sound, a cry, rising, to die out. He tripped and fell down, sprawling, and got up again, rubbing his knee.

Coming in, he found it quiet, and she was sitting in the chair by his own. He looked toward the stairs, but she shook her head, and told him the boy was asleep, so he sat down himself, going loose, hopeless, in the chair.

What the hell does it, he said, what starts it off?

But she shrugged, and he saw she had the knitting, and watched the needles begin, easily, moving in and out.

What a night, he said. What a goddamn miserable night.

It seemed nothing, and he grew restless, watching her, intent, and could say nothing, to break it. Getting up again, he asked her if she were tired, and so she put down the knitting, to follow him, blowing out the candle beside her, while he took the other from the table to carry up with them. But there was light enough, from outside, and so he blew it out, to leave it again on the table.

Upstairs, he felt the room deeper, or open, the light making a wideness, and breaking against the sides, pushing, to make a space. He could not know that she saw it, but hoped, and undressing, quietly, laid his clothes on the chair, and got into the bed. He looked back to see she had finished, and then felt her slide in against him, to sink back, on the bed, then turn.

A place, she said, but didn't, and put her hands on him, again gently, and he put his arms around her, still hoping. The room was very light, and the whiteness now altogether actual, seeming even a drift, of some wave, in, to make the room a space, of an intention, or where one might come to live.

Waiting, he went back against the pillow, easily, but somewhere he heard the scream, behind him, and asked if she would want him to go quietly, and being more, he thought, that I can do something, perhaps which she might wish me to. But she got up, and went into the other bedroom, opening the door then, so that he heard the sounds very close to him, a pain there, and continuing. Quiet again, she came back, but again it started, the boy calling, and she went back.

All right, he called, asking, and she answered, soon, and he lay back, tired, and a little lost. The moon seemed to sink, a crest reached and lost, and he watched it, catching the edge against the window, to try to hold it, but felt it pass.

She came in, standing at the door, and waited to see if the boy would now sleep, but he didn't, calling to her, and she went back.

What's the matter, he said, but she didn't hear. What's the matter, and she answered, again, soon, and he fell back again, to wait there, the night going deep, and on, he said, it must be late.

Then she got into the bed, and lay down, coming to him, then, but nothing, he thought, and heard it, the cry, and got up himself to run to the door, pulling at it, and yelled, what, seeing the boy sitting straight in the bed, staring, and crying, screaming, the sound driving in on him as he came.

What, he yelled, what, what, what, and got hold of the boy, by one arm, dragging him clear of the blanket, then bringing his own hand back, hard, to slap him, the head jerking back, and down. But useless, the screaming now louder, and he felt it useless, picking the boy up, to cradle him, holding him, and walking beside the bed's length, the moon still against them, a light, a light, he said, and went back to the other room to find her waiting with the candle.

IN THE SUMMER

I am not saying that it was ever to the point or that a purpose could be so neatly and unopposedly defined. Or that twenty-one or so years ago, on that day, or on this, he was then, or is now, there or here, that we could know him and see him to be what he is. I don't much care for that. I had my own time to do, a number of things to do. I had heard, then, that the growing-up of anything could become an involved and crippling process. I could see the sun each day, coming up, and then each night, going down. I gave my time to that.

She said: do you really believe that, do you really see things that way.

Of course, it isn't so neat, he said. He was being somewhat diffi-cult, he thought, to allow her to speak of things which didn't have to do with her, but her hands, in his own, were chafed, and rough, and his own, moving over them, in a kind of tired realization that they were not what they might be, said, here's a little warmth, take it.

No, I couldn't have to do with him, then, because I was afraid of him, of having him come too close to me, or to himself, for that matter. I knew then what I was, what gave me pleasure, or how I should best set about getting it. It was no sin, to know that. I got up early in the morning, each day, to get that jump on everyone else. They didn't see that I did, but just the same, I did.

So is love, in itself, a kind of inverse plunging, which I cannot say more about, or much more, than that.

She said: why love, what has that got to do with this, what you were saying about him.

And withdrew, a little, her hand from his hold which was to say to him, that she had become suspicious and was now thinking of something else. But he drank what beer he had left in his glass and took that occasion for speech, finishing.

Like that, he said, that I was then thinking of it, the beer. That was what I had in mind. And I could love that too, I expect. One thinks of hot days and it's not so hard then.

She said: but not the same way.

The same way, he said, no different. And that is what was wrong then. Wanting to give. That is itself a sin. There is no other sin that I can think of that is worse. And I should damn it more thoroughly, than I could myself, for considering it or any one thing. That I haven't the time for, now or then.

The question would be always the same in love, and is: can it be taken. How can I best take hold of it, in what multiple ways, and all of these with the obscenity of blindness. Since it will never be what I take.

She said: this is all the same, I know all this, and the kind who say it.

And he could not himself have made such a thorough round comment, as she had made, for which he didn't so much as remember, later, that she had said it but forgot then, in himself, that she was even there, or that he again had her hand, the fingers of which he went over, one by one, counting, making sure.

What summer is more beautiful, he began, and then began again. What summer is more beautiful than the one I can tell you about. Let us think of it as all orchards and that kind of smell, a freshness there, which one couldn't lose hold of if one wanted. From the house, between the single row of maples that stretched down over the slight hill to the field below, it was always to be going somewhere far from the house though I could be called to it by even the slightest of voices, to come back for whatever it was they wanted. And close to the top of this hill I had my coops, for my pigeons, and they were all different colors, different shapes. On the windy days I would let them out, with the clouds, and they would go up, very high, except for those who could not quite get there or loop in long fast circles, but would hang in the air, to wait for the others to come round or back, and then would start off, as leaders, only to be left again, and to wait. These were my fantails, which were awkward, strutting birds, with wide spread tails. Mine were white and one spring I had a very nice one but he wasn't banded and so he was never worth very much to anyone but myself. But that is another tragedy, and not this one.

We spent that summer at home and when my mother's vacation came, we didn't go anywhere, to the beach or up to the mountains, but stayed there in the town. I expect that I was a little sorry then,

but not too much. I had any number of birds that year and could not
be got very far from them, except to see someone else's, which got
me about, at least a little, here and there, to see the other boys of
my age, or the men who had not got beyond this time in their own
lives and whose garages or houses still sprouted with flycoops and a
variety of pens. It was something to do.

He had left the first part of that summer, to go to a camp, a
caddy-camp, some distance away, at a big hotel, in the mountains,
which his father thought would be good for him, to learn to take it,
and to make a little money. He was somewhat stronger than myself,
a year older, so in that way he went, without thinking much of myself
or that it was strange that I didn't go too. Another year I was to
have gone, he said. I would go, as it had then been agreed. But for
myself, I missed him very much, the first part, and would get cards
from him, these not very often, and painfully written, as a fifteen-year
old boy will write to one a year younger than himself, in a way that
neither can understand, being fragments thrown off from the very
force of his living. I wrote to him much the same things as we had
been doing when he was at home, that such and such had come or
gone, these all on the only postcards I could get, of the town-hall,
looking very grey and shoddy against the hard geometry of the square
with the surrounding and enclosing stones. It was not wrong, then, to
consider myself, in spite of the summer's warmth, and what I had to
do with it, still abject and though I could not then have thought so,
pathetic.

Sometimes I would go down to the barn which his father had moved
and built again, by himself, though we boys gave what help we could,
to be doing something during the fall he put it up. And there it was,
then, and maybe now, what tribute he could put into so much wood,
for his son, that he could move and put up again with his own
hands, to put the pony in, which he couldn't afford, yet would have.
I was allowed to ride the pony that summer, now and then, when he
was around but he fed it while his son was away, and would let no
one else do very much for it. So for most of the day it was staked out,
like a cow, under the apple trees for shade though not so near to any
of them that it would eat the apples and get sick.

The barn wasn't too big, just room enough for a good-sized box
stall and what hay the pony ate during the winter, and a place for

harness and saddle. And he hadn't finished it off altogether, being in a hurry as he was to get it done, so the pony could come, and only himself to do it. So a good number of the boards were nailed with only a single nail in the corners where the pony wouldn't go, though where the stall was and the way out to the main door he had fixed with two-by-eights, double-planked, which the pony would never break through.

A year before the boy and myself had hit upon one board in particular, soon after the pony came, when we were down in the barn, most of the time, that we lifted and put things under, pushing them far back, as far as we could reach, cigarettes and what else we had.

And reaching under there, then, that summer, I could get hold of the corner of the magazine and pull it out, without tearing the page I had got hold of, slowly, dragging it, and then the book, with the back off and the pages mildewed from having been under there so long. And on the first page could see the woman under the slightness of the slip, with its fine line of cloth covering only that much of the breasts which would have been in itself enough for the hand of a fourteen-year old. And where the cloth moved down the body against the flesh, to the leg, and there stopped, to end in a kind of torn edge, against the flesh, which I knew almost by heart, and then to the face, with the look of kind, that kind of, dismay, which then explained the man with his own face, in the picture, across from her, but coming closer, with his hands stretched out and wanting, about to, tear off the slip.

Or the book, which I can, perhaps, still quote, being those pages which I have no right to forget, or not quite so quickly, since it was there written, that '. . . she did not at first understand what he expected of her. But he came closer and then she knew that he was about to. . .'. As I myself was.

At least this much we had stored against a time when we should know more of it, that those pages should themselves secure us, that we should then know, all. But not enough then, to see what we were cheated of. Those times I came alone, that summer, to the barn, perhaps, what was I looking for, and here I am very near tears, or much closer than you may think, to look at me. That I should somehow have expected his own words to have been there, on the edge of the page, which would have been meant for me.

What embarrasses here is not altogether what you think but is that which will always be more sad than embarrassing. I am not sure that I speak now, even for myself, that I have not become the fact of much more than I intend. But I do speak of myself, nonetheless.

With the end of summer or toward the end of summer, since it had not quite come but only that slight feel of the days somewhat faint and beginning to go into another kind of color and tone, with that time I began to look for him to come home again, from the camp. Later I read of those fair lovers who lay, without sleep and all cares, on those no harder beds than love's own caring, but then I could not invoke them. That much you must understand. I had no idea of what part I should have in anything, much less in this. So he came home one day toward the first of September, with his father in their car, and drove into the yard opposite ours which was where he lived then, in a small white house, Cape Cod, as they call them, to which his father had added some dormer windows and inside, rooms, so that there would be places for them all. I could see them getting out of the car and then the bags and boxes coming out of the back, with all his things, and then I expect I wanted to go over and help, but didn't, and instead went down to the barn, since I knew he would come there, soon, to see the pony, if it was all right after the summer and his being away from it.

She said: he came.

He came, he said, but it wasn't sad. There was nothing there or in that that got me, then, and it wasn't until later that I got what I should have got there. It had been strong enough apparently to carry the summer with it, all that fine weather, into the colors of the fall, the cold, and then all that winter, sometimes in his house, sometimes in mine.

She said: what had you expected from any of it, being fourteen as you were, or any age, for that matter, what was it you wanted to get out of something like that, that you knew you couldn't, and didn't, later, much want, but just then wanted, as though you knew that later it would have to come to me, this kind of thing, to ask me what I thought and did I understand, as if there, in any of it, was what I was supposed to understand.

I don't know, he said, since then or there I haven't been for some-time. Sometimes it is just that I can't remember any of it or have like a kind of fog that which I felt then, to wonder about, and to put against, even, what I have now.

She said: you haven't anything, even with him here, it's yourself you care about, and want, that you can hurt both of us, or I don't care about him, if it's what you want me to do, that I shouldn't care.

A DEATH

Vestida con mantos negros
piensa que el mundo es chiquito
y el corazón es inmenso. . .
                                    LORCA

Ahead of them the path went round the trees, and into a clearing of stones, which had rolled from the higher points of the hill to make a sort of flat and broken plateau above the sea. Again, the children went in front, with Amos carrying the basket in one hand, and the other two crowding in back of him. She puffed at the cigarette for the last time, and dropped it, to step on it, and asked them all, how much farther it all was.

She was not a very pretty woman. Amos was six years old, and her one son. The facts sorted themselves like much too brief messages, not trivially but too quickly. She wanted to say something to the man now beside her, who was her brother, and his wife walked beside him on thick legs, wide and heavy at the ankles. Beginning to say it, she heard the children cry out, and there was Amos standing in the sun with the stone in his hand, in front of her, and then he threw it.

But that, at least, was not enough to bother them. James bound the wound, as he said, expertly, and soon the little girl had forgotten it, and ran once more after the others. The sun picked them out, in the shadows, and in and out they ran, around the rocks, and behind them, crouching, then waving the sticks again, and the parents sat in a small three-cornered circle watching them, and then looking at one another.

In her own head she now resolved, or arranged a pattern of hostility, a final war against them, but that was her love for Amos. If he cried, that was too much. Or if he did not cry. but hit her, as he would and did, she would rather it were in their own room at the hotel, and not here in front of the others. He is a very nervous child, she said, his father makes no gesture of love to him. Or of affection.

So they pitied her. What was it like, they thought. What ever could it be like, in the heathen country of New Zealand. James said, he'll get over it. He laughed. His wife smiled at her, and she felt the edge of it coming in like the sharpness intended, to cut at her politely and to wound her. So she got up, and said she would take a little walk, calling Amos, and the two of them left and went down the hill to the sea.

As they grew smaller, the wife smiled again. James was uneasy, and their own children bored and impatient. He began to pile small stones, one very carefully on another, to build a small house. He made a door and two little windows, with small sticks for supports, and then the little boy kicked at it, and it fell to pieces.

In New Zealand, he said, but his wife would not listen to him. She took the children in her arms, one against each leg, and smiled again at him. He was the man she knew, and she would hear nothing at all to the contrary.

Closer to the sea the rock became sharper, and lifted into big, over-hanging bunches. A few pine trees grew somehow out of them, but these were very stunted, and low. The water was very lovely and very clear. One saw to the bottom. The fish moved out from the shallows, and seeing people come, disappeared altogether.

Amos was a fisherman. He had his own little pole, with a little reel on it, and would sit hours by the water without bothering her at all. Sometimes her husband came too. The first fish Amos ever caught, after many days and even years of fishing, was one which her husband had put on the hook for him, without him any the wiser. In a way it was sad that that had been the first, but after that he caught some actually.

Looking at Amos, she now wondered what she would change, if she could. His eyes were blue, almost shut in the intensity of their color. Perhaps he would be a great man in spite of them. His hair had bleached almost white, and under it the darker tawny color came through. But his arms were very thin and stick-like, and his chest corded with little muscles. He was like a goat, an obscenely precocious goat, who had no use for people.

Taking off their clothes, she put them in a pile, and then put a stone on top of it. Amos giggled. She had forgotten the bathing-suits, and they were in the basket, high up on the hill with the others. Even so she slipped into the water quietly, and calling softly to Amos, drew him in after her.

Above them, James fumbled in his embarrassment. His wife smiled again, and watching him, thought only of his remarkable innocence. It was pleasant that it should be so. He was very unmarked, and untouched by so many things. His sister might well be a photograph, she thought, which he wished to be proper and in focus. Otherwise she was a nuisance, as, for example, she paddled away down there, with the boy, and seemed almost completely foreign. James coughed, he wanted not quite to see. The bodies went under the water, to leave the heads free, then they too ducked under.

Still watching him, his wife said, what do you think of it, James. As she had said, three days earlier, to a young man on the beach with them, do you see how he treats me?

But what was so simple about it. Make me happy, she said. Don't please think of her. James was very much in the middle and began to know it. He knew love was not multiple, or could not be here divided. He said, be patient with her. He let it all rest on kindness.

The water around them changed all that, on their bodies, very much on their bodies. Amos jumped up, shrieking, and she loved him more than she admitted. Look, she said. The small fish darted out, past their white feet, and then back again to the darker places. But Amos had seen them. It was lovely.

Then she left him, swimming out, and free of it. The water was buoyant, so that she hardly swam but floated, lifted out on the wash of the waves as they fell back. Beneath her the colors changed from the green to blue, and then a darker blue, and then black. She dove and felt the tips of her fingers touch bottom, and on her hands the weeds were very light and brushed them gently.

Far away she thought that the house was now gone. Her husband loved no one anymore. At last they were also free of him. He sat in a chair in the yard which he had made. There was no car. The street was long, and at the end there was a tram-stop. People spoke English but he answered them, *no se*. He was a Greek with rings in his ears, and his hands were folded in his lap.

So one could change it as he might. She held to that, and here the water helped her, taking her as she was. One saves all one's life, against the one instant it is all real, and all enough. Why, she said, tell me now otherwise! Tell me nothing.

If it is obscene, she said. Her husband's mother was obscene. Of her own husband she had known nothing, she had not even known his body. And when at last he grew sick, to die, she took off his clothes for the first time, and saw the body for the first time, dying.

Gulls flapped off the rocks behind her. Amos slapped at the water with a stick he had found. The quiet grew over all of them.

But what was to be done with James. His wife thought she knew, and yet he was strangely moved. The children were happy, they played behind them with the toys they had brought in the basket. So she attacked him directly, and asked him, what was it. He said he did not know.

Is it your sister, she said, and looked down, and away, to the form still clear to them, a white odd shape on the top of the sea. He answered that he did not think it was. She said, you must see the difficulties. He was not sure that he did.

But, corruption, she would have insisted if she had dared to. The small knotted boy giggled at them, he caught at his mother's skirt and giggled. She had neither sympathy nor time for that horror. She has had a difficult life, he said. And what is difficulty. He lifted the skirt, giggling at her own children, he said to them, look. It was not possible to be kind.

To that James agreed, and yet it was still possible. The children played happily in back of them. The little boy threw the ball to the little girl. She missed it, and ran off to bring it back.

What do you think, his wife said. But a small boat now came into view, and he pointed at it, and they watched it crawl out past the rocks to their left, and then begin to come down the coast.

Hearing the sound of the motor, Amos looked up, and out. There it was, very white, with a little line of exhaust trailing the back. His mother was also out there, and he thought of it. He wanted the boat to take him away, perhaps to put him into the front somewhere, but he would never have the courage to go. He felt for a stone under the water, and found one close to his toes, and then threw it out as far as he could at the boat.

It missed the boat, but fell beside her, splashing her face. It was usual, and yet she looked back at him, in anger, to see him squatted there in the water, and, she thought, shivering. She wondered if the man, standing upright in the boat, could see her. He had seen the stone. His hand was on the tiller, his other let him lean back a little, braced against the boat's side. He was not tall, but he was strong-looking, his chest heavy. Now he did look, at first at the boy, and then coming closer, looked down and saw her as she took a stroke to swim back.

At that even James was angry. They had all expected it. She had only done what she would, but his wife was now right beyond all question. They watched the two figures collect themselves. The boat was no longer visible. Slowly they came up the hill again, and now it was impossible for James to swim, or for his wife, or children.

You know, his wife said, what this will mean. For the last minutes she wanted to be clearly fair. James watched his sister coming toward them, and saw her smiling. Was it to be a simple thing? She was not ashamed. Amos dragged at her hand, she pulled him along almost without realizing it.

Such a lovely swim, she said. The water was so lovely and refreshing. And the boat, the wife asked. But did she really say it. Her own children were safe behind her and never again would she really let them go. Amos giggled, he pulled at his mother's skirt, raising it, and James saw the tight thigh, and the brown, close flesh.

Did you see the boat, his wife said. She knew it was her brother's wife. She knew her own husband was dead. She saw the faces all in front of her, and if she cried out at them, she was still in love with everything.

THE DRESS

Much was simple about Mary and Peter, and to describe them quickly, it was first of all two people, in a house into which not many others came. And three children, pushed into corners, and a friend or two who came to call. After ten years or so of living together, there were no very actual mementos, or none that either felt much disposition to recognise. There were no flags, and in fact few signs of even time except for the children, and a scar which traversed Mary from belly-button to bottom. Which both had *done*, but also for which Peter was in some sense guilty. Not her.

But, passing that, walking into the room, at this instant, saying something, Peter wanted one action, definite, to place them all in that place where time shall have no dominion. Louise, Mary's *present* friend, was a tall woman, dangling happy jiggly things hung from both ears with such weight that he was worried her ears might tear loose. The pain of speaking was in this way increased.

But. Now—for once he shook free of it, taking with him both Louise. And Mary. And through a small opening in the floor, pulled them down, into where *he* lived. Saying nothing, because there was nothing to say, *now* he led them through a tiny passage, obliging Louise in particular to crawl on all embarrassed fours, like the tiny and comfortable being she was. He snapped a whip. He turned on a light, and, in an instant, the cavern was flooded with a warm rich yellow searching glow. Peering into the two faces looking up at him, he saw, first, dismay. Then, laughter. And then, dismay. So back up they went, into the room, and sat there.

Mary's dress, half-finished, lay on the table, and this is what the two women had been talking about, planning, deciding, when he had, first, come in. It was a question as to whether this material, as an added border, and so, design, would be the best, the most interesting, or, on the other hand, that. Two materials lay beside the half-finished dress, in long narrow strips, and on one there was a quiet, rich, oblique design of some warm grey and blue and red. And on the other, a more excited, flaring, intense design of green, yellow and blue. Louise asked him what he thought would look best, and Mary, by her listening, also was curious to know. So he thought, *under* the dress will be, of course, Mary. So what is Mary like? Yet that necessitated returning to *under* the floor, so down they all went again, the women this time less hesitant, as he drew them on, and down, and also more curious to explore, should he let them, this sudden, exciting inclination.

He let them explore, and as the yellow light reached all corners of the underfloor cavern, the two women went, hand in hand, to one after another of the sights which were there. As, for example, the stalactites and the stalagmites. Which had been formed by the dripping, and which hung, like icicles, from the roof of the cavern. The dripping itself was from a fissure, a cleft or split. But also, a narrow opening in an *organ*, as was now the case. A cleavage. *Findo. To cleave*. Peter had accomplished this by a daily *expenditure*, and these objects, precariously enough arrived at and/or created, were important to him.

The women moved incautiously, because these things were not what he had *done*, not, that is, what they had done for him. Mary did many things for him, as she now did, certainly, in the present place—by moving there at all—and by looking, touching, exploring. Louise, striking one of the pendular accumulations with the hard heel of her hand, said, listen! And from the hanging, or rather the hanging up spikelike accumulation, came notes, with each blow, like those of Big Ben chiming the hour, in London. Peter brusquely silenced her, and it was then that both women reminded him of their reason for coming to the cavern at all.

So again they sat in the room, with the dress material across Mary's knees, while she bent over it, as if to catch, now, in some pattern of the varied cloth, an instance of her own person. Finally, in short, this was to be her own *person*, or at least was, from roughly, the knees to the neck, with arms and varied other areas left clear. Under it, of course, would be her own body.

Louise interposed the *idea* of, in New Mexico, Indian women, with their many layered dresses, built out into a raging, piled, and then formed piece of clothing. This, with the hair pulled back, long, and left to hang down. Also, they had straight backs, fine clear features, a race altogether of clean, dark women. Under this onslaught Mary buckled, adding for herself a host of other details, taken from pictures of Mexican women, Italian women, and the more known Spanish women. Peter himself saw his wife as *white*, and had known her as such. He added to the material which she held, on her knees, the memory of other materials, and, in particular, one thin worn black and purple-spotted dress, for which he had a great fondness. This dress, when she wore it, swelled into desirable proportions, the breast forward, the waist drawn in, and for the neck, low and round, of the dress, a leaving open of the bones, which formed the height of the body, wide, then certain, down, into the complexity of the *flesh*.

It was the friend's *premise*, however, to make the wife not a wife. This was where Peter himself was confused. To take Louise, too, into the cavern—she was with Mary and that allowed it. Louise, looking at him, now, was *older* than he was. As, in some crowded neighbourhood, this building is older than that one, and, because it is, insists on itself as in that way more rightly there. Under any dress the body is this or that, older or younger, whiter or darker. Under the floor he had the cavern to think about, but Louise could not think *about* it. She was either there or not. Mary likewise.

Mary, the young wife, getting up, put the cloth on the table where it had first been, and went out to see about supper. In the room behind them Louise and Peter heard her speak, then the maid answer, then Mary speaking again. Whether or not the children had always been in the room, as they were now, looking at both Peter and Louise, covetously, was not certain. Could he take *Louise* into the cavern? Alone?

In the cavern Louise stood back from him, crouched under the warm yellow light, and hidden behind the multiplicity of forms which crowded from all sides. He spoke, yet the voice in finding her became too changed to be recognized. It was not his voice. Had he thought of her otherwise, he might well have approached her. But he did not. Soon other faces looked down from that point at which they had entered the cavern, little faces looked down, three in number. This time Louise did not strike the coagulated, hardened and depending forms with her hand. No tone at all broke the silence.

Yet the relief was in the *body*, both his and hers, and also Mary's. Who was not present but was felt, among them, and each, Louise and himself, insisted on that knowledge. In the yellow light one group of stalactites and stalagmites appeared to be a castle. Another, not far from where Louise continued to *creep*, back, on hands and knees, was a snow scene, and reared, up and down, in sinuous, fixed motion.

When Mary re-entered the room Louise spoke to her, but Peter was unable to. He remained in the cavern. But concern soon brought him out, and closely listening he accepted the invitation of their words and re-addressed himself to the problem of material.

Was the dress to be final—is in effect how he addressed it. The *body* was not final, yet women, or rather his wife—she was final. Louise was not. In the cavern, revealed, or veiled? In that light it was Louise, entire, who was revealed. In the mind, or idea, of Peter.

Picking up the material again, Mary let it spread over her knees, and looked at Peter, and then at Louise. The concern was whether or not the dress was to be her own person, or Louise's. Or the Indian women. Or, in the cavern, all these forms were taken care of, redisposed, in, surely, a wide variety of *attitudes*. Peter wanted a dress, for Mary, that would not be Louise at all. He wanted desperately enough, to make the *body* present, all of it, by simply that clothing of Mary, which would not re-displace her, not again. Each time she left the room he thought she would never come back. He was left with Louise.

Left with Peter, Louise turned to Mary. It was Mary's suggestion that, in the cavern, they wear *no* clothes, because she was Peter's wife. But Louise wanted the *dress*. She arranged the dress on Mary, and then chose the intenser, more flaring design of green, yellow and blue, from the two materials either one of which she might have added. To finish the dress. Peter laughed but felt dismayed too. This was to be Mary's *own* person. Mary readjusted the half-done dress upon herself, and held the material, which Louise had chosen, against it. The dress, with the material, became her.

But the *cavern* was and *is* an underfloor hollow, with a *horizontal* entrance, and is made by the *subsiding*, or *giving inwards*, or *smashing in*, of *soil, walls*, etc. Cavern-dwellers are *prehistoric men* living in these huge or deep *hollows within solids*. Peter said.

THE BOOK

He was bringing the book in a gesture of final hope, something he had found in a bookstore just after leaving her. *Oh bright and sunny day,* and words to an old English time and tune, measure of clear voice and air. She liked to sing, in a high clear voice, a little thick at times, chirruped, like a secure bird. The book was a paperback collection of English Aires and Folksongs, edited by authentic people she would be careful to see.

Down the street, walking heavily along, it was time to be not drunk but the afternoon was heavy and slow, he was drunk with beer and dirtiness. All over his body, sluggish sweaty clothing under the dusty sun, walking more than he was used to, the streets were hard and barren.

She had a number of songs she would sing. At one time it is possible that she might have been trained to sing professionally. It was a leftover hope in that sense, a little of an ability put to fond memory's sake and trust to it to reappear, always. They do not forget what they meant to do, but just don't do it. She sang not happily altogether, not wildly, certainly, nor loudly, sadly, strongly, longly. Just enough to be the memory, turn on the radio, the victrola, and listen. Concerts and early training were the strengths she had.

She had painted also. She had been trained in that in a large gray building along a dark avenue of the city. It was a timorous place, yet aggressive with age and authority of that kind. He once rented a room on that street. He had to go through the living room of the owners to get to his own room, through theirs to the back. He moved his things in, sat on the bed for only a few minutes and then apologized and moved out. Had he apologized? The sins of walking are the sins of memory, and she was not in that at all.

He lit a cigarette and considered his direction. A drugstore lay on his left at some distance, a flat square with a few trees in a triangle beyond it, then, across, a row of usual businesses along the same avenue.

She was there somewhere in that maze. At another crossing of a street, a hotel for women, Y.W.C.A., kindest of all refuges, heaps, of people who must be secured, for a moment, against sex, age, and other identity.

Earlier, "I didn't expect you so quickly, I had just come down." He had called her, at the desk, a woman watching him in dull glasses, piled hair, but prim, and not friendly. Who came here? Ask for your wife, mother, sister, the girl friend, is she here? Like a morgue of women, that sex, all of them, beds and beds and beds of them. Think of the sound, snoring, wheezing, blowing, puffing, breathing, in beds in sleep.

"Not about that," he wanted to say. "Don't," she was saying, and she was crying. "I don't want to go through it all again. I can't tell you more. I don't know more. There isn't any more to tell."

Explain. I was raped on the boat, not raped but like that. I lost a thousand dollars in a purse, on the train. I bought a lot of Italian blouses. I do what I want to, now.

What is the English song? Something like, *I want to go where the birds go.* Not quite, but that flavor of old softness, a deep blanket of cold clear warmth. Hush, they are singing, *down in old Bethlehem the lights are low.* No but carefully, you can't get it right all the time. The note goes up there, then, one, two, down it goes. Lightly. *They came upon,* not so common, it is, *a statue, weeping at grief.*

It was a brutal dullness that he felt, walking. Having intended to do it, he wanted to do it, and with the book in his hand, wet with the sweat of his hand, from walking, it was not new. It was a dirty old plan, with the walking. The old book worn with the intention of taking it to her. As though next week he had remembered a plan which he had thought of and done, accomplished, paid bill of something or other. No history in that, nothing solved, no answer because he was being overcome by the action of walking toward her, the time climbing up on him as though it were a weight he accumulated step by step.

Can't you sing, too? No, I don't feel easy doing it, I try to hard enough, try too, hard enough. No but I can't. Can't you? No.

Would he ever see her again in this life, he thought. This day perhaps, again. Talking at lunch with food he did not like, want, to eat, a failure in that so reminiscent of his meals with her, and for years to come quite the same. Oh he wouldn't change. That was the song.

He had meant everything he had ever done. Not to do many things, to do a few also.

"Oh where do the birds go when the summer's sun is through?"

No, but closer, a little closer, each time. The words go along a line in movement with the song, the song is in that way a song, of words. That tell what? Oh common things, of women and men, lads and lasses, hay, corn fields, horses, old roads, stones and crows, roses and one begins, "I remember, I remember, the house." Not so common but later, earlier, into some practice of ear and voice he knew nothing of. Say it slowly.

"Waley. Waley. Oh, love is bonny. A little whi(high)le while it is new." That was the true one, the right one. Sing it. It was in the book which he held in his hand. A documented pair who had done the selection assured her, would assure her, they were all there.

Sing:

> *The street is the book is*
> *in the garden*
> *sitting on your knee*
> *my dear old England . . .*

Sing of her, that is the garden's insolence, that bent the seat she sat in, broke the thorn to get a better hold, to stick it in the face of winter's thorn, bleak wind and cutting frost, aghast upon the frozen pane, the wind doth drive upon, fast night, fast moon, stuck fast in ice today. English songs are pretty little songs with a right, bright tune which followeth.

The book in his hand had a slight weight, but the heat of the hand as pressed against it, holding it, was the bother of it. He had no idea as to which street would most quickly get him there. He wandered, a little drunk still, hence walking head forward steadily. People he supposed to be looking at him, or after, but he could not change his eyes. They went forward as his feet.

He listened slowly, closely, to all that she played him, on the phonograph. He had burnt out the fuses on two floors of the building in which they lived, fixing it better, more volume, more sound to it. The bump and grind of calypso, Charlie Parker. Listen to it. The song is, *oh where do the birds go, you don't see them any more now.* No but you can't hear it enough, so sweetly, so lightly. Hear it. Listen closely, then pick up the instrument and play it. Blow, this way, across, making the sound lift out of the long wood. Hold it firmly but do not over-press. A sound as in woods' hollow, from furtive shadow and water, the reeds and willows of the wood. Not to be learned in an instant. Listen, and again, listen. He sang with a sharp croak, oh shut the door behind you. She was always not shutting the bathroom door.

In a maze of people, streets, then brought to doors, one after another of them, or parks like deserted, contaminated areas, as if cut off, out, of the activity, as if to be rebuilt as parks one day, woods, hollows, water. A pipe dripped water into a stone basin. He wet his hands and then wiped them on his pants. He sat down to think of his direction.

"Not ever again," she said. No but one last time, say. This was outside the call of duty. One last look, book, like not forever, but one last time. Hey it's you! By god, it's you. I never expected to find you here like this. Oh say, what a happy day, you came my way, and that was a song. Sing it.

He got up no longer knowing where he was. He asked the man passing where it was, and got a vague answer. The drunk with the book. Look, the drunk's got a book. A new book. They wouldn't answer him but went past quickly, smiling, frowning. Perhaps he would try to sell the book to them.

He wasn't that drunk. He was heartbroken. He was hot, tired with walking, wanted to drink beer, wanted friends, a home, wife and friends and beer. He sang a song for that sound. He kept on walking but it wasn't fair any more.

You're not listening. Yes but he couldn't get the words. Like this, and one, and two, like this, and, there, you hear it, now, and one, and two. *The boy stood in the burning bush. His hair was all on fire. He thought that he would burn to death. And very soon expire.* Yes but not, like this. Song it is, wrong it is. He kept walking because the plan had been made, no longer to be thought of as anything else. Get the book to her. Get the goddamn book to her. Show her what you can do. The book with the songs.

FIELDING DAWSON

EARLY IN THE MORNING

The outdoor game yard of the Catholic nursery was still. Chairs were stacked to one wall beside a row of brightly painted tricycles. Blocks and balloonsize balls lay around.

The janitor sat on a kiddy chair facing a girl, a teacher's assistant, who stood not two feet away, throwing a ball above his head against the brick wall behind him. She threw, just missing his head; it bounced and she caught it.

They talked a little. She threw the ball girlishly, awkwardly but surely. The ball bounced above his head; she caught it with both hands and then held it out on the palm of one hand.

He sat in the tiny chair, hands clasping it between his thighs. He was an old man with gray hair and pink skin and bright eyes. She threw and caught the ball and then popped it in the air, just a few inches, caught it and did it again. Then she held it by her side, arching her hip so that the pleats of her skirt moved. His shoulders sagged; she shrugged. He grinned. She threw the ball over his head; it bounced against the wall and she caught it and popped it in the air like before. It hung in mid-air. Her fingers spread and the skin of her palms stretched tight. As the ball came down her hands jerked, she caught it; she popped the ball into the air again and she caught it. Each time she threw the ball, either in the air or against the wall, she took her eyes away from his. Each time she had the ball she held her eyes on his, while they talked. When she threw the ball she stopped talking. When she had the ball, she talked. She talked and smiled and shifted her feet and swung her shirt and moved her arms, talking and not talking, throwing the ball in the middle of a sentence, taking her eyes from

212

his, catching the ball, holding it, toying with it, looking at him and then throwing it, either in the air or against the wall, breaking a sentence, catching the ball, talking, throwing catching, talking, playing with it and talking. She threw it over his head against the wall. She caught it, moved her hips and threw, catching it. His mouth was level with her navel. She threw the ball and it bounced off the wall above his head and she caught it.

The door opened and screaming children rushed out, anchored by two laughing nuns. The girl threw the ball, caught the ball and slipped inside the building.

THE INVISIBLE GLASS

After he married Jeanette, it was easier to let—her—he went along with her. He was thirty years old, six feet tall, and a little fat. He had a good job, good enough, not as good as, he was sorry, he could do better, maybe, but Jeanette was pretty, their little home was nice, it might be—she had difficulty getting things in place, pictures, furniture—that magazine table, where she wanted, if she could find where she wanted it like Joan, Joan had a wonderful sense of—those drapes, did you ever see anything like those—oh, Dick, do you want—

The car ran fine, it wasn't—but got him where, the office where he worked was large with bright colors and modern furniture, Richard had a desk by the window.

"Dick," Sally said. She was a secretary. "Here's the report; Mr. Winters said bring it in before you go to lunch."

She dropped it on the desk. He glanced at it. "Thanks, Sally." He looked out the window. Horace sat on the edge of the desk. Horace grinned: "Good morning, friend."

Richard turned. "Hi—hey, could you give me a hand with these figures? I—this morning, I—"

They worked it out.

Richard parked the car, got out, closed and locked it and went up the walk, he saw the dog barking behind the window. He went inside, patted the animal and looked toward the kitchen. He called.

"I'm home!"

"Dick?"

"It's me."

He went in the kitchen, she glanced over her shoulder and said hello; as she said hello he crossed the kitchen to the refrigerator. She turned as he opened it.

"Coke?"

He scratched his neck, nodding, looking and finding it in the refrigerator. He took out the bottle, some ice and made the drink. He went in the living room, sat down in his chair and unfolded the paper. The dog barked, crossing the room to him. Dick patted the dog. The phone rang. He rose, and answered it.

"Hello?"

"Dick? This is Nan. Busy now? Leland and I thought maybe you'd like to come over."

"Wait a minute, here's Nettie," he said, feeling Jeanette slip in behind him. He handed her the receiver, quietly saying, "It's Nan."

"Nan?" Jeanette asked, face bright. Listening she nodded. "Um hum, well, let me ask Dick."

He had sat down and unfolded the paper and was looking at the television listings. Jeanette said,

"Dick?"

He looked at her.

The first martini made him giddy. "Let me have some more potato chips."

"Dick, you're already overweight!"

"I hate fat young men."

"I know," he laughed. "Leland, the cheese dip!"

They were talking about the Jackie Gleason show. Leland was imitating that comedian and Nan and Jeanette were egging him on. Richard sipped from the second martini and apologized: he had fallen asleep while the show had been on.

"Hey—where's my glass?"

They burst into laughter. "Glass?" Leland mocked. "It seems to be in your hand, kind of around your drink!"

"The other one!" Richard said angrily. "It was right here."

The girls were in hysterics. Leland chuckled. "What kind of glass, dad?" They all teased him.

On the way to the car he rough-housed with Jeanette. He was glad to be outside. Jeanette laughed and told him to stop, she pushed him away. They got in the car and he felt anger and confusion, he took the wheel, raised his shoulders, raced the engine, the car lurched into the street, where he stopped it.

"Why are we stopping?"

He glared out the windshield.

"*Drive*, Dick!"

They drove home. They had supper, watched television a while and went to bed early.

He woke feeling an urgency. He looked around the dim room, and after a moment the feeling paled and shifted into a necessity to know the time in which he was—he was ahead of himself, yet almost stopped in the middle: he looked at the clock. The indicated numbers said he had another hour to sleep. His heart sank and rose at the same time hurt and delighted, and in the odd polarity he looked at Jeanette beside him, and seeing her awry in her sleep, he also saw himself and felt a strange regret which was then halved by a necessity to move ahead and away, but to also backtrack and catalog feelings to return to the mood of the urgent awakening, and figure out what was significant in a dream which he must have dreamt that had awakened him as it had.

He backtracked through necessity and regret to the time in which he was, trying to figure out how the waking sensation had seemed important and why it had occurred with its particular evasive identity, and as if someone had then touched him, he distinctly remembered the waking feeling, and in the order of what was familiar to him, he felt out of place, and he tensed, knowing he would never know . . . he had felt the character of the dream, and now he was losing it by being aware of the self that tried to summon the self that knew. He pulled the covers around himself meaningfully: placating the safe-keeping mind which was alarmed.

He felt he was dwindling, as though he had once been large and all of himself.

He lay back despairing, staring out of his shrinking skull, watching running images and hearing himself breathing in a growing panic, realizing his metaphorical time of one hour was moving away from him, and his time-keeping consciousness flagrantly slanted into it, counting fifty eight minutes fifty seven seconds into fifty eight seconds snapping into fifty nine snapping into sixty, fifty nine minutes, one second, snap, two seconds, three going. He losed his eyes, counting, really exhausted.

And then an altogether understood sense of time seemed to direct him towards the activity of busy streets which included a superior sense of other things going on elsewhere. Possibly his time was part of another story, as accepted as it also seemed to act out another potential, as if his longing for completion was even originally incomplete, and that dimly envisioned world seemed nearly *thusly* X *and* familiar, young and old at the same time, and confounded by a painful necessity to begin quickly.

CAPTAIN AMERICA

Webster Groves was short and stocky, well dressed and his bushy mustache gave him the air of someone different which he mildly enjoyed and the gestures of his hands and fluidity of manner made him seem to be a plurality rather than something the *avant-garde* might regard as vaguely singular, or parenthetical, for which he seemed grateful, although he understood what that, in turn, might well signify. So he kept to himself, accepting the reality. He hadn't really made the team in school and didn't pretend he had. But he could tell wonderfully amusing stories about The Bench. His large mustache was a shade darker than the long light blonde hair on his head but it, the mustache, it was wonderful, gave him a forward quality that kept his head up. He worked in an art supply store in downtown Saint Louis and was indifferently happy selling canvas, tubes of paint, brushes, turpentine, stretchers, and such. Often his friends, casual or close, dropped in, "just to see Webster." There was something—charming—about him.

He was twenty nine, soft spoken and unpretentious. His manner held a mild flair for light humored sarcasm. He didn't have many really close friends . . . few do—certainly not in Saint Louis. But those that were, were distinct—as distinct as Webster himself was from them: they were not like him in either habit, appearance, desires or detail. They had the quality of what friendly people really are: dull.

Kirk, Ferguson, Craig, or even Manchester—Clayton, a mild mannered Impressionistic painter who sold reasonably well but never really got too serious—had a nice studio on the fringe of the city and from his wide windows you could see the distant Hotel Chase and the Park Plaza above the trees, overlooking Forest Park. When Webster went over to see Clayton after work they'd smoke Clayton's favorite Cuban cigars and drink espresso in little cups and look out the window in friendly silence. And then, pleasantly bored, Webster would leave. Go to Tony's—or home and eat supper; maybe take in a movie. Or read.— Or call up Valley.

Valley was tall and slender with soft round breasts and narrow

to sleep—wait for the return, the inevitable scent in time and space
to carry him across the vacant lot to that little house of hers.

That was what that was. He counted on it but never tried to make
it be. It was right. There. Wherever he was, whatever he was doing,
whenever the great Anything happened, he knew her reality existed
within it, identically off from him, for him. Never waiting but always
there. Eternal. It occurred. Then—anywhere, anytime, no matter what
was going on, the reality of Valley would appear into his life in sub-
stantial form. Like the dream sound of a distant trumpet call, clear
and keen, existent but untouchable, she beckoned. So now, at work, on
a bus, home in bed, at a movie, a party, out walking or while over
in Clayton's studio, smoking those Cuban cigars, drinking espresso
and looking out the windows at the Park Plaza hotel . . . some thing
from outside himself, between which he saw nothing, off from himself
spanned the space and distance like a bridge, like a weird reflection-
bridge from out of a prism, magic and shimmering, came to his eye
and within the invisible glitter a form appeared to make whatever
he was doing cease to exist. And rather than quickly phone her, he
woke slowly, let her fill the air so when he called, it would be his hand
on the instrument and his lips speaking words and the reality of her
voice surprising him because all the rest was already fulfilled and
what remained to be done: was. So he walked and walked, acted and
gestured, spoke mildly of school or art—letting the sound of her flesh
fill him, slowly, on wings, until he was blindly on his way to her.

Then there was no time. The distance between himself and Valley
did not exist. He bought a bottle. The bus ride was accomplished and
he walked across the vacant lot on the footpath to her front door as
the nearing sea of her reality rose to drown his identity. Gone when,
after he knocked she opened the door, he said,
"Hi."
And went in.

She broke ice cubes into glasses while he opened the bottle. They
drank and talked and she became expansive and he listened. Then
they made love and then she fell asleep, he with his fingers touching her wrist, she with the knowing sense that Webster was there

beside her; he listening to her breathing regularly and wondering if
it might come from another thing, the thing from the old world—or
a more knowing world where the dream sound of a distant trumpet call
and the invisible presence of the unknown soldier were the flesh and
blood, the universe, the stuff of reality within which men and women
existed. The hum, like the hum of doom—of despair and loneliness
and death, the language of an unknown man who fell in an unknown
field in an uncharted time.

BLOODSTAR

You bet. Not till Tuesday. Okay.

He hung up, stepped out of the telephone booth.

One.

He sat at the bar and thought.

Thoughts and images: her guitar and singing voice. Embraces all the rest: in importance, in fact. That need not lead to other facts; that did lead to other facts. Get receptive. Stuck there, like a burr in your hair. Maybe it was most of her; there's a fact.

The bartender put the beer in front of him. He paid.

Lesbians.

After the kodachrome photographs

On the Swiss Alps: skiing with a handsome man. Sun sparkling on snow-white, red ski clothes, snow; gleaming accoutrements.

On the Carribbean with another fellow on a yacht. Glistening, spanking white; bright green stripes, red stripes. Colored flags.

Along the beach in Nice: arms linked with another man's, running into the water laughing: hair flying behind her tan body. Photographs in color: blonde hair blonde, golden body golden, white rim above white breasts, white line around white waist, between white thighs; white line of sea foam, flurry of waves. Silver white beach: dazzling in that sun. Blue, ultramarine, blue, green sea. Invisible winds: soft sweep across flesh, water, earth. Photographs, color sound hold it—great—another? Laughter. They kiss. Hey! Take one of me like that! Two men trade places and he kisses her as the other shoots. Then they lift and carry her wriggling body into the sea

were passed around, held against the light of the lamp on the table, she stood up, finished her glass of beer and touched the snoot of the police dog who rose with her; she passed into the other room. He refilled her glass, his own and the beautiful girlfriend's glass while she sat at the other end of the table, handsomely sullen in the glare of the lamp as the shade had been tipped, the light flayed out.

fix the shade why don't you.

okay.

He straightened it and they waited in silence; drank beer. She returned to the room with her guitar and sat down. She took a drink. She tightened the strings, tested their tone; finally she began to sing.

Three years before, when he had been in school, he received a letter one afternoon. It read:

my dear sweet friend,
i have met the most beautiful woman
you could see. if you ever come to
n.y. i want you to meet and know
her. i have told her very much
about you. when you come, phone.
if i had a flower, a violet, i
would send it to you; however,
it is winter in n.y. and bitter
cold. there are no flowers. there
is hope. i have found hope. i
send some of my hope to you. a
gentle hug. a small kiss.

Time passed.

. . . sure it's late . . . yes of course I'm drunk . . . no I don't have a job you do? In forty-five minutes? Just time enough . . . yes me. I want some hope too. Never mind. Too long ago . . . sure I understand, tomorrow, okay, tell your beauty hello . . . years . . . right, no, Army. Kilmer . . . till Sunday evening . . . at noon? Tomorrow at noon . . . right. Promise. Carny Taylor? Nice. See you.

He came down Broadway in the early morning snow. It was near eight. He crossed Union Square and later Fourteenth Street, headed down University Place towards the bar, AWOL bag in his hand and dressed as he was in the olive drab of the U. S. Army: in one month, Germany. The Atlantic Ocean Crossing: February, 1954. But his feet were getting wet. GI low quarters weren't made for snow. He crossed

Thirteenth, looking in a bar with a glance, seeing opening preparations just as the clocks struck 8 in the churches: on Fifth Avenue, Twelfth Street, Tenth Street and Broadway. Eight O'clock. Up too early. A mild hangover. The snow felt good. He leaned his head back and closed his eyes, letting the flakes hit his face.

Tuesday, two years later
he called her:
Yes, Miss Taylor, Fourth Floor. You will? Thanks.
He lit a cigarette in the phone booth and waited, the receiver in his left hand. He watched the bartender serve a man a beer. His own stood on the bar, waiting for him.
Miss Taylor—
Carny? I'd like a large hopechest—
You! How are you—are you out now?

They talked about Europe, things in common, and even got a little loaded at lunchtime; she confessed she was high and didn't know how she would finish out the rest of the day.
He realized as she talked: I put in my life. Without photographs. Over the rim of my friendly glass, I see you. He laughed out loud. A puzzled look came over her face. She had been explaining her job to him.
What is it? she asked.
Nothing, he said.
Nothing? Tell me, I'd like to share it with you.
No, he said. I'll tell you something, though. I'll tell you a story about Germany. It's to the point.
I'd like to hear it, she said.
I met a girl in Heidelberg who was bright and attractive, he began, sitting back in the chair, offering her a cigarette; she took it, he took one for himself both of which he lit; he exhaled and in the smoke: even in the eyes, but like a clouded or filmy thing, just behind the front transparent part that I took to be withdrawal at first, from lack of confidence, all of which was true enough. But as it later turned out, you can never be sure about what is something else when first you encounter it. So she was full of doubt. You want to go faster? We talked, walked, drove, danced and laughed around Heidelberg. She had

an old yellow Mercedes convertible which could scarcely run but which we drove everywhere. So what was it, I kept asking myself: that thing, like a burr in your hair, a nettle, refusing to let loose of you. She asked if I believed in the stars telling things. We were out walking, then, one night, up near the Schloss, the Castle, and there was a tall stone tower which rose into the dark sky. When she was a girl, one night she had wandered into the tower, gone up the circular flight of stone steps to the top, come through a trap door and there, in the tiny circular topmost cubicle was a giant man: beard darker than night and as thick as hands clung to his jaw, eyes like luminous blades, revolving, slowly whirring, covering her. He did drawings of her, told her of her past: of a sunny day in Rotterdam when she had gotten on a streetcar; of her future; of the art and magic of the universe and revolving galaxies spangled with stars like all seeing eyes. When she returned the next night he was not there. She returned again and again to the old tower. But he had vanished. Years passed. She grew up. The war came and she idolized Nazi fliers like Americans idolized movie stars; every German girl kept photographs. When the war was over, she went to Belgium, rented a room in a boarding house; she met a woman of her age, they became fast friends. They swore in blood to always love the other: it was in the stars for them. They separated for a time; she returned to Heidelberg. What was it, she kept asking herself, about this woman that so fascinated her. One day she passed the tower: suddenly she knew! She knew! She wrote her friend, told her everything. The friend wrote back; they were to meet in Berlin. She went. Gladly! Her heart happy in anticipation. They met, made plans—she had known an old friend in Dresden and they would go. An adventure into Communist Germany! They went to Dresden. The friend was gone. The city was in ruins, streets bare, skies grey, overcast; Russian soldiers paced guard in their ugly and unkempt uniforms. The two women wandered over the city, exploring the ruins. They discovered a restaurant she had known as a child, long before the war. They went in, sat in a booth; the waiter came and they ordered. The waiter said they could go in the back, if they wished.

What is this? they asked each other.

They went in the back.

The room was bathed in blood red light; couples danced to cool American jazz records; moving figures, faces and shadows were murky red forms. They sat at a table. A woman approached them, sat down and smiled and other women joined them, talked in many languages and drank with them. Across the room, through red smoke, over the rows of liquor bottles and large purple mirrors behind the bar, a mask hung on the wall: a glass mask whose blood red star shaped eyes bubbled. Under the mask, red neon said: BLUTSTERREN

A decade later she ascended the long flight of steps to the Heidelberg Schloss for the last night of Fasching festival, she, in costume, a princess in her gown. It was late, approaching midnight. At midnight the Queen of Fasching would be chosen. The party would last all this night as it had lasted for four days. As she went up the dark steps she noticed a figure descending, far above: a shadow had moved. It is nothing, she told herself, someone coming home early from the party. The figure came closer—they met, a hand took her arm and the voice apprehensively questioned: Dresden? and the eyes glowed and whirred like bloody stars on revolving blades and the beard, darker than night, the beard like claws on a jaw moved as the voice repeated: Dresden? like a wind come clanging out the craters of the moon: *Dresden? Dresden? Dresden?*

HUBERT SELBY JR.

ANOTHER DAY ANOTHER DOLLAR

They sprawled along the counter and on the chairs. Another night.
Another drag of a night in the Greek's, a beat all night diner near the
Brooklyn Army base. Once in a while a doggie or seaman came in for
a hamburger and played the jukebox. But they usually played some
goddam hillbilly record. They tried to get the Greek to take those
records off, but he'd tell them no. They come in and spend money.
You sit all night and buy nothing. Are yakiddin me Alex? Ya could
retire on the money we spend in here. Scatah. You don't pay my
carfare. . . .
24 records on the jukebox. They could have any 12 they wanted,
but the others were for the customers from the base. If somebody
played a Lefty Frazell record or some other shitkicker they moaned,
made motions with their hands (man! what a fuckin square) and
walked out to the street. 2 jokers were throwing quarters in so they
leaned against the lamppost and carfenders. A warm clear night and
they walked in small circles, dragging the right foot slowly in the hip
Cocksakie shuffle, cigarettes hanging from mouths, collars of sport-
shirts turned up in the back, down and rolled in front. Squinting.
Spitting. Watching cars roll by. Identifying them. Make. Model. Year.
Horsepower. Overhead valve. V-8, 6, 8, a hundred cylinders. Lots a
horses. Lots a chrome. Red and Amber grill lights. Yasee the grill on the
new Pontiac? Man, that's real sharp. Yeah, but a lousy pickup. Can't
beat a Plymouth fora pickup. Shit. Can't hold the road like a Buick. Outrun any cop in the city with a Roadmaster. If ya get started. Straight-
aways. Turns. Outrun the law. Dynaflows. Hydromatics. Can't get
started. They'd be all overya before ya got a block. Not in the new
88. Ya hit the gas and it throwsya outta the seat.

Great car. Ain't stealin nothin else anymore. Greatest for a job.
Still like the Pontiac. If I was buyin a car. Put skirts on it, grill light,
a set a Caddy hubcaps and a bigass aerial in the rear . . . shit, that's
the sharpest job on the road. Your ass. Nothin can touch the 47 Continental convertible. They're the end. We saw one uptown the other
day. What-a-fuckin-load. Man!!! The shitkickers still wailed and they
talked and walked, talked and walked, adjusting their shirts and slacks,
cigarettes hanging from their mouths then flipped into the street—ya
shoulda seen this load. Chartreuse with white walls. Cruise around in a
load like that with the top down and a pair of shades and some sharp
clothes and ya haveta beat the snatch off witha club—spitting after
everyother word aiming for a crack in the sidewalk; smoothing their
hair lightly with the palms of their hands, pushing their d.a.'s gently
and patting them in place, feeling with their fingertips for a stray hair
that may be out of place and not hanging with the proper effect—ya
should see the sharp shirts they got in Obies. That real great gabadine.
Hey, did yadig that sharp silverblue sharkskin suit in the window?
Yeah, yeah. The onebutton single breasted job with the big lapels—and
what's to do on a night like this. Just a few drops of gas in the tank
and no loot to fill it up. And anyway, where's to go—but yagotta have
a onebutton lounge. Ya wardrobe ain't complete without one. Yeah, but
I dig that new shawl job. It's real sharp even as a sports jacket—the
con rolled on and no one noticed the same guys saying the same things;
and somebody found a new tailor who could make the greatest pants
for 14 skins; and how about the shockabsorbers in the Lincoln; and
if we had a Buick instead of a Plymouth the otha night we woulda
rapped up when we turned third; and the guy on New Utrecht made a
great pair for 10 and so what, whose got the loot anyway; and they
watched the cars pass giving hardlooks and spitting; and who laid this
broad and who laid that one; and someone took a small brush from his
pocket and cleaned his suede shoes then rubbed his hands and adjusted
his clothing and someone else flipped a coin and when it dropped a foot
stamped on it before it could be picked up and as he moved the leg
from the coin his hair was mussed and he called him a fuck and
whipped out his comb and when once more neatly in place it was
mussed again and he got salty as hell and the other guys laughed and
someone else's hair was mussed and they shoved each other and someone else shoved and then someone suggested a game of mum and said

Vinnie should start and they yelled yeah and Vinnie said whatthefuck, he'd start and they formed a circle around him and he turned slowly jerking his head quickly trying to catch the one punching him so he would replace him in the center and he was hit in the side and when he turned he got hit again and as he spun around 2 fists hit him in the back then another in the kidney and he buckled and they laughed and he jerked around and caught a shot in the stomach and fell but he pointed and he left the center and just stood for a minute in the circle catching his wind then started punching and felt better when he hit Tony a good shot in the kidney without being seen and Tony slowed down and he got pelted for a few minutes then finally pointed and Harris said he was fullashit, he didn't really see him. But he was thrown in the center anyway and Tony waited and hooked him hard in the ribs and the game continued for another 5 minutes or so and Harry was still in the center, panting and almost on his knees and they were rapping him pretty much as they pleased, but they got bored and the game broke up and they went back in the Greek's, Harry still bent and panting, laughing and went to the lavatory to wash.

They washed and threw cold water on their necks and hair then fought for a clean spot on the dirty apron that served as a towel, yelling through the door that Alex was a no good fuck for not havin a towel forem, then jockeyed for a place in front of the mirror. Eventually they went to the large mirror at the front of the diner and finished combing their hair and fixing their clothes, laughing and still kidding Harry, then sprawled and leaned.

The shitkickers left and they yelled to Alex to get some music on the radio. Why don't you put money in the jukebox? Then you hear what you want. Comeon man. Don't be a drag. Why don't you get a job. Then you have money. Hey, watch ya language. Yeah, no cursin Alex. Go get a job you no good bums. Who's a bum. Yeah, who? They laughed and yelled at Alex and he sat, smiling, on a small stool at the end of the counter and someone leaned over the counter and turned the radio on and spun the dial until a sax wailed and someone yelled for service and Alex told him to go to hell and he pounded on the counter for service and Alex asked if he wanted ham and eggs and he told Alex he wouldn't eat a egg here unless I saw it hatched and Alex laughed—scatah—and walked slowly to the coffee urn and filled a cup and asked if he was going to buy everybody coffee and they laughed

and Alex told them to get a job, you all the time hang around like
bums. Someday you be sorry. You get caught and you won't be able
to drink this good coffee. COFFEE!!! Man, this is worse than piss.
The dishwater upstate tastes betteran this. Pretty soon maybe you be
drinking it again. Yourass I will. I should report you. Then I'd have
some peace and quiet. You'd die without us Alex. Who'd protect ya
from the drunks? Look at all the trouble we saveya. You boys are
going to get in trouble. You see. All the time fuckaround. Ah Alex.
Can't talk like that. Ya make us feel bad. Yeah man. Ya hurt our
feelings. . . .

Alex sat on his stool smoking and smiling and they smoked and
laughed and walked over to the mirror near the front door and
adjusted their clothes and combed their hair, carefully. Cars passed
and some tried to identify them by the sound of the motor then looked
to see if they were right, raising their shoulders and swaggering back
to their seats if they were. Occasionally a drunk came in and they
would yell to Alex to get up off his ass and serve the customer or tell
the guy ta getthehell out before he was poisoned with Alex's horse
meat and coffee and Alex would pick up the dirty rag and wipe off the
spot in front of the drunk and say yes sir, what you want and they'd
want to know why he didn't call them sir and Alex would smile and
sit on his stool until the drunk finished and then he'd walk slowly
back, take the money, ring it up, then back to his stool and tell them
they should be quiet, you want to scare good customers away and Alex
would laugh with them and spit the cigarette butt out of his mouth and
turn his shoe on it; and the cars still passed and the drunks still passed
and the sky was clear and bright with stars and moon and a light
breeze was blowing and you could hear the tugs in the harbor chugging
and the deep ooooo from their whistles floated across the bay and
rolled down 2nd avenue and even the ferry's mooring winch could be
heard, when it was quiet and still, clanging a ferry into the slip . . .
and it was a drag of a night, beat for loot and they flipped their cigarettes out the doors and walked to the mirror and adjusted and combed
and someone turned up the volume of the radio and a few of the girls
came in and the guys smoothed the waist of their shirts as they walked
over to their table and Rosie grabbed Larry, a girl he laid occasionally,
and asked him for a halfabuck and he told her to go fuckerself and
walked away and sat on a stool. She sat beside him. He talked with the

guys and every few minutes she would say something, but he ignored
her. When he moved slightly on his stool she started to get up and when
he sat down she sat. Larry stood, adjusted his pants, put his hands in
his pockets and slowly walked out the door and strolled to the corner.
Rosie walked 6 inches to his right and 6 inches to his rear. He leaned
against the lamppost and spit past her face. You're worse than a leech.
A leech yacan get rid of. You don't go for nothin. Don't bullshit me
ya bastard. I know yascored for a few bucks lastnight. What's that to
you? And anyway it's gone. I aint even got a pack of cigarettes. Don't
tell me. I aint ya father. Ya cheap motherfucker! Go tell ya troubles ta
jesus and stop breakin my balls. I'll break ya balls ya rotten bastard,
trying to kick him in the groin, but Larry turned and lifted his leg
then slapped her across the face.

Three drunken rebel soldiers were going back to the base after buying drinks for a couple of whores in a neighborhood bar and being
thrown out when they started a fight after the whores left them for a
couple of seamen who had just paid off. They stopped when they heard
Rosie shout and watched as she staggered back from the slap and Larry
grabbing her by the neck. Go giter little boy. Hey, don't chuall know
you're not to fuck girls on the street. . . . They laughed and yelled and
Larry let go of Rosie and turned and looked at them for a second then
yelled at them, ta go fuck their mothers, ya cottonpickin bastards. I
hear she's good hump. The soldiers stopped laughing and started crossing the street toward Larry. We'll cut yur niggerlovin heart out. Larry
yelled and the others ran out of the Greek's. When the doggies saw
them they stopped and then turned and ran toward the gate to the base.
Larry ran to his car and the others jumped in and on the fenders or
held on to the open doors, and Larry chased the doggies down the
street. Two of them continued running toward the gate, but the third
panicked and tried to climb over the fence and Larry tried to squash
him against it with the car but the doggie'd pulled his legs up just
before the car bumped the fence. The guys jumped off the fender and
leaped on the doggie's back and yanked him off and he fell on the
edge of the hood and then to the ground. They formed a circle and
kicked. He tried to roll over on his stomach and cover his face with his
arms, but as he got to his side he was kicked in the groin and stomped
on the ear and he screamed, cried, started pleading then just cried as a
foot cracked his mouth. Ya fuckin cottonpickin punk and a hard kick

in the ribs turned him slightly and he tried to raise himself on one knee and someone took a short step forward and kicked him in the solar-plexus and he fell on his side, his knees up, arms folded across his abdomen, gasping for air and the blood in his mouth gurgled as he tried to scream, rolled from his mouth then spumed forth as he vomited violently and someone stomped his face into the pool of vomit and the blood whirled slightly in arcs and a few bubbles gurgled in the puke as he panted and gasped and their shoes thudded into the shiteatin-bastard's kidneys and ribs and they stomped his head and he groaned and his head rolled in the puke breaking the arcing patterns of blood and he gasped as a kick broke his nose then coughed and wretched as his gasping sucked some of the vomit back in his mouth and he cried and tried to yell but it was muffled by the pool and the guys' yells and Larry kicked him in the temple and the yellow-bastard's eyes rolled back and his head lolled for a moment and he passed out and his head splashed and thumped to the ground and someone yelled the cops and they jammed back into and on the car and Larry started to turn but the prowl car stopped in front of them and the cops got out with their guns drawn so Larry stopped the car and the guys got out and off the car and slowly walked across the street. The cops lined them against the wall. The guys stood with their hands in their pockets, their shoulders rounded and heads slumped forward, straightening up and raising their arms while being frisked, then resuming their previous positions and attitudes.

Heads popped from windows, people occurred in doorways and from bars asking what happened and the cops yelled for everybody to shutup then asked what was going on. The guys shrugged and mur-mured. One of the cops started yelling the question again when an M.P. and the 2 doggies who had continued running—holding the third one suspended between them, head hanging limply and his toes dragging along the ground—came up to them. The cop turned to them and asked what this was all about. Those goddam yankees liked takill our buddy heuh, nodding to the soldier between them, his head rolling from side to side, nose split and busted, cheek gashed, eyes closed, mouth and ear split, face and front of his uniform covered with blood and puke, blood dribbling from his head. Larry pointed at him and stepped toward the cop and told him there's nothin wrong with him. He's only foolin. The

guys raised their heads slightly and looked at Larry and chuckled and
someone murmured he's got some pair of balls. The cop looked at the
soldier and told Larry if he's fooling he's one hell of an actor. The
chuckling grew louder and a few in the crowd of onlookers laughed.
The cops told them to shut up. Now, what in the hell is this all about.
The doggies started to speak but Larry outshouted them. They insulted
my wife. Someone said o jesus and Larry stared at the doggies waiting
for them to say something so he could call them a goddam liar. The
cop asked him where his wife was and he told him right over there. Hey
RosiE! Comere! She went over, her blouse hanging out, her hair hanging in lumps, lipstick smeared from Larry's slap, her eyelashes matted
and the heads of pimples shining through many layers of old dirty
make-up. We was standin on the corner talkin when these three creeps
started makin obscene remarks to my wife when I toldem ta shutup they
came after me. Aint that right? Yeah, they insulted me, the go—Yuh
dirty hoarrr. How could yawl be insulted??? Larry started toward him
but the cop rapped him in the gut with his club and told him to take it
easy. And you'd better watch your mouth soldier. All yuhgoddam
yankees are the same. A buncha no good niggerloving bastards. That's
all yuare. The cop stepped over to the soldier and told him if he didn't
shut up right now he'd lock him up and your friend along with you.
He stared at the soldier until the doggie lowered his eyes, then turned
to the crowd and asked if anyone had seen what had happened and they
yelled that they saw the whole thing that the drunken rebels had started
it, they insulted the boy's wife and tried to beat him up and—the cop
told them ok, ok, shut up. He turned back to the soldiers and told them
to get gack to the base and have someone look after their friend, then
turned to Larry and the others and told them to beat it and if I see any
of you punks in a fight again I'll personally split your skulls and—
Hey, wait a minute. The cop turned as the M.P. walked up to him. This
aint going to be the end of this officer. These men have rights and it's
my duty to remind them of them. They might want to prefer charges
against these hoodlums. What in the hell are you? A Philadelphia
lawyer? No sir. I'm just doing my duty and reminding these men of
their rights. All right, you reminded them now go back to the base
and leave well enough alone. You know these neighborhood bars are
off limits. Yes sir, that's true, but—but nothing. The M.P. started stam-

mering something, then looked to the three soldiers for support, but they had already started back to the base, the two dragging the third, blood splattering as it fell from his head.

The bodies went back in the doors and bars and the heads in the windows. The cops drove away and Larry and the guys went back into the Greek's and the street was quiet, just the sound of a tug and an occasional car; and even the blood couldn't be seen a few feet away.

They slammed around the lavatory washing, laughing, nudging each other, roaring at Larry, splashing water, inspecting their shoes for scratches, ripping the dirty apron, pulling the toilet paper off by the yard, throwing the wet wads at each other, slapping each other on the back, smoothing their shirts, going to the mirror up front, combing their hair, turning their collars up in the back and rolling them down in front, adjusting their slacks on their hips. Hey didya see the look on the bastards face when we threwim off the fence? Yeah. The sonofabitch was scared shitless. A buncha punks. Hey Larry, how's ya gut. That was some rap that bastard giveya. Shit. I fuck cops where they eat. . . . Someday you boys going to get in trouble. All the time fighting. Whatayamean Alex? We was just defendin Larry's wife. Yeah, they insulted Rosie. They roared, stamped, and banged their fists on the counter and tables. Alex grinned and said Scatah. Someday you be sorry. You should get a job. Hey, watch yalanguage Alex. Yeah. No cursin in fronta married women. They laughed and sprawled along the counter and on the chairs. All the time fuckaround. Someday you get in trouble. Ah Alex, don't talk like that. Ya makus feel bad. Yeah, man, ya hurt our feelings. . . .

A PENNY FOR YOUR THOUGHTS

He didnt think of her breasts at first. He simply noticed how attractive she was. And too it was extremely unusual to see a young girl without makeup. She probably was no more than 18. He was waiting for the subway after work and she was standing among the crowd with a few friends. She wore a black coat and black kerchief. Her skin appeared very white and her eyes were dark and sparkled. He kept glancing at her. He stood near them on the train and was surprised when they got off at his stop. He walked slowly and tried to listen to their conversation, but the only thing he heard distinctively was her name: Marie. A block from the station she said goodbye to her friends and turned along the avenue and he continued home.

The next morning he saw her on the station waiting in the same spot where he usually waited for the train. He stood near her again and tried to determine the color of her eyes, but he couldnt (at least not without staring) and was amazed again at her lack of makeup and how beautiful she was. Not a glamorous beauty, but a quieter, deeper and natural beauty . . . yet an exciting beauty! He tried not to be too conspicuous and turned his head away from her as much as possible and watched her from the side of his eye. They got off at DeKalb Avenue and he walked slowly up the stairs behind her and her girl friends hoping he might see a bit more of her leg, but she held her coat tightly around her and with straining and falling behind as she climbed the stairs he was still only able to see the calf of her leg. It was very attractive though. Even with those flat slippertype shoes on. She turned at the exit and walked off in a different direction than the one he had to take so he stood for a moment watching her until the light turned green and she and the rest of the crowd rushed across the street, then turned and went to his office.

He didnt see her that night on the platform. He looked around and had almost convinced himself that he should wait for another train, one that would be less crowded, but there was a large open area just inside the train that was large enough for 3 or 4 people and the train remained there for a few seconds with the doors open and he

felt guilty and conspicuous standing there when there was all that room
and suppose someone he knew should ask him what he was waiting
for or what if there should be some kind of a police investigation for
some reason, what could he say? and there are witnesses to prove there
was room in the train—he stepped forward quickly just before the door
closed.

After dinner that night he stretched out on the couch and consciously tried to conjure up an image of Marie. All he could see was
a vague outline, his wifes voice making it impossible to concrete the
image. He stopped trying and got up from the couch and went out to
the kitchen and helped his wife with the dishes, his wife surprised, but
saying nothing.

About 10 oclock he said he was going to bed as he was bushed
from the extra work in the office and was relieved when his wife said,
no, she wouldnt come to bed now, but would finish the ironing first.
He lay in the bed and thought of Marie. He thought of her dressed
in a beautiful tight sheath with dark stockings, but the image continued
to blur. He had never seen her with her overcoat off and without a
kerchief around her head. Actually he didnt have the slightest idea of
what her body looked like except what he assumed from looking at
her legs and face, and she obviously wasnt fat, but he still didnt know
exactly how she looked. How about her tits? She might be flatchested.
. . . Cant really tell with an overcoat on. That wasnt possible though.
She must have a nice pair. Large and firm. Sure. . . . She must. . . .

He ate breakfast just a little faster the next morning wanting to be
certain to get to the station in time to get the train she always took, yet
he didn't want to be obvious and perhaps have his wife ask questions.
Marie was there on the platform and he got on the train with her and
her friends and rode to work trying not to stare, but listening to her
voice and watching from the side of his eye and hoping her coat would
fall open when she reached up to adjust her kerchief, but it didnt.
While still watching her coat and hoping, he looked at her face and
noticed the small blemishes on her right cheek, but it didnt bother him.
It really didnt affect her attractiveness (beauty). And anyway it was
just a small spot. Probably temporary and nothing that would scar
her skin. He did wish though that she didnt go to work with her hair
set every morning, thought she does look much prettier than Alice
with her hair set. Maybe in the warmer weather she doesnt, but thats

a long way off. Actually it was only the front she kept set. The back hung loose. It was long, wavy and very pretty. If she put something on it to make it blacker and shinier it would really be something, but it was very nice the way it was. Really nicer that Alices, but that was something else. He was just curious about this girl. She must be 10 years younger than he. It's just that shes unusually attractive. Good Lord, cant a guy look at a girl and find her attractive without something being made of it. Alice certainly wouldnt mind. . . . It was their stop and they got off and he turned waiting once more for the light to change then went to work.

They rode the same train home that evening, but it was still impossible to determine their size. It must be the way she stood and held the coat around her that prevented his seeing. He stared at her intently hoping for an opening in the coat and didnt notice the front of her hair and it wasnt until later, when he was telling his wife about her, that he realized he hadnt looked to see what her hair looked like without the pins. When he mentioned the girl he saw on the platform to Alice he tried to do so with an *in passing* attitude, but he wanted to be certain he didnt over do it. He was certain she didnt think twice about it as the conversation drifted to a natural tangent after he mentioned how attractive this girl was and it was a shame she didnt put her makeup on properly instead of smearing it all over. You know how these kids do it, and then they were talking about high school or something and he felt better, much better. Now when he thought about Marie he wouldnt feel guilty. And anyway, why should he? Theres nothing wrong with that.

He saw her everyday, twice, for the next 4 days and he watched her the entire time from the moment he saw her on the platform until they parted at 3rd avenue . . . yet still he didn't see them. And this was January. So long before spring and lighter coats that would be allowed to fall open and so much longer to summer when only dresses and blouses were worn—and he stared and stared. . . . *Hello. I hope you dont think Im too forward, but Ive seen you everyday for quite some time now and I am sure you have noticed that I have been staring at you. I suppose it is a little unusual to just speak to a girl on the subway like this, but it is just that you are so attractive*—a train came in and they got in the rush and he tried to reach her, but couldnt get through the crowd or continue his mental conversation; and then the train stopped at their stop and he got off and stayed a few feet behind and watched her and tried to go back to where they were on the platform and he was telling her how beautiful she is and she was about to smile (shyly perhaps) and tell him he was right, that she had noticed him looking at her and he would be able to understand (from her tone and attitude) that she was flattered—but he couldnt get back there and whenever he tried to isolate just them, alone, he suddenly tried to remember the color of Alices eyes. He tried pushing the thought from his mind, then tried shoving it away, but his hand felt no resistance and it just flowed around it like an amoeba, an enormous amoeba; he tried gripping it; kicking it; dragging it; but it just floated and flowed. He even closed his eyes for a moment as he stood on a corner waiting for the light to change, but the thought wouldnt move so he stopped trying to keep it out of his mind and consciously thought of his wifes eyes and it slowly disappeared; then he tried to make his wifes eyes bigger and bigger so he could see what color they are, but it failed. It was impossible. But they must be blue. Shes so fair. They must be. They have to be. Blue Blue BLUE!!! Still he couldnt believe they were. But that doesnt mean anything. You know yourself how you forget things like that. But Maries eyes are brown. A deep dark brown. And they sparkle. Dont they? But thats different. How can you doubt I love Alice? I really know the color of her eyes. Its just trying to force it like this. Thats why I cant remember. . . .

Hello sweetheart. He bent and kissed Alices hair (of course theyre green. Its ridiculous. I knew) and asked her whats for supper.

He went to bed early again, giving some excuse about not feeling well, smoked a few cigarettes and thought of her. He wondered what would happen if he werent married, not that Im not happy after 4 years of marriage or anything, you know, but I just wonder. Academically so to speak. Id have a car of course—but I wouldn't be living here and would never have seen her anyway—have to start again. I live here—he put the cigarette out and rolled over on his side dismissing all the meaningless things that were ruining his thoughts. He was single and he had an apartment of his own near Fort Hamilton with a nice radio-phonograph console, indirect lighting and even a small bar (Id have the money) and he knew her from work and they went out and stopped at his apartment for a nightcap—maybe they went to the Casino or some place on the Island—and he put on the radio and played soft

music and when he gave her her drink he held her hand and kissed
her and he slowly undressed her and she was bashful and flushed
slightly and he kissed her and reassured her and told her he loved her
and she grabbed him and kissed him hard and he led her, gently, to
the bedroom and they lay down and he felt her stocking under his
fingertips and he played with her stocking for a few moments then
the smoothness of her thigh and she turned, sighing, and the train
came in and he held up his hand and pushed at it and tried to punch
the hundreds of motormen, but it ran right through the room and through
the bed and he held her and whispered, still trying to push the train,
and all those damn people were walking by . . . o goddam it! he
slammed the door! slammed it again and again and again, running
back to her and kissing her and slamming the door again I love you,
I LOVE YOU, frantically trying to unbutton her blouse and a large
trailer truck went by and he struggled to get her blouse off and Alice
asked him if he felt alright. Youre turning and tossing so much. Are
you sure you feel alright honey? and he turned and mumbled something and lit another cigarette and she continued to talk as she undressed
and he nodded and mumbled and smoked, hoping he hadnt blurted out
something, and anyway its not like it was real and he didnt love Alice
. . . o well. . . . But its not really wrong. This is not at all like those
guys who have girl friends on the side. This is something different.
Ive never been untrue to Alice. I even told Alice about her—yes sweetheart I will. Did you lock the door—she reached up and pulled the
cord and the room was dark again and he put out his cigarette and
tried to keep his mind blank, not wanting to fall asleep thinking about
her and perhaps say something in his sleep. . . . He couldnt get her
out of his mind and kept waking with a start, listening for something
and when he awoke about 3 or 4 he was so excited he tried waking
Alice, but she didnt awaken when he touched her lightly so he stopped
trying, afraid he might say something with his excitement and sleepiness, so he just lit another cigarette and thought about work or something . . . anything, until he felt calmer, then put out the cigarette and
finally fell asleep.

He was exhausted in the morning and he told Alice to call the office
and tell them he wouldnt be in, that he wasnt feeling well. He told her
he thought he might be getting the virus and thought it better to take
it easy for a day or two than to take a chance on getting sick. He stayed

in bed all that day and the next, which was Friday, and just lolled
around most of the weekend. On Monday he said he felt better and
Alice suggested he wait an hour before going to work in order to avoid
the rush hour, but he said that was ridiculous. Theres no need for any
such thing. I can go at the regular time. Alice was stunned by his brisk
manner and stared for a moment, then continued setting the table when
he lowered his eyes.

He rushed to the station and didnt slow down until he saw Marie at
the end of the platform. It seemed as if weeks had passed since he
stood on the platform next to her and he was certain she had been aware
of his long absence and probably wanted to talk to him. There certainly
wouldnt be any harm in speaking to her—the train came in and it was
unusually crowded and he pushed his way in and Marie and her girl
friends just did get in the door hitting her girl friend on the shoulder,
and they screeched slightly at the difficulty and he smiled and almost
spoke, but caught himself—yes, yes of course. Alices eyes are green
and her hair is cut in sortofa d.a. More people got on at the next stop
and he was jabbed against her side and he thought it would be easy to
simply let his arm rub against her breast or he could lower his hand
and the next time there was a push his hand would rub against her
ass and he looked and looked but he couldnt see. Incredible, but he still
couldnt see. Still didnt know if she had a big pair or not. Not that
that mattered either. Just a case of curiosity. No, no. Nothing like that.
Dont be silly. I wouldnt really do it. Would be easy enough though.
Especially in a crowd like this. It really would be an accident. But if
I could just see how big they are. I mean. . . .

There seemed to be no way he could find out. Would he have to
wait until spring or even summer? It was ridiculous. Why in the name
of christ didnt she stop clutching her coat. It isnt that cold. She could
let the goddam thing open in the subway. It was warm enough. Or if
it was a tight one, a fitted coat, then at least there would be an outline
to see and allowing for the thickness of the coat you would have some
idea of just how big her tits are. He didnt expect them to be gigantic
(there's nothing wrong with Alices. Theyre not too small. Ive said that
before. I dont really mind. That has nothing to do with it) just large
and firm. She seemed to have nice wide hips. If she has a slim waist
and a big pair . . . all white and smooth and when she lays on her back
theyd probably fall to the side slightly and her nipples will probably be

rosy and the trains and people and trucks kept forcing him away from her and they parted at Third Avenue each night and he thought about it and again, 4, 5 maybe more times he thought of waking Alice in the middle of the night, but he smoked, turned on his side and his thighs cramped and his stomach twinged and he kept looking and looking and they parted at the corner each morning after the light changed and she clutched that goddam coat and he looked and looked and he couldnt see and he didnt sleep and he was always keyedup and tensed and Alice knew it was the job and she didnt want to let him know she was upset worrying about him so she tried to ignore it and talked to him during mealtimes so he would relax enough to eat (he really wasnt eating much lately and lost weight) and she smiled and tried to be casual when asking him about work and his evasiveness confirmed her thoughts about the job fraying his nerves and still he looked and looked and Alice worried and he continued to lose weight and she thought of suggesting a visit to the doctor, but was still fearful of seeming alarmed and didnt want to upset him so after supper she suggested a movie. Its Friday and theres a good double feature playing tonight. One of them is supposed to be very funny and you know how hard youve been working lately honey. Yeah, I guess I have, not knowing what she was talking about, but afraid to ask. It might relax you to sit in a movie. He nodded and they went to the movie and he sat watching and smoking and then he started chuckling, then laughing and he relaxed in his seat and stretched out his legs and Alice leaned against him and held his arm and glanced at him occasionally, and they laughed.

And then Marie was standing in the aisle, in front of him, looking up at the rear of the balcony and then seeing her friends she smiled and walked past him, up the aisle. At first he was a little surprised, but of course there was no reason why she shouldn't go to this movie. Then, of course, when she started to open her coat he tried to see her tits, but couldn't. All he could determine was that she was wearing a black sweater. And her hair wasnt set and looked nice in the darkness of the movie. Then she was gone. Sitting somewhere behind him. He wondered if she noticed him. Dont imagine she saw the ring on Alices hand. Might be alright if she knew. Married men are more attractive to some women.

He concentrated on the movie, laughing and whispering to Alice and then Marie walked by with another girl. He really didnt notice it was she until she had passed and was on her way down the stairs. He continued watching the movie but, watched the staircase from the side of his eye. He felt his muscles tensing and consciously tried to relax. He didnt want Alice to get any ideas. He fought his muscles. Watched the movie. The staircase. 15 maybe 20 minutes. He thought perhaps she had left. But of course that was silly. She just got here. And anyway, he did notice that she wasnt wearing her coat. He waited. And waited. Finally he heard their voices and they came to the top of the staircase, stood for a moment then walked past him and up the aisle. He looked, but the railing in front of him was on a level with her chest as she walked by and he was too amazed to try to look as they walked past him up the aisle. It was fantastic. Unbelievable. All he wanted to do was see how big her goddam tits were and this railing is in the way. How inthehell. . .

Maybe theyll come by again. If we were sitting back a row. How could I ask Alice to move. I insisted on sitting here to stretch out my legs. There might be something I could say. Better not. She might think it strange. Theyll come by again and when they go up the' aisle I'll be able to see. Maybe I should tell Alice that thats the girl I told her about. She may have noticed me staring. No, I dont think so. A good kid that Alice. He looked at Alice and smiled and she smiled back and asked how he liked the show and he said good. Very good. Her smile broadened and she squeezed his arm and he waited for Marie to go by again trying to look behind him but they were all the way up and he couldn't see that far without turning completely around and looking deliberately and being obvious. He just sat, smoked, watched the movie and waited. He heard faint footsteps and voices and 3 girls passed and went down the stairs and Marie was one of them. He sat up higher in his seat and started turning his head slowly toward the aisle and adjusting his eyes testing to see how large an area he could see without moving his head too far. He reached a point where he could see more than necessary while still, apparently, looking at the screen. He froze himself in the position and waited. His neck muscles started to stiffen and his eyes burned but, he didn't move. He closed his eyes briefly then opened them and waited. When she came by he wouldnt have to move and he would see. . .

Then Alice tugged at his arm and pulled him toward her slightly. Would you go down and get me a pack of cigarettes honey. Im all out.

He glared for a moment (after spending all that time getting ready and she might come any minue) and almost yelled at her to get her own damn cigarettes. You should have made sure you had enough before we got here, but then he thought perhaps they arent in the Ladies Room and are downstairs at the candy counter. He mumbled a quick ok and dashed down the stairs to the candystand. They were standing around a soda machine talking. He bought the cigarettes then stood to one side and looked at them. She did have a nice pair. Not gigantic, but just right. And her waist was beautifully slim and when she turned he could see that they were firm, really firm, and not just held up with a brassiere. Of course they might hang a little without a brassiere. Thats only natural. But they wouldnt sag. And her mouth was lovely. O, I bet she'd bite. Her thighs must be so smooth. . .

The girls dropped their cups in the bucket and started walking toward him. He turned and climbed the stairs two at a time and dropped back in his seat and handed the cigarettes to his wife, trying to breathe normally, and fixed his eyes on the proper spot. He sat and waited and when they climbed the stairs to their seats he watched them bounce—just slightly—and she passed so close he could smell the soap she had washed with and he could reach out and pat her ass. He stretched out and lighted a cigarette and struggled with a conductor, a train and an usher that kept coming through the room but he kept closing doors and pulling down shades and she was naked on the bed and he kissed her and he turned in his seat and sat up and crossed his legs and was motionless and thoughtless for just a second then put his arm around Alice and rubbed his nose against her ear. She looked at him and smiled, kissed his cheek and snuggled closer to him and rubbed his arm, singing inside at seeing him relaxed and smiling and loving the way he caressed her cheek. She lifted his hand to her lips and kissed his fingertips. He put his arm around her, kissed her neck and said lets go home. But we havent seen the other picture silly. I know hon, but lets go anyway. I want to talk to you. He caressed her neck with the tip of his fingers and looked into her eyes. Ah Harry, dont. Please dont. You know I cant do anything now.

He dropped his hands and stared at her for a moment then slammed back into his seat. O for christ sake. Whats wrong Harry? Nothings wrong, goddam it. Nothing. Why don't you just leave me alone. . .

JACK KEROUAC

SEATTLE BURLESQUE

I walk in just in time, to see the first dancer.

Aw, they've got little Sis Merriday up there, girl from across the bay, she oughtnt be dancing in no burlesque, when she shows her breasts (which are perfect) nobody's interested because she aint thrown out no otay hipwork—she's too clean—the audience in the dark theater, upsidedown, want a dirty girl—And dirty girl's in back getting upsidedown ready before her stagedoor mirror—

The drapes fade back, Essie the dancer goes, I take a sip of wine in the dark theater, and out come the two clowns in a sudden bright light of the stage.

The show is on.

Abe has a hat, long suspenders, keeps pulling at them, a crazy face, you can see he likes girls, and he keeps smacking his lips and he's an old Seattle ghost—Slim, his straight man, is handsome curlyhaired pornographic hero type you see in dirty postcards giving it to the girl—

ABE   Where the hell you been?

SLIM   Back there countin the money.

ABE   What the hell d'you mean, money—

SLIM   I've been down at the graveyard.

ABE   What were you doin there?

SLIM   Burying a stiff.

and such jokes—They go through immense routines on the stage before everybody, the curtains are simple, it's simple theater—Ever-

244

body gets engrossed in their troubles—Here comes a girl walking across the stage—Abe's been drinkin out of the bottle meanwhile, he's been tricking Slim into emptying the bottle—Everybody, actors and audience, stare at the girl that comes out and strolls—The stroll is a work of art—And her answers better be juicy—

They bring her out, the Spanish dancing girl. Lolita from Spain, long black hair and dark eyes and wild castanets and she starts stripping, casting her garments aside with an 'Ole!' and a shake of her head and showing teeth, everybody eats in her cream shoulders and cream legs and she whirls around the castanet and comes down with her fingers slowly to her cinch and undoes the whole skirt, underneath's a pretty sequined virginity belt, with spangles, she jams around and dances and stomps and lowers her plaid-hair to the floor and the organist (Slim) (who jumps in the pit for the dancers) is wailing tremendous Wild Bill jazz—I'm beating with my feet and hands, it's jazz and great!—that Lolita goes slumming around then ends up at the side-drape revealing her breast-bras but wont take them off, she vanishes offstage Spanish—She's my favorite girl so far—I drink her a toast in the dark.

The lights go bright again and out come Abe & Slim again.

"What ya been doin out in the graveyard?" says the Judge, Slim, behind his desk, with gavel, and Abe's on trial—

"I've been out there burying a stiff."

"You know that's against the law."

"Not in Seattle," says Abe, pointing at Lolita—

And Lolita, with a charming Spanish accent, says "He was the stiff and I was the undertaker" and the way she says that, with a little whip of her ass, it kills everybody and the theater is plunged into dark with everybody laughing including me and a big Negro man behind me who yells enthusiastically and claps at everything great—

Out comes a middleaged Negro dancer to do us a hotfoot tap-dance, hoof, but he's so old and so puffing he cant finish up and the music tries to ride him (Slim on the Organ) but the big Negro man behind me yells out "Oh ya, Oh ya" (as if to say, 'Awright go home')—But the dancer makes a desperate dancing panting speech and I pray for him to make good, I feel sympathetic, here he is just in from Frisco with a new job and he's gotta make good somehow, I applaud enthusiastically when he goes off—

It's a great human drama being presented before my all-knowing desolation eyes—upsidedown—

Let the drapes open more—

"An now," announces Slim at the mike, "presenting Seattle's own redhead KITTY O'GRADY" and here she comes, Slim leaps to the Organ, and she's tall and got green eyes and red hair and minces around—

(O Everett Massacres where was I?)

Pretty Miss O'Grady, I can see her basinettes—Have seen them and will see her someday in Baltimore leaning in a redbrick window, by a flowerpot, with mascara and her hair masqueraded in shampoo permanent—I'll see her, have seen her, the beauty spot on her cheek, my father's seen the Ziegfield Beauties come down the line, 'Aint you an old follies girl?' asks W. C. Fields of the 300-pound waitress in the Thirties Luncheonette—and she says, looking at his nose, 'There's something awfully big about you,' and turns away, and he looks at her behind, says, 'Somethin awfully big about you too'—I'll have seen her, in the window, by the roses, beauty spot and dust, and old stage diplomas, and backdoors, in the scene that the world was made out to present—Old Playbills, alleys, Shubert's in the dust, poems about graveyard Corso—Me'n old Filipino'll pee in that alley, and Porto Rico New York will fall down, at night—Jesus will appear on July 20, 1957, 2:30 P.M.—I'll have seen pretty pert Miss O'Grady mincing dainty on a stage, to amuse the paying customers, as obedient as a kitty—I think "There she is, Slim's broad—that's his girl—he brings her flowers to the dressingroom, he serves her"—

No, she tries as hard to be naughty but caint, goes off showing her breasts (that take up a whistle) and then Abe and Slim, in bright light, put on a little play with her.

Abe is the judge, desk, gavel, bang! They've arrested Slim for being indecent. They bring him in with Miss O'Grady.

"What's he done indecent?"

"Aint what he's done, he *is* indecent."

"Why."

"Show him, Slim."

Slim, in bathrobe, turns his back to the audience and opens his flaps—

Abe stares and leans almost falling from the judge desk—"Great

day in the morning, it cant be! Who ever saw a thing like that?
Mister, are you sure that's all yours? It's not only indecent it aint
right!" And so on, guffaws, music, darkness, spotlight, Slim says
triumphant:

"And *now*—the Naughty Girl—*Sarina!*"

And jumps to the organ, ragdown jazz drag, and here comes
naughty Sarina—There's a furor of excitement throughout the theater—
She has slanted cat's eyes and a wicked face—cute like a cat's mous-
tache—like a little witch—no broom—she comes slinking and bumping out to the beat.

> Sarina the fair-haired
> bright
> Bedawnzing girl

She immediately gets down on the floor in the coitus position and
starts throwing a fit at heaven with her loinsies—She twists in pain,
her face is distorted, teeth, hair falls, shoulders squirm and snake—She
stays on the floor on her two hands supporting and knocks her works
right at the audience of dark men, some of em college boys—Whistles!
The organ music is lowdown sex-down-there what-you-doin down there
blues—

How really naughty she is with her eyes, slant blank, and the way
she goes to the righthand box and does secret dirty things for the
dignitaries and producers in there, showing some portion of her body
and saying "Yes? No?"—and sweeping away and coming around
again and now her hand-tip sneaks to her belt and she slowly undoes
her skirt with tantalizing fingers that snake and hesitate, then she
reveals a thigh, a higher thigh, a pelvic corner, a belly corner, she
turns and reveals a buttock corner, she lolls her tongue out—she's
sweating juice at every pore—I can't help thinkin what Slim does to
her in the dressingroom—

By this time I'm drunk, drank too much wine, I'm dizzy and the
whole dark theater of the world swirls around, it's all insane and I
remember vaguely from the mountains it's upsidedown and wow, sneer,
sleer, snake, slake of sex, what are people doing in audience seats in
this crashing magician's void handclapping and howling to music and
a girl?—What are all these curtains and drapes for, and masques?

and lights of different intensity playing everywhere from everywhere,
rose, pink, heart-sad, boy-blue, girl-green, Spanish-cape black and
black-black? Ugh, ow, I dont know what to do, Sarina the Naughty
One is now on her back on the stage slowly moving her sweet loins
at some imaginary God-Man in the sky giving her the eternal works—
and pretty soon we'll have pregnant balloons and cast off rubbers in
the alley and sperm in the stars and soon walls'll be built to hold her
protect inside some castle Spain Madkinghouse and the walls will be
cemented in with broken beer glasses and nobody can climb to her
snatch except the Sultan Organ who'll bear witness to her juices then
go to his juiceless grave and her grave be juiceless too in time, after
the first black juices the worms love so, then dust, atoms of dust,
whether as atoms of dust or as great universes of thighs and vaginas
and penises what will it matter, it's all a Heaven Ship—the whole
world is roaring right there in that theater and just beyond I see files
of sorrowing humanity wailing by candle light and Jesus on the Cross
and Buddha sitting neath the Bo Tree and Mohammed in a cave and
the serpent and the sun held high and all Akkadian-Sumerian antiqui-
ties and early seaboats carrying courtesan Helens away to the bash
final war and broken glass of tiny infinity till nothing's there but
white snowy light permeating everywhere, throughout the darkness and
sun—pling, and electromagnetic gravitational ecstasy passing through
without a word or sign and not even passing through and not even
being—

But O Sarina come with me to my bed of woes, let me love you
gently in the night, long time, we got all night, till dawn, till Juliet's
rising sun and Romeo's vial sink, till I have slaked my thirst of Sam-
sara at your portal rosy petal lips and left saviour juice in your rosy
flesh garden to melt and dry and ululate another baby for the void,
come sweet Sarina in my naughty arms, be dirty in my clean milk,
and I'll detest the defecate I leave in your milky empowered cyst-&-
vulva chamber, your cloacan clara file-hool through which slowly drool
the hall-gyzm, to castles in your hassel flesh and I'll protect your
trembling thighs against my heart and kiss your lips and cheeks and
hair and love you everywhere and that'll be that—

At the drape she parts her bra and shows the naughty teats and
vanishes inside and show's over—lights come on—everybody leaves—
I sit there sipping my last possible shot, dizzy and crazy.

I dont make no sense, the world is too magical, I better go back to my rock.

In the toilet I yell at a Filipino cook, "Aint those beautiful girls, hey? Aint they?" and he loth to admit it admits it to the yelling bum at the urinal—I go back, upstairs, to sit out the movie for the next show, maybe next time Sarina'll fly everything off and we'll see and feel the infinite love—But my God the movies they show! Sawmills, dust, smoke, gray pictures of logs splashing in water, men with tin hats wandering around a gray rainy void and the announcer: "The proud tradition of the Northwest—" then followed by color pictures of water skiers, I cant make it, I leave the show by the side left exit, drunk—

Just as I hit the outside night air of Seattle, on a hill, by redbrick neons of the stagedoor, here come Abe and Slim and the colored tap-dancer hurrying and sweating up the street for the next show, even on an ordinary street the tapdancer cant make it without puffing—I realize he has asthma or some serious heart defect, shouldnt be dancing and hustling—Slim looks strange and ordinary on the street and I realize it's not him's making it with Sarina, it's some producer in the box, some sugar candy—Poor Slim—And Abe the clown of Eternity Drapes, there he is talking as ever and yakking with big interested face in the actual streets of life, and I see all three of them as *troupers*, vaude-villeans, sad, sad—Around the corner for a quick drink or maybe gulp a meal and hurry back for the next show—Making a living—Just like my father, your father, all fathers, working and making a living in the dark sad earth—

I look up, there are the stars, just the same, desolation, and the angels below who dont know they're angels—

And Sarina will die—

And I will die, and you will die, and we all will die, and even the stars will fade out one after another in time.

CITY City city

Boys pushing through the combination inter-group deactivator, for juvenile delinquent kicks, and sometimes just young children when they tried to shove through to their ball, had brought up before Congress the subject of laxity of Deactivation. "It's a grave peril to our freedoms," said a spokesman close to sources in Master Center Love (MCL). "It shows a disrespect for ancient tradition in CITYCITY*CITY* that was accepted without cavil by the older generation. A great many lives of our children, too, are endangered, when their non-deactivated rubber balls fall into a No-Zone and the game of 'push-me-in' takes place, where boys line up behind the brave volunteer and forcibly shove him through the air barrier of the deadly No-Zone where he struggles, choking and turning blue and causing irreparable damage to his lungs, until the ball usually is handed to him by a No-Zone child, as a courtesy, and then ensues the even deadlier game of pulling him back with the pushed-in hand of the leader of the file in Zone, which sometimes fails and results in the death of the child trapped to choke in No-Zone. These practices, plus the delinquent practice of running and throwing oneself against the No-Zone air barrier, which is called Sexing, must be dealt with at the root of their cause; mere punitive punishment, increase of electrocutions, alone, serves no real preventative courtesy to the ideals of Master Center Love and all it has stood for since the Twenty-Eighth Century and the blood shed so willingly before the year One."

This was on the Brow Multivision set, just a little rubber disc adhering to the brow, turned on and off at the breast control; the sensation to a newcomer was of seeing, hearing, smelling, tasting, feeling and thinking the sensation of the vision, which was being waved out of Master Center Love Multivision Studios. M-80, of Zone Block 38383939383-338373 (a number most difficult to refer to, without a Multigraph), (but referred to and duly recorded and Destinated in Master Center Love), walked down the street in the early morning sunshine. M-80 was kid of thirteen. He had pushed the Multivision down from where he usually kept it on the back of his ear, listened a minute,

to the speech about juvenile delinquents, and now was about to slide
it back, when the commercial came on and he felt a delicious wave of
ecstasy from some spiel about a new Drug . . . "They were saying
I couldnt be happy, couldnt be high in the cloudless sky, glad, raving
to joy, but no, say, hear me, I went and got myself a tube of 17-JX,
we call it Jex, and I took out two tablets, and swallowed with water,
and instantly, almost at once! there stole over me the incomparable
ecstasy of a REALLY free and at the same time POLITE compound, I
said to myself 'These MCL chemists who prepare this Drug for the
people of CITYCITYCITY show that they really know the meaning of
LOVE: they have gone all out to provide myriallions and myriallions
with the Best, the Most Polite, Courteous, Loving that ingenuity
can devise and Merits buy . . !" But M-80 wasn't listening to the
announcer; he was busy enjoying the four or five seconds of bliss
allowed by the commercial, as a teaser. People all over CITYCITYCITY
were putting in calls this minute to the Super Drugway; soon you'd
see them flying around, to their destination; "nobody'll even be on
the street", sneered the boy, who wanted to play. "U-21'll stay home
and try his old Drug, and H-30'll sleep on it . . . Golly! Atheism!
There's a pool of water—a real pool of water!" His heart thumped.
He had never seen a pool of water in his life, except in Multivision
in their history shows, showing how, in the days before rain was
diverted from CITYCITYCITY, moisture used to fall from the skies and
form in the streets and blocks of old cities. "There's been a leak!"
thought the kid frantically. "What'll they say? Wow!" He rushed up
to the pool. Marvelously it reflected the blue perfect sky, with a little
ripple only. It was a clean puddle, just a little dust on the edges. He
touched it wonderingly, squatted. It was only 8 in the morning and
he was the only one who'd seen it. He ran his finger around, stepped
in. "It's just like when they electrocute a block and forget to sweep
out a dead man ash. Golly zoo Athies! Romanticism! This is going to
kill dad." He ran to his house, singing happily some gurgled crazy
kidyell of happiness. "Ha, ha, ha," he crashed into the house, interrupting his father, T-3 at breakfast. "What's it, kid?"—wiping his
mouth. "A pool of water? Who ever heard of such a thing? Lemme
see." They went out together, their crepe-foam shoes sliding softly over
the steel-plate street with its bolts at intervals like shiny knobs. The
pool lay in a depression formed by an old accident, when an insane

old man had thrown the Computer of Merit out of the front window
and put a dent in the street. "Hmm," said T-3, Prime Minister of Block
38383939383-338373, a tall handsome man with thick temple gray and
a bushy head of hair still jet black in parts, frowning thickly now,
"it looks like somethin went wrong somewhere. Couldnt be the Raindar,
the Umbrella Command never had any trouble with electronics that I
know of, tho there's a theory among some of the MCL wiseguys, about
infiltration of Activation agents in the Command . . . a joke on somebody. Let's see . . . a leak in the next plate? But the water wouldn't
get through from the No-Zone. What the divine hell could it be? Aw
well, it's a puzzle. I'll bring it up with the girls. Son, the day women
took over all the central organization of world government, wow, look-
out, that was it . . . The day my grandfather envisioned, he told me
too, when women get a hold of the whole works and you have to kow-
tow every morning to a dike martinet, that's your red wagon . . ." T-3
called M-80 "son" but in actuality he was only adopted; all the children of the world, after birth in Central Deactivation, where Deactivator disks were riveted into their breastbones prior to Connection in
their given Zone Block, were assigned to various parents, according
to the Computer of Infinite Merit in MCL (one of the most, if not
THE most complicated mechanical brains ever put together; its central
secret feature obtained around a mathematical principle relatively
unknown, something to do about the chasing of the Zero to Infinity,
a constant process that kept equations spinning dizzily on the Dial, you
saw thousands of them flashing on and off, vibrating, sending off waves
of computation that you could almost sense sprinting to keep up with
the race of the zero and still turn out Estimates of Merit, General and
Local, by which the government was run). Some people even went so
far as to state that Master Center Love itself was a computation, ever-
changing, from the Computer of Infinite Merit, but the truth was,
Master Center Love had for centuries emanated from the inner core of
the High Women of the world, whose system of succession had never
been revealed . . . It was *Political.* M-80 was assigned to his Zone
block by the computation of the machine. His real (seminal) parents
he would never know, because they were in other Zone Blocks.

The world was the earth; every square inch was covered with electrical steelplate. The ocean had long ago been covered with earth
acquired from surrounding planets. CITYCITYCITY was the world; every

square inch of the world steelplate was covered with the Three Types
of Levels of CITYCITYCITY. You saw the skyline, of steel skyscrapers,
far away; then beyond that, like a ballooned imitation of the same
skyline, rising way beyond and over it, vastly larger, the second level
of CITYCITYCITY, the CITY level; beyond that, CITY, like a dim cloud,
rose huge on the horizon a vast phantasmal skyline so far away you
could barely see it, yet it rose far above the other two and far beyond.
Those three levels were to facilitate the ingress of sunlight into the
various people-flats. The CITYCITYCITY Tri-Levels were: one tenement
ten miles high; the second, fifty miles; the third, a hundred miles high;
so that from Mars for instance, you saw the earth with its complete
CITY everywhere looking like a prickly ball in the Void. The prickles
represented one vast domicile of millions upon millions upon myrillions. In each Zone Block lived only about 2,500 people; but there were
billions of Zone Blocks. M-80 was our hero's name; but it was also
the name of billions and myrillions of other boys, each with his zone
number. His full name was, thus: M-80 38383939383-338373 . . . Population kept increasing continually. It was necessary at intervals to electrocute entire Zone Blocks and make room for a new group culled from
slags and miscalculations in the system. Deactivation which prevented
people from leaving their own Zone Blocks, was a necessary caution
against the chaos which would have resulted from an overpopulated
Movement over the crowded steelplate of the world. Migrating to other
planets was out of the question; especially after centuries of Self
Enforced Deactivation. Other planets in the immediate vicinity of earth
had been denuded of life and turned into Deactivator Bases and Laboratories, Deactivating all that part of the universe around the earth.
Outside raged the life of the Universe, where Activation reigned. Many
were the space ships from unknown planets who'd come crashing
against the No-Zone of earth and disintegrated in mid-air; many the
meteors met the same fate. Nobody questioned the wisdom of Master
Center Love in refusing to have any contact with the rest of the universe. Activated . . . a word written in black letters dripping with red
ink . . . ACTIVATED, you'd see it written on superseptic toilet walls of
the CITYCITYCITY, with lewd drawings. It was a word whispered in
dark sex rooms, turned into a colloquial dirty-word. "Activate me." For
all anybody knew, the rest of the universe was completely hostile as
well as Activated; no one was taking any chances. But for centuries

there had been a steady infiltration of Activationists, and of Activationism. Congressional Committees had investigated. Traitors were found; at least they seemed to be guilty of Activationist activities. The means were through propaganda via Multivision and via certain subversive drugs with telepathic compounds by which the Activationist was said to telepathize propaganda around Master Center Love . . . One Activationist was believed to be behind one of the famous boners in the history of CITYCITYCITY. Everybody was lying around one day enjoying the afternoon comedy show, Jexed to the gills ("I'm telling you I was HONORED that afternoon, why I was *so* honored . . .") when somebody at Master Center threw the Panic Switch, which sets off the Warning throughout the world of the impending destruction of the Outer Zone Barrier. (Also it is the switch that transmits directly individually to a single Zone Block ten seconds before it is to be electrocuted.) Using it as a warning of impending destruction of the Outer Zone Barrier naturally has never been known to be needed. Zone Blocks are eliminated at the rate of sixteen a day, but with the world so vastly populated, densely, deeply 100 miles down and 24,000 miles around, it was rare that a Zone Blocker could remember at some time in his life witnessing the doom of his nextblock neighbor on either of the four sides. You could see four other zone blocks but you couldn't put your hand through the No-Zone Air, unless pushed, and at great pains, into it. "Yes I remember seeing the north Zoneblock next door here, burned, in '306 . . . it was awful . . . everybody turned black . . . you saw em come runnin outa the house at the warning and still runnin on the steelplate and then they burn black and crisp up . . . there warnt any smoke much . . . I hope never to see it again."

"You think it'll ever happen to our Zone Block?" (a kid).

Wherein comes the famous saying of the world, "If it does you only got ten seconds to worry about it."

The goof at Master had thrown this switch, but for every Zone Block in the world, so that for a moment, everywhere in the world in the trillions of billions of Zone Blocks up and down and all around the globe people rushed out of their houses screaming, sending a human vibration, they say, into the sky, that was said to have almost destroyed the No-Zone Air Barrier, and was the supposed intention behind the plot. Studies were being made century after century to ascertain the effect of such a vast human vibration on the Electronics Wall (Great

E Wall) . . . Nothing had ever been unearthed concerning the mystery of the panic broadcast. But it was Activationist work.

Ideas of Activation had been brought onto the earth-globe via the only form of Activated life in the universe that was capable of penetrating the Great Electronics wall: beings on a level of certain rarity that enabled them to swim, veil-like, pale as ghosts, through the Wall and through the people of earth, yet communicating thoughts and ideas. For a long time they were said to be Tathagatas from a Buddha-land but this was refuted in the year '682 by a great Mechanical Scholar who said: "The incidence of supernormal and superreal existence, or is-ness, on a level of communication via mental conception, is .0008753 impossible, and therefore, After the Zero, on a basis of .3578 returning from the Void Echo Decimal, of no pathoactive significance." It was established then, that these beings were normal beings in a different vibration, not supernormal beings beyond life. Nothing beyond life had as yet found the light of scientific verification. These Beings, these Activation Agents, were the terrors of the world; the troops of Devils of Gothic times were replaced by these pale phantasmal insinu-ators from Outside, called Actors. This name was referred philologically back to ancient times when disorderly elements were known as "actors" in early trade unions; it all tied up psychologically; now the "actors" were almost impossible to detect and came from other worlds. It was strange. It was always sunlight because of the Raindar Umbrella that prevented moisture from wetting the dangerous electrical hotplate which was the world. The streets were usually empty. Except in the morning, on Market Days, when Drugs, L-Pumps, Computers of Merit, various gadgets, doodads, delicacy pills, etc. were exchanged at the proper marts. Illicit Actor Fumes were sold in forbidden little jars; Actor Fumes came from the emanation which an Actor left when it passed thru a jar, apparently by intention; the sniff of it had the peculiar effect of inducing a certain blissful feeling that was accom-panied by a vitamin lapse, or false recharge, that made it impossible to inject L (Love, the official CITYCITYCITY drug, used by everyone from birth, by law); with the effect of actor fumes, a man of this world was left wide open for telepathic messages from Actors infest-ing the air; nothing Multivision could send out could combat this, once the victim had a sniff of Actor Fumes, or Ghost, as it was called; it was so powerful and so sweet to the senses the weaker elements of the population were all addicted; it was easy to get, the Actors saw to that, by merely passing themselves through every jar in the world; jars became illegal. Actors began fuming themselves in people's breast-pockets; all an addict had to do was bend down and sniff, but this never had the total effect of a good enclosed jarful; the Breast Sniff became the minor evil of the two. Breastpockets of any kind were abolished. Later, pants pockets; cavities of all kinds in clothing, walls, surfaces. Certain addicts became adept at storing fumes in their mouths; certain sexual defectives found all kinds of new thrills. Juvenile delinquents hung around corners holding their hands cupped, after dark, to catch fumes if any. "Man, I'm zoned."

"What's wrong with Master Center World Drugs, that a little whiff of Actor Fumes, or Ghost as it is known in the street, Jar Bang or Breast Sniff, gets everybody going in the wrong direction? Activationism is behind this; research, unending struggle in our laboratories and computatoriums and Mechanical Universities, in our whole Machine, must be banded together to find a solution to this invasion which may only be the prelude to an unheard-of catastrophic deluge from Outside." They called it "Outside," like 20th Century (Pre One) (PO) jailbirds. "The world is going up in flames!" cried the prophets of doom. "All respect for ancient values is deteriorating. People wander off into the realm of Activated thoughts, influenced by Fumes. Or if not that, outcries are raised against the Computer Administration, complaints that such and such a Zone Block was chosen instead of another . . ."

"Five Zone Blocks in my very district have been electrocuted in the past 156 years counting yesterday's Elimination—yet nothing, NOTHING is being done to ascertain why the Computer Administration has not launched an Investigation into possible administrative defects at Center Love that may have played a role in this needless slaughter of District Seventythree."

"Now wait a minute, you can't tell District President that any kind of indelicacy has been involved. My dear man, let us take an instance, District Seventyfour, right next door, three million people and more, have had to put up with as many as eight Zone Block eliminations in the past 150 years, this means twenty thousand District Seventyfours have had to be Eliminated, Security bless their souls . . .

"No, if the world is to keep up its Security Calm, and panic and dissolution and restlessness are to be dispelled, it's going to have to be a new inner movement in the Master Center Love, radiating NEW vigor via Multivision to the Multitude, NEW ideals of Love, a NEW DEAL in Master Center Love, then you'll fumes'll fade, then your prophets of doom will say 'we should have known better, this old steelplate that only looks like an old marl spike in the universe, is built on solider ground than the ground of Activation spooks with their head-in-the-clouds attitude towards realities of life.' Overpopulation has always given the people what it wants. There may come a day when Depopulation may come to be necessary at last . . . this is the day when Master Center Love shall have to disappear from the cup of this universe . . . this will be the day for the invasion and the rape of CITYCITYCITY by Activators from Outside . . . and centuries of human effort, mechanical genius and Love shall have turned to dust of failure . . . Overpopulation, now a Legislation 86 Centuries old, stands behind You, and You, and You, and You, and You, and You, and You, and You, and You, and You, and YOU YOU YOU! Let not Depopulation come to Master Center Love!"

The Computer of Infinite Merit worked out supermathematically not only the amount of hours put in by everybody in the world listening to Multivision Love Broadcasts, but because of its contact with the various multibillion disks upon the breastbones of mankind, by a method of such high mechanical mystery, almost mystical in its far-reaching significance and political depth, it computed the intensity of the communicant's attention to Love. These complicated figures were broken down by Data Divisions of the General Computer Command, and it was the sum of these figures that had to do with the Merit accumulated by both the individual of a Zone Block and the whole Zone Block together in common merit. When a Zone Block was chosen for Electrocution, Elimination from life, it was because of the low Merit Average of the whole 2500-odd community. Home Computers of Merit were in use, by which people could keep track of their own average; but some people just didnt care. The Loveless Brothers didnt care. The Loveless Brothers didnt even bother to tune in their Multivision and would have nothing to do with either general Drugs or L the Love Drug. These were the bums of the community, and usually were seen in the streets, sitting, talking. They had homes, they had their cells like everyone else. They contributed dismal scores to the general average of a Zone Block, and of course they were resented and even persecuted. So shiftless were they, sitting there all day with no place to go because Deactivated at birth, and yet not oriented to life in their Zone Block due to their refusal to imbibe the proper drugs, they became motionless and dreamy. Kids never paid attention to Loveless Brothers, brushed them aside sometimes.

It was dusk. The air was filled as always with the vague, dull odor of burning atomic rubber from the continually flying myriads of guided freight missiles bringing uncounted goods from the Drugway and the "Nutrish" (the Nutrition Commissariat). Shoving a Food Pill down his throat, swigging it down with a dash of synthetic dry water, little M-80 ran out to wait for his father, T-3, hoping for news about the official reaction to the pool of water. M-80 stood there, wrinkling his nostrils because he'd never liked that smell of dry rubber of the Synoids flying around up there, tho after a lifetime of smelling it he couldnt quite detect it either. No one else seemed to mind. "M-80 has got too many ideas in his head."—"He certainly complains a lot."—But M-80, standing there, his hair motionless in the dusk, eyes lowered, wondered if he ever would escape. If there was such a thing.

Even when he saw his father stepping out of the Ministry Van. The Van was made of steel and was operated by two armed guards who came each morning, flying in silently (but always leaving a faint odor of wet ashes in the still air, smouldering, all-pervasive, nauseating to M-80 when he stepped out for afterbreakfast play). The guards opened the Dezoning door, the most secretly guarded door of the realm unless you name the door of Master Center Love the inner bedroom of the Love Exec. The minister of Zone Block Number so and So stepped in as ordered, with briefcase, as contact was made with his breast-disk by the diskfinder in the guards' hands. Two guards were used to point this diskfinder, to offset the possibility of one guard, without being resisted, turning the diskfinder on the wrong subject in some attempt, as there had been many in older times, to effect an escape from Deactivation into the inner Sanctums of Master Love from which this one heavily guarded carrier was limitedly sent to fetch the ministers of the realm, duly elected. When the Minister, partially and temporarily Activated and saved from belly strain by the soothing counter-action of the diskfinder in the rocket room that takes him there, is ordered to step out into the steelplate of Master Center Love, their occurs a reverse process, the diskfinder's taken away. Deactivation takes on full force again but now a marvelous new sensation takes place, like walking into heaven. Master Center Love is neither Deactivated nor Activated, there is no such arbitrary conception there; as a result, Deactivation immediately ceases, and the Minister is free to get on with the day's business with the other Ministers and Districters, all from a variety of different Zone Blocks and all similarly brought to work. The formula for the arbitrary conceptionlessness of neither Deactivation nor Activation had been developed in the machine known as the Brain Halo, which divined equations, proof of equations, disproofs of equations, balancing them all together, so skillfully, so complicated, a thousand wires running into a million larger ones that grew and snaked and vined their way in the tangled Wire Room of the Brain. This formula was put to use in Deactivation Headquarters of Master Center Love and sent through. But everyone remained with his Deactivation disk, immune, till the return to the No-Zone of the general Zone Block world of CITYCITYCITY. Who in Master Center Love was *not* Deactivated? It was the highest known sacrilege to say that anyone on earth could ever be Activated; that anyone had not been born Deactivated was absurd, ridiculous, lies. "If there's someone there in that Woman Room that aint Deactivated, and goes around traveling to the other universe, and's running OUR universe, then I hang up my tube and lay back and become a Loveless Brother cause brother, that means we're all being played a wood—and I dont mean chemical wood."

You'd hear sometimes on murmurous afternoons speeches among the people emanating from noisy SLEEPSLEEPSLEEP Halls, where you went to sleep up the Love, or to talk. "I dont give a gerl dang toot; if Master Sinner Love sends me out to that blue horizone with a shot of electrical ouch in my arse, I'm damn sure I aint gonna believe in em on the way out." etc. "Yesh, call me a Loveless Brother if I dont feel the same damn glassed way, gas me."

"What did they say Pa?" yelled M-80 rushing up as his father stepped from the Ministry Van onto the good old steelplate of 38383939383-338373 . . . (that happened to be the queer number of this particular block, and was noted for its strangeness, and commented upon by old citizens, and looked on as a bad sign: "We'll get it soon for sure!")—His father looked worried: lines showed under his eyes. "I've had a strange day, Em child. Wait, let me gather my thoughts, before we talk, let those guards go. I've never felt so oppressed before . . . it's been a strange day."

"—the water—"

"Precisely, the water, the water has not everyone worried . . . I don't understand . . . it's something about something about something I just didnt hear when the door closed . . . And tomorrow I'll know what it's all about but they just left me in the dark today . . . Something about a similar incident at such and such a time, water leaking into a Zone Block, something about Activation activities, always that of course," (aside) "they'll find a reason in their black gowns to give a name to everything, hell and heaven and both the east and west of themselves, and have funerals on the sly when the winds dont bring honor"—"they'll find a god damn name for our death in this block."—He went in to his wife, and to supper, and a quick tune-in on Multivision to see if there was any talk yet, any hints from the more casual commentators, any mad gloved hand maybe he could find in the program tonight, always so dull and the same—"Love is Patience, what is my rush to call it dull!" he reprimanded himself, and worried . . . He was a man on the verge of a nervous breakdown, but held himself together physically and sometimes physically he'd feel the straining of his components, about to fall, break down too; he did 32 pushups every morning; once he'd wanted to do as many pushups as his age, but now he was a good old healthy taped-together Drugfed CITYCITYCITYite of 198 and that was out of the question. Nothing on Multivision that he could see; tho for a half hour he lay dreamily listening to some own thought of his suspicions of some point in a sly remark he imagined he heard during a commercial, "but a commercial, what's the matter with me, looking for news in the commercial? . . . but that's where it is," he couldn't help having the eerie afterthought, full of sinister self-assurance. His hair stood on end. Burn, burn . . . this was the secret thought of all CITYCITYCITY . . . not, as in ancient times, Death, Death, I'll grow old and die, but now old age and death had been checked, so much so that there was a better chance of death by Block Electrocution than by death from really old age in the 300's (which no one, curiously, wanted, it apparently being too long a time for life of any mentally conscious kind.) One eminent Mechanic had said: "The quotient of care-to-live decreases in ratio to age; past the 250 mark the quotient is near nil; at 300 there is no substantiality to the quotient warranting the continuance of a living organism." Famous pessimists had reached very old age and left messages of horror to their Block before, senile and most-asleep in the torpor of 400 and 500's, they went up in smoke with the others on the Shock Day. Shock Day . . . the name was written as by great dark clouds on the blue horizon, some calendars depicted the imagined scene of Shock Day with the homily in large letters, "Trust in Love to take you there." Or, "Be polite to the forces of your Love." And some Alexandrinisms like "Love, You'll Burn it" were featured as jokes in the salons of intellectuals around MCL Hexagon. The Hexagon housed over 20 million government employees and provided Deactivation free while they were there; when fired, they were thrown back into the humdrum ZoneBlock life. In the Hexagon, L Pumps to facilitate the intake of L from Center via L Drug were also provided for government workers. Everyone had L drug free at birth, by law. It was contained in a steel amulet riveted to the outside of the breast-disk just below the place where the Merit Numbers showed counting like the counters on a speedometer. For instance, T-3's disk had a large T-3-38383939383-338373 engraved and fretted, and right under that, the merit counters, and the amulet containing the life-supply of Love Drug. But with an L pump there was no need to pump in the Love Drug yourself; that was for the working people of the world, the "Pumpers," while, for the more fortunate the L pump just worked it in for you. The general theory that you cant have a world completely populated with unoccupied masses here prevailed, of course, for tho it would have been easy to relieve Pumpers of their all-day duties as self L-pumpers of Love Drug, authorities in Master Center Love, perhaps unrightly influenced by some ancient traditions still adhered to in the heat of change and progress, still held that somewhere in the world there must be *some* physical motion and effort, besides the mechanical motion of the machine, for reasons of courtesy to the forces of "nature," perhaps for reasons of unconscious psychological imitation of the machine now that motion was no longer really necessary—The highest CITY-CITYCITY Love Official could be motionless the livelong day receiving her (the highest officials were woman) L and her Multivision in a quiet room, stay like that for months, years, a whole lifetime, it wasnt necessary to move any more. So the "Pumpers" complained of their bitter lot. You saw their darkened faces snarling in the windless air.

Nothing moved but a few slow futile sinister gestures of speakers, generally you'd lie there pumping in your Love looking out the window at the empty afternoon steelplate. Sometimes a Loveless Brother shuffled by, cupping his hands together to catch some Action . . . The air however swarmed with freight missiles gayly rushing to their destinations. The Machine was doing the moving for man and still man wanted less and less to move. "Blimey crackerjacks, but if them rich sonsaguns can sit there all day their lard tail on the couch of foam from midnight to midnight and all the kicks in the book, why can't we?"

"It's because you cant have all the people in the world *rich!*"

"Some's got it and some aint."

"Some crap thru burlap and some fart thru silk I say."

"Here I am pumpin and pumpin all day wasting myself to the bone while these lazy pale tat cottonpickin mother activators go around getting themselves free-rided thru ecstasy. Why do *I* have to struggle through and them just loaf!"

"Pumpers and Mumpers aint got no jemumpers!" sang the kids in a favorite street song. Streets had no sidewalks or curbs. "Galumpers and galumpers . . ." "And if the rich got curbs, I got blurbs, in Love Magazine," sang the popular W-70, the Sleepsinger at the Hall.

In the morning Ministers went to work, flying in the Ministry Van with the two unfriendly diskfinder guards. It was the rule never to speak to them, only to answer when spoken to. This was a precaution taken in Master Center Love, among many others, to establish a gulf of personality between Minister and guards, to obviate any chance of friendship, favor, preference stepping into the picture of impersonal daily flight to work in the mornings and back to the home Zone-block at night. No Minister had ever been able to escape his block, or escape the Ministry Van enroute to MCL or find his way out of MCL once delivered there to that marvelous wave of neither Activation or Deactivation that equalled everything out and made you free—but the walls were thick. The walls of the Kremlin had never been so thick, the walls of Jugurtha lesser guarded.

MP's stood around with diskfinders, ready to pull an errant Minister into a Van with the force of the magneto . . . M-80's, Pop, popularly known as Tee, stepped out of the van and felt the arbitrary conception fade from his disk and from his brain. "Here you are, Tee. Heard the latest on your pool of water?"

"No, what . . ."

"You *havent* heard?"

"No"—

Someone was nudging the speaker, he clammed up, grimly his lips came together. People were whispering. Ministers and Districters standing all over the steelplate plazas, smoking Jex, rifling thru their briefcases, arguing, waving . . . it was the customary half hour recess before opening of the day's Session. A ripple of attention seemed to be focusing on Tee this morning, but you couldnt always tell, it seemed to be going in other directions too. At least one of the gathered 9,000 Ministers of the "G" area of cITYcITYCITY daily received notification of the decision to electrocute his block and himself; you heard sometimes lamentable moans rising from the dignified halls of Congress. "When an electrocution takes place brother you gets flown back by the dim guards now and grim they are by now, and you're stepped out on the steelplate of your block and told to stay there, via diskfinder, and the warning is immediately sounded by the guard, setting off the 10 second panic switch all set to go in the Computer works—you see people running out of the apartments, you see upset pumps of L and Comps of Merit spilled and people crawling on the steel begging for mercy but it lasts only a few seconds, and your last glimpse is of the Minister himself standing there in the airless void smelling of dim burnt rubbery ashes with one hand in his coat lapel, like Napoleon, eyes to heaven, boom, up goes the block in sizzles and crackles of hot smoke, as the guards fly away . . . everyday routine with them . . . to them it's known as Hot Dog Day—

"Ah well, such is Overpopulation," was the popular saying.

Taps, some called it.

And this is what happened to our Minister T-3. He was informed and notified that day. Confirmation. Look out, he ran back to the toilet and threw up and they put the diskfinders on him and dragged him back to the Van, tho he would have willingly walked, straight and unafraid of death, tho inwardly trembling. But once he'd been sick and straightened up in the toilet and even combed his hair and adjusted clothing for a grand finale to his life in front of his cohorts . . . they dragged him, like a hoodlum who hasnt done anything, like a saint who's suddenly afraid to die.

It all began at 9 AM. In the committee room Districter G-92 (Goldie) who'd never liked Tee because Tee had voted against his idea in '754—*O, where had the love of the people wandered?*—Goldie's bill was to centralize Love further into MCL and not concentrate so much on spreading it among the people, who only wasted it. It was a reactionary move by a reactionary thick-headed usurper of other people's natural rights, plainly. Tee had organized a group of Ministers and even two Districters to prepare opposition to this measure . . . For just a Minister Tee had shown remarkable strength. Goldie was the kind of Districter who should never have been promoted from Minister nor elected among the people of his block in the first place. But with some front he'd put on, carefully cultivated for years, to advertise himself as a tireless champion of some kind, for some Cause, whatever Cause they wanted (tho they never caught him taking his secret nap in the afternoon chair . . . tireless, indeed), he'd worked his way up high in MCL and was even highly regarded by Women in the high Courts . . . ("shows how much real love they must have up there, not pumped in") —

Is there such a thing as real love? was a popular question.

So now Goldie had a look of triumph on his face, and since Districters were always notified before Ministers at Special Sessions, Tee now divined "My block's getting it this morning (I got ten minutes or less to live) and he knows it"—But a motion was started up by Tee's friends, to pass a vote around on an Anti-No Zone Pushing bill, aimed to curb the juvenile delinquents and put a stop to the practice altogether by anyone, punishable by individual electrocution. Tee's friends wanted poor Tee to live at least an extra hour . . . to gather his soul up. "Soul" was a popular superstition. Tee saw clearly the reason for the move and the measure. He saw despicable Goldie, showing his teeth, looking oddly like ancient pictures of the Devil with his long sinuous ears and the curve of his arched brows and the particular demonism in the glitter of his eyes or of the glasses before his eyes or of both in conjunction, something hellish Tee prickled all over to see it.

He suddenly saw snakes swarming all around Goldie, the undulating motion of thousands of Ministers. "Life is a snake. What do I lose when I lose the snake? I lose my writhing properties."

He stood up. Goldie was putting in a counter-measure to make the announcement of Electrocution Elimination at once. This meant Tee had ten minutes to live instead of an hour. The giant loudspeaker thundered: "LOVE."

Everyone hushed. The great Voice of Love came over the micro-
phone. "ZONE BLOCK ANNOUNCEMENTS. PROPOSED AMENDMENTS AND
EMENDATIONS OF PROGRAM. MEMBERS OF THE MINISTRY HAVE
REQUESTED IMMEDIATELY THE VOTE ON THE ANTI-NO ZONE PUSHING
BILL. MEMBERS OF THE DISTRICT REPRESENTATION HAVE IN A SUBSTITUTE
MOTION TO ANNOUNCE THE BLOCK ELIMINATIONS AND THEN VOTE. O,
LOVE, HERE ARE THE NUMBERS OF THE ZONE. BLOCKS TO BE ELEC-
TROCUTED THIS MORNING AND THEIR MINISTERS NUMBER 3838393938383-
338373, MINISTER T-3 . . . (Voice pauses for speech).

And the Voice of the Woman droned off and Tee stood still, all
the eyes of the men who had tried to help him, showing piteously in
a general stare towards him, and the eyes of his enemies burning to
leer his way. The two Van guards approached at once, unsheathing and
turning on their diskfinder, both clutching to special side handles on
it, pointing at Tee.

"Farewell sweet friends, sweet fellow students of young and happy
days . . ." cried Tee to the assembly—"May the hope of the sun or
whatever the sun, or hope, or hopes themselves, multiplied, put together
by whatever measurements of light, or of actuality, come to you—
either by grace, intention, by self assistance, by courage, will, compas-
sion to live—and you find love, real love, if such a thing there be,
if such a world indeed there here be now, if—"

O, LOVE HERE ARE THE NUMBERS OF THE ZONE BLOCKS. NUMBER
8386294853008-290490, MINISTER Y-16—" boomingly interrupted the
Voice of Love, cutting Tee's speech short, because the time allotted
for speech was ten seconds and no more; many's the doomed Minister
in his heat of sadness and eloquence who ran over his time—One
distinguished Mechanic had made this estimate: "If Ministers were
allowed liberal uninterrupted speech time at the announcement of the
Electrocution of their blocks, and assuming that the average length of
these speeches would be seven minutes, at the barest minimum, the
time consumed and taken at the expense of the work of Love is
calculated at sixteen million four hundred and thirty six thousand five
and hundred twelve man-years, which, multiplied to the man-quotient,
would have meant the loss of 764,096,264,740,862,398 tats of man-
power (.Mp), (minus deduction for electronical loss) (and leak).
Therefore the ten second rule is imperative to our Machine."

MANHATTAN SKETCHES

THE CAFETERIA—a glittering counter—decorative walls—but nobody notices noble old ceiling of ancient decorated in fact almost Baroque (Louis XV?) plaster now browned a smoky rich tan color— where chandeliers hung (obviously was old restaurant) now electric bulbs within metal casings or shades—. But general effect is of *shiny food* on counter—walls are therefore not too noticeable—sections of ceiling length mirrors, and mirror pillars, give spacious strange feeling—brownwood panels with coat hooks and sections of rose-tint walls decorated with images, engraved— But Ah the counter! as brilliant as B-way outside! Great rows of it—one vast L shaped counter—great rows of diced mint jellos in glasses; diced strawberry jellos gleaming red, jellos mixed with peaches and cherries, cherry jellos topped with whipcream, vanilla custards top't with cream; great strawberry shortcakes already sliced in twelve sections, illuminating the center of the L. . . Huge salads, cottage cheese, pineapple, plums, egg salad, prunes, everything—vast baked apples—tumbling dishes of grapes, pale green and brown—immense pans of cheesecake, of raspberry cream cake, of flaky rich Napoleons, of simple Boston cake, armies of eclairs, of enormously dark chocolate cake (gleaming scatological brown)—of deepdish strudel, of time and the river—of freshly baked powdered cookies—of glazed strawberry-banana desserts—wild glazed orange cakes—pyramiding glazed desserts made of raspberries, whipcream, lady fingers sticking up—vast sections reserved for the splendors of coffee cakes and Danish crullers—All interspersed with white bottles of rich mad milk—. Then the bread bun mountain—. Then the serious business, the wild steaming fragrant hot-plate counter—Roast lamb, roast loin of pork, roast sirloin of beef, baked breast of lamb, stuff'd pepper, boiled chicken, stuff'd spring chicken, things to make the poor penniless mouth water—big sections of meat fresh from ovens, and a great knife sitting alongside and the server who daintily lays out portions as thin as paper. The coffee counter, the urns, the cream jet, the steam—But most of all it's that shining glazed sweet counter—

showering like heaven—an all-out promise of joy in the great city of
kicks.

But I haven't mentioned the best of all—the cold cuts and sandwich and salad counter—with pans of mountainous spreads of all kinds
that have cream cheese coverings sprinkled with chives and other
bright spices, the pink lovely looking lox—cold ham—Swiss cheese—
the whole counter gleaming with icy joy which is salty and nourish-
ing—cold fish, herrings, onions—great loaves of rye bread sliced—so
on—spreads of all kinds, egg salads big enough for a giant decorated
and sprigged on a pan—in great sensuous shapes—salmon salads—
(Poor Cody, in front of this in his scuffled-up beat Denver shoes, his
literary "imitation" suit he had wanted to wear to be acceptable in
New York cafeterias which he thought would be brown and plain like
Denver cafeterias, with ordinary food,—).

SIXTH AVENUE CAFETERIA, poorer but emptier—People in cafeterias smile when they're arriving and sitting down at the table but
when they're leaving, when in unison their chairs scrape back they
pick up their coats and things with glum faces (all of them the same
degree of semi-glumness which is a special glumness that is disappointed that the promise of the first-arriving smiling moment didnt
come out or if it did it died after a short life)—and during that short
life which has the same blind unconscious quality as the orgasm, everything is happening to all their souls—this is the GO—the summation
pinnacle possible in human relationships—lasts a second—the vibratory
message is on—yet it's not so mystic either, it's love and sympathy in
a flash. Similarly we who make the mad night all the way (four-way
sex orgies, three-day conversations, uninterrupted transcontinental
drives) have that momentary glumness that advertises the need for
sleep—reminds us it is possible to stop all this—more so reminds us
that the moment is ungraspable, is already gone and if we sleep we
can call it up again mixing it with unlimited other beautiful com-
binations—shuffle the old file cards of the soul in demented hallucinated sleep—So the people in the cafeteria have that look but only
until their hats and things are picked up, because the glumness is also
a signal they send one another, a kind of "Goodnight Ladies" of perhaps interior heart politeness. What kind of friend would grin openly

in the faces of his friends when it's time for glum coatpicking and bending to leave? So it's a sign of "Now we're leaving this table which had promised so much—this is our obsequy to the sad." The glumness goes as soon as someone says something and they head for the door—laughing they fling back echoes to the scene of their human disaster—they go off down the street in the new air provided by the world.

Ah the mad hearts of all of us.

MEANWHILE THE MAN READING THE PAPER before the big green door is like an Arab in city clothing, felt hat, bow tie, plaid pants, like Aly Khan he has black hair bulging from the sides under his hat—He sits semi-facing cafeteria (where us Egyptians wait) under this damn 20-foot door that looks like it's going to open behind him and a green monstrous 5-foot-hand will come out, wrap around his chair and slide him in, the great door swinging back shut and no one noticing. (And on each side of the great door is a green pillar!) Inside, that man will be made naked and humilated—but actually gladdened—he's shaking his head sadly at the paper—he's moving his foot up and down nervously as he reads—he's jutting up his lower lip, deep in reading—but the way he holds the paper vertically folded and now bending it over like a little woman to follow the print you can see his mind's really goofing—and he's waiting for something else. The big green door holds itself up like a lamb to sacrifice to the sun at sea dawn over him, and it has wings.

An immense plateglass window in this white cafeteria on a cold November evening in New York faces the street (Sixth Avenue) but with inside neon tubular lights reflected in the window and they in turn illuminating the Japanese garden walls which are therefore also reflected and hang in the street with the tubular neons (and with other things illuminated and reflected such as that enormous 20-foot green door with its red and white exit sign reflected near the drapes to the left, a mirror pillar from deep inside, vaguely the white plumbing and at the top of things upper right hand and the signs that are low in the window looking out, that say Vegetarian Plate 60¢, Fish Cakes with Spaghetti, Bread and Butter (no price) and are also reflected and hanging but only low on the sidewalk because also they're practically

against it)—so that a great scene of New York at night with cars and
cabs and people rushing by and Amusement Center, Book store, Leo's
Clothing, Printing, and Ward's Hamburger and all of it November clear
and dark is riddled by these diaphanous hanging neons, Japanese walls,
door, exit signs—

But now let's examine it closer. Riddled and penetrated and
obscured and rippled and haunted and of course like kaleidoscope
over kaleidoscope but above the glittering street are the darkened or
brownlit windows of Sixth Avenue semi-flophouses and beat doll shops
and blackdust plumbing shops and Waldorf Cafeteria Employment
Office closed, red neons through windows at other end—Furthest up
in dark is the focus of this entire human scene: this is a fourth floor
unwashed window with the shade not drawn more than a foot but
ever so thin brown filthy lace or muslin curtain (and now the light
went off!) failing to hide the shadow of an iron bed. Now that it's
gone off the mirror pillar is suddenly revealed all the way to its entire
length because my attention had been on the actual window and the
reflected pillar was just barely touching the edge of the window and
I didnt know it. Most amazing of all now this reflected mirror pillar
hanging in the street is at the same time reflecting the tubular neon,
the real one inside, not the imaged one outside, and also reflects parts
of the wall I didnt mention that are not Japanese but checked red and
green. There are no more lights in those windows up there, I'll tell
you what happened: some old man finished his last quart of beer and
went to sleep—either that or he was hungry, wanted to sleep it off
instead of spending 55 cents for fishcakes at Automat—or an old
whore fell weeping on her bed of darkness—or they saw me noticing
the window four stories and across the street down the mad city night—
or now that the light is off they can see me better across these con-
fusions of reflected light (I know now that paranoia is the vision of
what's happening and psychosis is the hallucinated vision of what's
happening, that paranoia is reality, that paranoia is the content of
things, that paranoia's never satisfied). Other signs, the window ones,
are reflected this way:

DELICIOUS
HOT CHOCOLATE

and across this goofiness cars flash by and the asses of pedestrians hurrying in the cold flash by, when it's yellow cabs the flash is
brilliant yellow streak, when people the flash is memoried and human
(a hand, bag, a burden, a coat, a package of canvases, a dull, above
it the floating white faces)—When it's a car the flash is dark and
shiny and staring into it for all signs of flashes sometimes you only
see soft clicking oncoming and outgoing of glow from neon lights
intertwined in the street—and the white line in the middle of Sixth
Avenue, and just the barest indication of a piece of litter in the gutter
across the street unless just the gutter's reminder, without looking but
just absorbing as you stare the people pass and you know what they
are (two Texans! I knew it! and two Negroes! I knew it!) a beat
gray coupe flashed through looking like something from Massachussetts
(eager Canadians come to bang in New York hotels)—now the backward "Hot Chocolate Delicious" letters are shifting their depths as
my eyes rounden—they dance—through them I know the city, and the
universe—Now and finally right next to this part of the plateglass
window that I've been staring at for half an hour, peeking through an
area of six inches between the drapes and the window is a sidewall
mirror which is reflecting everything that's happening to the right of
me up the street, in fact to places I cant even see, so that while staring
into my "flasher" I suddenly saw a cab coming out of the corner of
my eye and it just never arrived, just disappeared—it was coming from
the right in actuality, in reflection from the left, and I had been watching the flash of actual rightward going cars and cabs—In that six-inch
area also are the people, observing the same laws of movement and
reflection but from not so great a distance because they are closer
to the plateglass, specifically closer to the miraculous mirror, and aren't
outflung in the road appearing from far off. While observing this
"flasher" a car came and parked in it, that is, a very shiny new fender
is seen (obscuring, for instance, the white line in the middle of road)
and in that fender that's round those crazy little images of things and
light seen on round shinies (like when your nose hugens as you look
closer) those little images but too small for me to observe in detail
from a distance are playing—they're playing only because a red neon
is flashing and every time it's on I see more of them than otherwise—
and actually the main neon crazy image is playing on the silver rim

of a headlamp of an Oldsmobile 88 (as I look and see now) as it flashes on and off red, and I hear above the clatter and sleepiness of cafeteria dishes (and swish of revolving door with flapping rubbers) and voices moaning, I hear above this the faint klaxons and moving rushes of the city and I have my great immortal metropolitan-in-the-city feeling that I first dug (and all of us) as an infant . . . smack in the heart of shiny glitters.

(IT STARTS TO RAIN)

PEOPLE GOING BY—The poor lonely old ladies of Lowell who come out of the 5-and-10 with their umbrellas open for the rain but look so scared and in genuine distress not the distress of secretly smiling maids in the rain who have good legs to hop around, the old ladies have piano legs and have to waddle to their where-to . . . and talking about their daughters anyway in the middle of their distress.

The big cow-lick Irishman with camel's hair belted coat who lumbers along his lips loosened in some sullen thought and as tho it wasnt raining in his huge dry soul—

The fat old lady incredible-burdened not only with umbrella and rain cape but underneath bulging pregnantly with hidden protected packages that stick so far out she has trouble avoiding bumping people on sidewalk and when she gets in the bus it will create a major problem for the poor people who are now, in their own parts of the city headed for the bus, unsuspecting of this—

The sharp little rich Jewish lady in a fur coat who lofts an umbrella that catches the eye it's so expensive and designed (red on brown) so beautifully, cutting along with that surefooted bandy legged gazotsky waddle that distinguishes her from other ladies, the great high civilization peasant woman of swank apartments with a hairy husband Aaron who deals in high finance with the gravity and hirsute slowness of an ape, she's headed home with a package and the rain like other things does not distress her—

The Irish gentleman all bundled tightly in a dark green-slick raincoat, collar up, tight at his ravelled chin, hat, no umbrella, a little anxious as he proceeds somewhat slowly to his objective and lost in thought of his job or wife or by God anything including feelings of homosexual deterioration or that Communists are secretly controlling his life at this very moment by thought-waves from a machine projecting from a submarine five miles offshore, maybe a teletype operator at U.P., thinking this as he goes down Sixth Avenue the name of which was changed to Avenue of the Americas some years ago to his complete disgust, going along surrounded by this entire night of dark rain in this moment of time that he occupies with a white scared sidelook at something on the bottom of the sidewalk (which isnt me)—

The young darkhaired plump pimply guy of thirty in a blue cloth jacket, from Brooklyn, who spends Sunday afternoons reading funnies (Mutt'n Jeff) and listening to ballgames on the radio, cutting along from his job as shipping clerk in an office near the New Yorker on 45th Street and thinking, suddenly, that he forgot the new key to the garage he had made this noon, forgot it on the dispatcher's desk in that empty blue light but it's raining so goes on home and he too surrounded by rainy night and the Hudson and East Rivers but can only be interpreted in terms of his garage keys (at this moment)—

—Roy Cohn, Ingrid Bergman, it seems they now went by separately—

—The strange old crazy lady from out of town who waddles like going over firewood in the yard of the farm she comes from, or did, before she moved to the upstairs flat in a wooden tenement block in New Brunswick, with her companion looking for a place to eat, her feet in those half heeled old lady black shoes very tired and so tired she lags behind her companion (similar but not so eccentric or unspeakably individual and tragic old lady) and sees this cafeteria, yells "Here's a place to eat," companion answers: "It's only a cafeteria and the food is awful in those places, George told me to stick to little restaurants"—"But there arent any!" (and quite naturally, they're on Sixth Avenue and the restaurants are all on sidestreets mostly, the ones with white tablecloths etc. although they will hit such restaurants if they keep distressing in the rain on up six more blocks to near Radio City)—So they decide, or that is Companion decides my Cafeteria is nowhere and my old eccentric lady with her curly gray hair and great low hanging appurtenances that touch the sidewalk such as umbrella, packages held low-dangling and almost underhanging from a lump blue-veined marble white old lady dear crazy finger and the low

hem of her enormous oldlady greatcoat that looks like it was made
to be a thick shroud to hide the atombomb in in the middle of an air-
field at dawn so nobody could tell what it looked like—this poor crazy
old lady is like my aunts, from Winchendon, Maine, etc., from woods
who come gawking out of the forest of the night to see great glittering
New York and are so themselves the raw creatures of time and earth
that in New York they are completely lost, dont lose their woods look,
suffer on smooth sidewalks of concrete the same pain and awkwardness
and womanly Gea like distress and ecstatic agony that they suffer in
pinecone rows beneath the cobwebby moons of New Hampshire or even
(name it) Minnesota—and so are *really* doomed as in this case never
not only to find a restaurant that will glowingly symbolize New York
for them so they can go home and tell the glorious story in detail by
the pantry window, the little one that looks out on the woodpile and
one Arctic star—they wont even find *any* restaurant and'll wind up
in a big beat Greek lunchcart six feet by ten because their feet will
have given out and they'll capitulate to something in New York they
wouldnt even think of accepting in Winchendon or Fergus Falls and
never will they tell this shameful story without a true sense of forest
sistership anyway in a non-existent goddamn New York.

As far as young women are concerned I cant look at them unless
I tear off their clothes one by one including this last girl (with her
Ma) wearing a green bandana and cute little face and long newlook
coat, and low heels, walks throwing her thighs loosely as tho floppy
and not as much control as her youth would indicate, and the big coat
hides her figure lines but I figure her lovelips is sweet, you get to
it via white lace panties, and she be fine. This is almost all I can
say about almost all girls and only further refinement is their lovelips
and will do.

ROAMING THOSE SUBWAYS I see a Negro cat wearing an ordinary
gray felt hat but a deep blue, or purplish shirt with white, shiny
pearl-type buttons—a gray sharkskin suit jacket over it—but brown
pants, black shoes, deep blue ordinary one-stripe socks and gabardine
topper short and beat, with edgebottoms rain-ravelled—carrying brown
paper bag—his face (he's sleeping) is big powerful fighter's sullen
thicklipped (*thick Afric lip*) but strangely pudgy sweet face—dark

brownskin—his big hands hang, his fingernails are pink (not white) and are soiled from a laboring job—Looks like Joe Louis only a Joe Louis who has known nothing but the freezing cold Harlem winter mornings when old blackbums infinitely beater than old Cody Pomeray of wino Denver go by with wool caps pulled over their ears with no prospects for the future whatever except horrible violent persecution in below zero filthy snows—His look is wild, frightened, almost tearful as he wakes from a nap and looks across aisle at redfaced white man in glasses and gray clothes with a big red ruby on his finger, as if that man wanted to kill him especially . . . (in fact man has eyes closed and chews gum). Now cat has seen me and looks at me with a kind of dawning simple interest but falls right back to sleep (people have watched him before).

This cat is coming from a job in Queens where undoubtedly there is a wire fence and he carries some kind of mop and goes about bareheaded. Now his big Harlem hat is on again (did I say ordinary? it has that wild level-swooping Harlem sharpness worked in, an *Eastern* Hat, thousands of cats in the street). He makes me think too of that strange Negro gurgle or burble in the voice that goes with the strangely humble almost clownish position of the American Negro and which he himself needs and wants because of a primarily meek sweet Myshkin like saintliness mixed with the primitive anger in his blood. When he leaves he walk-waddles out, from side to side, clicking, lazy, half asleep, "What you doin? what you doin?" it, and he, seemed to say to me—Damn, now he gone, he gone, I love him.

But now let's examine these American fools who want to be big burpers and ride in the subway with starched white collars (Oh G.J., your abyss?) and "business" clothes and yet by God they laugh and strain eagerly to their friends just like happy Codys, Emils, Jimmys of time—this one's a small businessman, actually a good guy I can tell by his pleading laugh—the kind that chokes and says "O yes say it again, I loved you that time!" And woe! woe! upon me, now I see he's a cripple—left foot—and his face is the face now of a serious frowning eager invalid maybe like the face of that rollerboard monster on Larimer Street who must have turned it huge and eager from his bottoms when he saw him, young Cody, come ball-bouncing down the street from school in a slant of tragic lost afternoons long departed from *the memory of love*, which is the secret of America—lost too, this subway invalid, in the folds of his own thick bustling manlike neck muscles—carrying a paper file envelope—chatting with tall younger fellow in glasses whom he admires and to whom he leans of course with that love of older man for younger man and especially of sick man for healthy dumbman everywhere.

NOW, STILL WANDERING, a lovely bakery window: a cherry pie with little round hole in the middle to show glazed cherries—same with all crust pies, including mince, apple—fruit cakes with cherries, nuts, glazed pineapple sitting in erect paper cups—wonderful custard pies with their golden moons—powdered lemon-filling layer cakes— little extraspecial cookies two toned—also two toned chocolate icings on round beautiful chocolate cakes with sprinklings of brown crumbs around bottom edges and lovely ravelled arrangements in icing itself— done with bakers' trowels—Those fat scrumptious apple-pineapple cakes that look like bigger editions of Automat-cakes, lumpy icing with a glaze—Everybody's watching as I stand there scribbling it all down— Wild raggedy coconut cakes with a cherry in the middle . . . like wild white hair.

The traceries of a tree against the gray rainy dusk—

It gave me a shudder of joy to see a cake with pink icing on top all raveled, with a red cherry in the middle, the sides around all covered with chocolate chip!

But across the street a bleak rectory. On the lawn in front are two twenty-foot spruce trees—the building is that peculiarly pale *orange* brick, color of puke, cat's puke—done up English style, or Saxon, with fort ramparts over the door, the oaken door but pale brown oaken not dark with three little glazed windows on top for decor and one in middle for the purpose of looking to see who's coming in—on each side of gray concrete *frame* to all this with the carved oldprint word *Rectory* are jolly Charles Dickens English lamps—then two little narrow slit windows about a foot wide, four foot down— at base of this bunched entrance is cellar window behind concrete protective curb of some kind (nameless, crazy, like the Christmas tree shrubberies in front of suburban law offices and the little wire fences around shrubs)—shape:—

all crazy, useless, supported by 1-foot tall fenceposts made of iron but look as if taped, with a noose on top

(with a curb to separate this, elevate, or emphasize its elevation from sidewalk and something never used or understood by anybody except those incurable *sitters* like me and Cody)—

Above castle ramparts and Gothic windows of rectory front is a brick gable with a regular American window that has venetian blinds, above that a grey concrete cross that looks like the stanchions you see around War Memorials in parks in the South and like crosses on cemetery main offices. Warm rich orange lights burn in rectory at dusk. This is certainly nothing like Proust's Combray Cathedral, where the stone moved in eccentric waves, the cathedral itself a great refractor of light from "outside"—

AH YES, ST. PATRICK'S CATHEDRAL—the altar of St. Joseph at my right a symphony in brown—His brown vestments with the traditional waist cord, the flickering brown candle racks—the brown confessional in back in its swarming nameless church shadows where old men whisper laryngitishly in your ear, with a rich wine, port wine red velvet drape and somewhere a priest is eating grapes—A curious young woman in a muskrat fur coat is hanging around there lighting candles—What's her truck with St. Joseph?—He who now with demure plaster countenance, holding the insubstantial child with feet and face too small and body too doll like, presses cheek against the painted curls, supports in mid air lightly against his brown breast the Son, with unstraining but rather greeting hand, downward looking into candles, agony, the foot of the world, all the angels and calendars and spirey altars behind him, eyes lowered to a mystery he himself wasnt hipped to yet he'll go along in the belief that poor St. Joseph was clay to the hand of God (statue), a humble self-admitting truthful Saint—with none of the vain freneticisms of Francis, a Saint without glory, guilt, accomplishment or charm—a self effacing grave and demure ghost in the Arcades of Christendom—He who knew the desert stars, and spat with the Wise Men in back of the barn—arranger of the manager, old hobo saint of haylofts and camel trails—Old lady in black coat and gray hair (Ma Tante Justine) socks the necessary action, the coin, into the candlelight concession and Joseph acknowledges with that ungraspable imperceptible sigh of statues—

RAIN'S OVER, HOME IN JAMAICA, LONG ISLAND, night—happens to be a fog—distant low of a klaxon moaning horn—sudden swash of locomotive steam, either that or crash of steel rods—a car washing by with the sound we all know from city dawns—reminds me of Cambridge Mass. at dawn and I didnt go to Harvard—Far away a nameless purling or yowling of some kind done either by (raised, vibroned) a train on a steel curve or skidding car—grumble of a truck coming—small truck, but has whistle tires in the mist—a double "bop bop" or "beep beep" from railyards, maybe soft application of big Diesel whistle by engineer to acknowledge hiball-on-the-air from brakeman or car-knocker—the sound of the whole thing in general when there are no specific near-sounds is of course sea-like but also almost like the sound of the living structure, so as you look at a house you imagine it is adding its breathing to the general loud hush—(ever so far, in the hush, you can hear a tiny SQUEE of something, the nameless asthmas of the throat of Time)—now a man, probably a truckdriver, is yelling far away and sounds like an adventurous young fellow playing in the darkness—the harmonies of air brakes stopping on two intervals, first application, the sound of it melting and echoing the second application and harmonizing—A cluster of yellow November leaves in an otherwise bare and sheepish castrated tree send up a little meek PLICK as they rub together preparing to die. When I see a leaf fall, I always say goodbye—And that has a sound which is lost unless there is country stillness at which time I'm sure it really rattles the earth, like ants in orchestras—Moan, the terrible sound now of the Public Address System in the Milk Factory, the voice like it's coming out of a stovepipe full of screens and amplified—a voice like night—a big steelrim cricket—(it's stopped)—I heard it once so loud "Please turn off the water," a woman, a rainy night, I was shocked—A car door slamming, the click, the velvet modern hinge-click before the soft slam—

The soft cushioned new-car slam, flump—

Some man in hat and coat up to something pompous, secret, sheepish—

The area breathes; it seems to want to tell something intelligible to me—

WILLIAM BURROUGHS

VAUDEVILLE VOICES

Totally Green Troops in the Area

Totally green troops in the area, K9—You are assigned to organize combat divisions at the Venusian Front—Appalling conditions—Total weapons—Without innoculation and training your troops will be paralyzed by enemy virus and drugs—Then cut to pieces in the pain-pleasure signal switch—The enemy uses a vast mechanical brain to dictate the use and rotation of weapons—Precise information from virus invasion marks areas of weakness in the host and automatically brings into effect the weapons and methods of attack calculated always of course with alternate moves—They can turn on total pain of The Ovens—This is done by film and brain wave recordings mangled down to a form of concrete music—A twanging sound very much like positive feed back correlated with The Blazing Photo from Hiroshima and Nagasaki—They can switch on electric pleasure leading to death in orgasm—(The noose is a weapon—The weapon of Kali)—They can alternate pain and pleasure at supersonic speed like a speed up tough and con cop routine—

You are to infiltrate, sabotage and cut communications—Once machine lines are cut the enemy is helpless—They depend on elaborate installations difficult to move or conceal—:: Encephalographic and calculating machines, film and TV studios, batteries of tape recorders—Remember you do not have to organize similar installations but merely to put enemy installations out of action or take them over—A camera and two tape recorders can cut the lines laid down by a fully equipped film studio—The ovens and the orgasm death tune in can be blocked with large doses of apomorphine which breaks the circuit of positive feed back—But do not rely too heavily on this protection agent—They are moving to block apomorphine by correlation with nausea gas that is by increasing the nausea potential—And always remember that you are operating under conditions of guerilla war—Never attempt to hold a position under massive counter attack—"Enemy advance we retreat" —Where?—The operation of retreat on this level involves shifting three dimensional coordinate points that is time travel on association lines—Like this: :

East Clinic Information

Clinic outside East St Louis on stilts over the wide brown river took in a steady stream of distant events—That week they could stay on the nod—Time there after a rumble in Dallas—Music runs back to the '20s—Ten year old keeping watch—Cracked pavements—Sharp scent of weeds that grow in suburbs—Pool hall and vaudeville voices—

So we turn over steady stream of distant events and we flush out traces of a time that meanwhile i had forgotten—Wet air thick and dirty on the garage—Sharp scent of memory pictures coming in— Looked for him he was gone—I met everybody in deserted cemetery with wooden crosses—There was a mulatto about—

"True?—I can't feel it—Yes you have his face—Healed and half healed skin—Put it on—Without you i on pavement"

"Perhaps if you had helped me—Good bye then—That silver film took it away from me—Well fade out—"

Trails my Summer dawn wind in other flesh strung together on scar impressions of young Panama night—Pictures exploded in the kerosene lamp spattered light on naked rectum open shirt flapping in the pissoir—Water from his face—The street blew rain from spurts of his crotch—Young faces melted to musical clock hands and brown ankles—Dead nitrous streets—Fish smell in doorways—

Look at the wired electric maze of the city—Stop—No good—Wait a bit—The long mat—It was an errand boy from the death trauma— No body walks out on one—In heart or brain spread out they fight on blocking his time—The boy who entered the '20s had his own

train—Room in the half light source of second wind spread the difference between life and death—Boneless mummy was death in the
last round—

So we turn over what he did not know: : Window people and
sky pictures fade out at dawn—Hurry up—Hands crowd—In the tremendous flash your brain splintered on empty flesh—Bleeding boneless panting death in the last round—The gate from darkened eyes of
wine still loaded with physical skin—Put it on? ? : : *End Of The
Line*—

"Remember I was fish smell and dead eyes in doorway—Errand
boy from last stroke of nine—Room in the half light beside you—
Great wind voices of Alamout its you?—My duty has been remitted
muttering: 'Not think any more of your harsh thoughts'—But who am
i to say more?—Empty is the third in vacant lot—Duty remitted—
Sound of fear and i dance—Crumpled cloth bodies empty—Ash from
falling tracks—Open shirt flapping wind from the South—The throat
designed to water—I stay near the basin and shadow pools—Invisible
man on webs of silver cut tracks—Vapor trails writing the sky of
Alamout and back i shall go—Indications enough in the harbor—
Muttering of dry rivers—Fish smell and dead eyes in doorways—The
sirocco dances to sound of the crowds—Harsh at this time of day—
Vultures in the street—"

"Know the answer?—Around in vacant lot 1910—Weeds growing
through broken towers—His face screen went dead—Smell of healed
and half healed scars—Silver film at the exits—Wont be much left—
Little time so I'll say: 'Good night'—Not looking around—talking
away—Now the Spanish flu would not be again steady stream of
distant events in green neon—You touched from frayed jacket—impro-
vised shacks—mufflers—small pistols—quick fires from bits of drift
wood—Shadow voices muttering in the dog rotation—Acoustic qualities couldn't reach flesh—Between suns desolate underbrush—Sharp
scent of weeds that grow in old Westerns—Battered phonograph talking distant events—Important thing is always courage to pass without
stopping—"

"Naked boy on association line—I stay near right now—Be shifted
harsh at this time of day—The levanto dances between mutual erections fading in hand—trails my Summer afternoons—Slow fingers in
dawn sleep tore the flesh from words—Fish smell and dead train

whistles—Open shirt flapping—Wind of morning in the harbor—My
number is K9—I am a Biologic from frayed jacket sitting out in lawn
chairs with the St. Louis suburb—Not looking around—Talking
away—Arab drum music in the suburban air—Fading khaki pants as
we shifted this pubescent banner on the pissoirs the river and the
Summer dawn—Semen in other flesh open shirt flapping spurts from
beyond the tomb showed a brass bed—Many names murmur of human
nights—I am dying cross wine gas far now—I am really dying—
Remember hints as we shifted commissions, stranger like death in your
throat?—Breathless flute through Al's body from beyond the tomb—
Slowly fading against the silk of seas my name—"

Soccer scores—The driver shrugged—His sound i could describe
to the open street car passing whiffs of Spain—Long empty face—His
eyes the evening breeze where the awning flapped—Violence roared
past the Cafe de France cleaving a heavy summons—Mr Bradly, hurry
up—Wind Ariel closed your account—Hurry up please its street—
Harbor lights gently moving water smiles dimmer at the edges—Arab
memory of flesh far now—Such people made a wide U turn back to
the '20s—Expectancy growing in vaudeville voices—

"Totally green troops in the area—We come to shape the five new
combat divisions through clear process in The United States—Slow
your brain area trade—Impressions of Present Time played electrical
music—Faded guards blew red nitrous fumes over you—Khaki pants
fully understood all of idiot Mambo spattered to control mechaniza-
tion—Hot sex words crackling paper and punching holes in it—"

Rectums naked in whiffs of raw meat—Jissom fell languidly bare
feet afternoons—A Mexican about twenty shifting Johnny's knees—He
was in the room on genital smells finger shared meals and belches—
Feeling like scenic railways in sleep—Suitcases all open—On association line electric spasms—Burning outskirts of the city—Dark street
life of a place forgotten—

"Invisible passenger took my hands in dawn sleep of water music—
Broken towers intersect cigarette smoke memory of each other—Healed
hands like ice—Wont be much—Screen went dead—He dressed hastily
shirt flapping—stared out from darkened eyes of wine gas—"

"Good bye then—I thought—" He walked through dawn mirror
of Panama—Memory hit spine outside 1920 movie theatre—Sat down
open shirts flapping—Many did not listen—Silver film at the exits—

Weilest du?—Dead nitrous flesh—Dirty look through glass—Who is that naked corpse?—

"Know the answer?—Flash from The Great Feed Back—Shivering naked under red fuck lights—Bird calls and frogs from the vacant lot—Music runs back to the afternoons—Laughing suburb boys—"Rub spit on it"—Words cut across his neck like the head was sewed on—Rectums strung on nitrous holes—It should work—Involving this aphrodisiac ointment in Spanish fly and pants slide exploded photo turnstile through flesh—Who is the third who try once more?"

"Reduced to two—Face it—Yes, you have his face—Purpose suffocating—Goodbye then—Well, fade out—The face from exploding star—It can happen here the twanging tones as well—I am mapping a complete list of names before choosing their perspective beyond exploding star—Survival list many parents scan at leisure in new worlds to get use of perspective children's names—Recorders fix nature of absolute calendar—Faded photo cruelties answer him—Click this ostepathic planet trailing "Daddy Longlegs" con su medicina—The old time junky look orient myself negative wires clicking through electric maze of The American Cemetery—Hours late they all in front of The Old Howard—Strata half healed over the grey veil—Out of Present Time past the crab guards at dirty pictures?—Pleasure maze out across his neck sewed up with black laughter—Voice fading like his head was sewed on—"

"Clearly the whole defense must look for recorder mutations"

"Again at the window of cigarette holes—We were there on some boy—Our carbon dioxide ran out—Ticket exploded in the air—Human dreams suffocating under explosive fragrance—(Cough noises)—I have delayed return in Weimar youth—Clicking through electric maze hit a long run of photo turnstiles—Distant 1920 music—Outskirts of the code i have endeavored to decode through ruined texts—The resulting message ("Legal Joint") reduced to two words showed strata of healed and half healed scars like any explorer out of present time past the crab guards—Like his head was sewed on the real writer and said: : 'I'm going to look for— Will try to get over to Paris—Purpose soffocating' "—(Cough noises)

"He's dead— Take him away—Did you say something?—She rattled the plates in a big building—Come along ladies and gentlemen—Screaming on the deal in many lips?—She didnt get it—Cut the image

like back in the restaurant—Wait a bit—No good—Half healed electric
needs—Dead scars—Leave him to me—Wont be much left—For a
room in the shoe shine boy Swedish river of Gothenberg?—Release
without more ado what?—When i left you hear little tune cut the
image—"

"I am surrounded through cafes and restaurants—Rabble rousers
fade in in coffee cup reflections—Blood?—There is no Jewish blood
flash scarlet invitations to young anti-Semites—Tourist as all the Jewish
people i see myself impoverished tired hustler—Anti-Semite is buried
forever in my deferential nods—Today i am as old in years as flapping
human genitals in Mexico—I am surrounded—Bodies and water everywhere—Blood runs in the pale door—My early rabble rousers give
off a stench of rotten lips departed—Nothing here—I know you are
wind voices"

BERSERK MACHINE

My trouble began when they decided I am 'executive timber'—It happens like this: : A big blond driller from Dallas picks me out of the labor pool to be his house boy inna prefabricated bungalow—He comes on rugged but as soon as we strip down to the ball park over on his stomach kicking white wash and screams out: "Fuck the shit out of me—!"

So I give him a slow pimp screwing and in solid and when this friend come down from New York the driller says: "This is the boy I was telling you about—"

Friend looks me over chewing his cigar and says: "What are you doing over there with the apes?—Why don't you come over here with The Board where you belong?"—And he slips me a long slimy look—

Friend works for The Life Time Change—"We don't report the news—We *write* it." And next thing I know they have trapped a grey flannel suit on me and I am sent to this school in Washington to learn how this writing the news before it happens is done— I sus it is The Mayan Caper with an IBM machine and I dont want to be caught short in a grey flannel suit when the lid blows off—So I act in concert with The Subliminal Kid who is a technical sergeant and has a special way of talking—

"What are you doing over there?—Beat your mother to over here—Know what they mean if they start job for instance?—Apparent sensory impressions calling slimy terms of the old fifty fifty jazz—Assembly points in Danny Deever—By now they are controlling shit house of the world—After that Minraud sky— Their eggs all over—These officer come gibbering into the queer bar don't even know what buttons to push—('Run with the apes?—Why don't you come across the lawn?')—And he gives me a long slimy reponsible cum grey flannel suit and I am Danney Deever in drag writing 'the news is served, sir.'—Hooded dead gibber this is The Mayan Caper—A fat cigar and a long white nightie— Non payment answer is simple as Board Room Reports rigged a thousand years—Set up excuse and the machine will process it— Moldy pawn ticket runs a thousand years chewing the same argument— I Sekuin perfected that art along The Tang Dynasty—To put it another way IBM machine control thought feeling and *apparent* sensory impressions—Subliminal lark—These officer don't even know what buttons to push—Whatever you feed into the machine on subliminal level the machine will process— So we feed in 'dismantle thyself' and authority emaciated down to answer Mr Of The Account in Ewyork Onolulu Aris Ome Oston—Might be just what I am look—"

We fold writers of all time in together and record radio programs, movie sound track, TV and juke box songs—All the words of the world stirring around in a cement mixer and pour in the resistance message "Calling partisans of all nation— Cut word lines— Shift linguals— Free doorways—Vibrate 'tourists'— Word falling— Photo falling— Break through in grey room—"

So The District Supervisor calls me in and puts the old White Smalz down on me—

"Now kid what are you doing over there with the niggers and the apes? Why don't you straighten out and act like a white man? After all they're only human cattle— You know that yourself—Hate to see a bright young man fuck up and get off on the wrong track—Sure it happens to all of us one time or another—Why the man who went on to invent Shitola was sitting right where your sitting now twenty five years ago and I was saying the same things to him—Well he straightened out the way you're going to straighten out—You can't deny your blood kid— You're *white white white*— And you can't walk out on Life Time Change— There's just no place to go. ."

Most distasteful thing I ever stood still for—Enough to make a girl crack her calories— So I walk out and the lid blew off—

Gongs of violence and how—Show you something— Berserk machine—

"Shift cut tangle word lines— Word falling— Photo falling—"

"I said The Chief Of Police skinned alive in Bagdad not Washington D.C."

"Switzerland freezes all foreign assets"

"Foreign assets?"

"What? British Prime Minister assasinated in rightist coup?"

"Mindless idiot you have liquidated the commisar—"

"Terminal electric voice of C— All Ling door out of agitated— Word falling— Photo falling— Time falling— Image falling—"

Spectators scream through the track—The electronic brain shivers in blue pink and chlorophyl orgasms spittting out money printed on rolls of toilet paper, condums full of ice cream, Kotex hamburgers— Police files of the world spurt out in a blast of bone meal—Garden tools and barbecue sets whistle through the air, skewer the spectators— Crumpled cloth bodies through dead nitrous streets of an old film set—Grey luminous flakes falling softly on Ewyork Onolulu Aris Ome Oston—Pan God of Panic piping blue notes through empty streets as the berserk time machine twisted a tornado years and centuries—Wind through dusty offices and archives—Board Books scattered to rubbish heaps of the earth—Symbol books of the all powerful board that had controlled thought feeling and movement of a planet from birth to death with iron claws of pain and pleasure—the whole structure of reality went up in silent explosions—. paper moon and muslin trees and in the black silver sky great rents as the cover of the world rained down—Outside a 1920 movie theatre in East St Louis I met Johnny Yen— His face showed strata of healed and half healed fight scars— Standing there under the luminous film flakes he said: "I am going to look for a room in a good naborhood."

THE TICKET THAT EXPLODED

Silence to say good-bye

These our actors bid you a long last goodbye — Johnny Yen playing the flute in a shower of ruined suburbs —

"Man like healed and half-healed scars under the story — A street boy's good-bye" —

Ancient Rings Of Saturn in the morning sky — The Old Doctor raises his blue hands — Silence at this old doctor twice — Hello yes good-bye — Indications enough in empty room, Miranda — Sex Garden caught in doors of Panic — Izzy The Push, Limestone John, Hamburger Mary, Jacky Blue Note, Silence to the sick lies —"Marks? — What Marks?" — Identity fades in empty space — Last intervention, The Subliminal Kid — Helped me with fingers fading —

"Indications enough showed you your air — Like good-bye then, Willy The Rat — Remember i was movies played good night — Known end of the line outside 1920 movie theatre — Bring The Doctor on stage — Call the point — Last rotten terminal" —

His face showed strata of last good-byes: "Like healed and half-healed scars, KiKi" — Some clean shirt and walked "No good no bueno — Adios, Meester" — Poo Poo The Dummy talking away in empty room "Green Tony and Willy The Rat on the last saucer, boss" —

"Errand boys" —

"I'm not taking any vaudeville voices — Bring The Doctor on — I'm going to rat on everybody" —

"Few more calls to make tonight" —

"We do our work and go — The ticket that exploded posed definitive arrest" —

"Perhaps, Inspector Lee" —

"Few more calls to make tonight left fingers fading Mr. & Mrs. D — Exploded Sammy The Butcher — Indications enough just ahead, Inspector Lee, we do our last film — Alteration in the morning sky — Like a street boy exploded the word — Last round from St. Louis

melted flesh identity — Hands work and go — Our street boys picking
up show — No word — No flesh — The actors melted — Indications
enough it wasn't easy — Radio silence to answer your air — Remember i was the ship gives no memory pictures — Johnny Yen, in last
good-bye fading scars — Played the flute of Ali — Played the flute in
KiKi — Some clean shirt and man like good-bye — Ding-dong bell
no good no bueno — Stranded actors walk through Poo Poo The
Dummy — The Orchid Girl fades into memory picture on outhouse
skin forgotten — Green Tony the last invisible shadow — Call The
Old Doctor twice on last errand? — Caught in the door of Panic, Mr.
& Mrs. D Last round over — A street boy's morning sky — Flesh
tape ebbing from centuries — Remember i was movie played you a
long last good night" —

End of the line for vaudeville voices — Last round in a shower
of ruined September — Last film flakes — The globe is self just old
second-hand door — Indications enough just ahead — Boys on roller
skates before stranded — Our revels at Rings of Saturn — Last September on stage — Last parasite just went up, Mr. Martin — I fold
thy strong tape — Bitter price on our ticket? — 'Bye then — Broken
dream and dreamer of the sick lies — The brain of Gothenberg on
stage — Last intervention gives no flesh identity — For i last errand
boy — Adios in the final ape of history — Fading shelter in the dog's
death trauma — Intervention — Last round over — The pipes are
calling, Mr. Bradly Mr. Martin — The story done when you reach
September — So we'll say good night — Showed you your air — The
pipes your summons — All are wracked and answer — Adios to the
sick lies — Adios to thy strong tape — Caught in the door of Gothenberg — Courage to question erogenous second hand trade — Story
of absent world just as empty as ding dong bell — Silence to the
stage — These our actors erased themselves into air far from such
as you, Mr. Bradly Mr. Martin — September faded leaves not a wrack
behind — I foretold you all spirits are going—

Johnny Yen: (His face shows strata of healed and half-healed fight
scars — Under gray luminous film flakes as the cover of the world
rains down) "I'm going to look for a room in a good neighborhood" —

Ali The Incandescent Street Boy: "You come Ali — You no go
body" —

KiKi: (Some clean shirt and walked out) "You can look any

place — No good — No bueno — Adios, Meester Bradly Meester Martin" —

Poo Poo The Dummy: (Flares of good bye over the irridescent lagoon) —

Miranda The Orchid Girl: (Trailing tendrils of stinging sex hairs, fades into bird calls and frogs from the vacant lot) "good-bye then" — Not looking around, talking away —

Green Tony: "On the last saucer, boss — A big bank roll" —

Willy The Fink: "I'm not taking any rap for those board bastards — I'm going to rat on everybody" —

Izzy The Push, Jacky Blue Note, Hamburger Mary, Limestone John: "Call The Old Doctor twice? He quiets you — Hello yes goodbye — A few more calls to make tonight" —

Mr. & Mrs. D: "The ticket that exploded posed little time so we'll say good night" —

Sammy The Butcher: (Definitive arrest) —

Inspector J. Lee: "We do our work and go — Proceed with the indicated alterations" —

The Fluoroscopic Kid: "Now picking up show — No word — No flesh — The lot" —

The Subliminal Kid: "It wasn't easy get to be radio be tape recorder on — Friends are — Showed you your air" —

Mr. Bradly Mr. Martin: "Man like good-bye — What in St. Louis after September? — Faded story of absent world just as silver film took it — Remember i was the movies — Rinse my name for i have known intervention — Pass without doing our ticket — Mountain wind of Saturn in the morning sky — From the death trauma weary goodbye then" —

Hassan i Sabbah: "Last round over — Remember i was the ship gives no flesh identity — Lips fading — Silence to say good-bye —"

Nov. 14, 1962
Paris
William Burroughs

LEROI JONES

THE SCREAMERS

Lynn Hope adjusts his turban under the swishing red green yellow shadow lights. Dots. Suede heaven raining, windows yawning cool summer air, and his musicians watch him grinning, quietly, or high with wine blotches on four dollar shirts. A yellow girl will not dance with me, nor will Teddy's people, in line to the left of the stage, readying their *Routines*. Haroldeen, the most beautiful, in her pitiful dead sweater. Make it yellow, wish it whole. Lights. Teddy, Sonny Boy, Kenney & Calvin, Scram, a few of Nat's boys jamming long washed handkerchiefs in breast pockets, pushing shirts into homemade cummerbunds, shuffling lightly for any audience.

"The Cross-Over", Deen laughing at us all. And they perform in solemn unison a social tract of love. (With no music till Lynn finishes 'macking' with any big-lipped Esther screws across the stage. White and green plaid jackets his men wear, and that twisted badge, black turban/on red string conked hair. (OPPRESSORS!) A greasy hipness, down-ness, nobody in our camp believed (having social worker mothers and postman fathers; or living squeezed in light skinned projects with adulterers and proud skinny ladies with soft voices). The theory, the spectrum, this sound baked inside their heads, and still rub sweaty against those lesser lights. Those niggers. Laudromat workers, beauticians, pregnant short haired jail bait separated all ways from 'us,' but in this vat we sweated gladly for each other. And rubbed. And Lynn could be a common hero, from whatever side we saw him. Knowing that energy, and its response. That drained silence we had to make with our hands, leaving actual love to Nat or Al or Scram.

290

He stomped his foot, and waved one hand. The other hung loosely
on his horn. And their turbans wove in among those shadows. Lynn's
tighter, neater, and bright gorgeous yellow stuck with a green stone.
Also, those green sparkling cubes dancing off his pinkies. A-boomp
bahba bahba, A-boomp bahba bahba, A-boomp bahba bahba, A-boomp
bahba bahba, the turbans sway behind him. And he grins before he
lifts the horn, at deen or drunk becky, and we search the dark for
girls.

Who would I get?
(Not anyone who would understand this.) Some light girl who had
fallen into bad times and ill-repute for dating Bubbles. And he fixed
her later with his child, now she walks Orange st. wiping chocolate
from its face. A disgraced white girl who learned to calypso in voca-
tional school. Hence, behind halting speech, a humanity as paltry as
her cotton dress. (And the big hats made a line behind her, stroking
their erections, hoping for photographs to take down south.) Lynn
would oblige. He would make the most perverted hopes sensual and
possible. Chanting at that dark crowd. Or some girl, a wino's daughter,
with carefully vaselined bow legs would drape her filthy angora against
the cardboard corinthian, eyeing past any greediness a white man
knows, my·soft tyrolean hat, pressed corduroy suit, and "B" sweater.
Whatever they meant, finally to her, valuable shadows barely visible.
Some stuck-up boy with "good" hair. And as a naked display of
America, for I meant to her that same oppression. A stunted head of
greased glass feathers, orange lips, brown pasted edge to the collar of
her dying blouse. The secret perfume of poverty and ignorant desire.
Arrogant too, at my disorder, which calls her smile mysterious. Turning to be eaten by the crowd. That mingled foliage of sweat and
shadows: *Night Train* was what they swayed to. And smelled each
other in The Grind, The Rub, The Slow Drag. From side to side,
slow or jerked staccato as their wedding dictated. Big hats bent tight
skirts, and some light girls' hair swept the resin on the floor. Respectable ladies put stiff arms on your waist to keep some light between,
looking nervously at an ugly friend forever at the music's edge.

I wanted girls like Erselle, whose father sang on television, but
my hair was not straight enough, and my father never learned how
to drink. Our house sat lonely and large on a half-italian street, filled
with important Negroes. (Though it is rumored they had a son, thin

with big eyes, they killed because he was crazy.) Surrounded by the
haughty daughters of depressed economic groups. They plotted in their
projects for mediocrity, and the neighborhood smelled of their despair.
And only the wild or the very poor thrived in Graham's or could
be roused by Lynn's histories and rhythms. America had choked the
rest, who could sit still for hours under popular songs, or be readied
for citizenship by slightly bohemian social workers. They rivaled pure
emotion with wind-up record players that pumped Jo Stafford into
Home Economics rooms. And these carefully scrubbed children of
my parents' friends fattened on their rhythms until they could join
the Urban League or Household Finance and hound the poor for their
honesty.

I was too quiet to become a murderer, and too used to extrava-
gance for their skinny lyrics. They mentioned neither cocaine nor Bach,
which was my reading, and the flaw of that society. I disappeared into
the slums, and fell in love with violence, and invented for myself a
mysterious economy of need. Hence, I shambled anonymously thru
Lloyd's, The Nitecap, The Hi-Spot, and Graham's desiring everything
I felt. In a new english overcoat and green hat, scouring that town
for my peers. And they were old pinch faced whores full of snuff and
weak dope, celebrity fags with radio programs, mute bass players who
loved me, and built the myth of my intelligence. You see, I left America
on the first fast boat.

This was Sunday night, and the Baptists were still praying in their
"faboulous" churches. Though my father sat listening to the radio, or
reading pulp cowboy magazines, which I take in part to be the truest
legacy of my spirit. God never had a chance. And I would be walking
slowly towards The Graham, not even knowing how to smoke. Willing
for any experience, any image, any further separation from where my
good grades were sure to lead. Frightened of post offices, lawyer's
offices, doctor's cars, the deaths of clean politicians. Or of the imaginary
fat man, advertising cemeteries to his "good colored friends". Lynn's
screams erased them all, and I thought myself intrepid white com-
mando from the West. Plunged into noise and flesh, and their form
become an ethic.

Now Lynn wheeled and hunched himself for another tune. Fast
dancers fanned themselves. Couples who practiced during the week
talked over their steps. Deen and her dancing clubs readied avant-

garde routines. Now it was *Harlem Nocturne,* which I whistled loudly
one saturday in a landromat, and the girl who stuffed in my khakis
and stiff underwear asked was I a musician. I met her at Graham's
that night and we waved, and I suppose she knew I loved her.

Nocturne was slow and heavy and the serious dancers loosened
their ties. The slowly twisting lights made specks of human shadows,
the darkness seemed to float around the hall. Any meat you clung to
was yours those few minutes without interruption. The length of the
music was the only form. And the idea was to press against each other
hard, to rub, to shove the hips tight, and gasp at whatever passion.
Professionals wore jocks against embarassment. Amateurs, like myself,
after the music stopped, put our hands quickly into our pockets, and
retreated into the shadows. It was as meaningful as anything else we
knew.

All extremes were popular with that crowd. The singers shouted,
the musicians stomped and howled. The dancers ground each other
past passion or moved so fast it blurred intelligence. We hated the
popular song, and any freedman could tell you if you asked that white
people danced jerkily, and were slower than our champions. One style,
which developed as italians showed up with pegs, and our own grace
moved towards bellbottom pants to further complicate the cipher, was
the honk. The repeated rhythmic figure, a screamed riff, pushed in
its insistence past music. It was hatred and frustration, secrecy and
despair. It spurted out of the dipthong culture, and re-inforced the
black cults of emotion. There was no compromise, no dreary sophistica-
tion, only the elegance of something that is too ugly to be described,
and is diluted only at the agent's peril. All the saxophonists of that
world were honkers, Illinois, Gator, Big Jay, Jug, the great sounds of
our day. Ethnic historians, actors, priests of the unconscious. That
stance spread like fire thru the cabarets and joints of the black cities,
so that the sound itself became a basis for thought, and the innovators
searched for uglier modes. Illinois would leap and twist his head,
scream when he wasn't playing. Gator would strut up and down the
stage, dancing for emphasis, shaking his long gassed hair in his face
and coolly mopping it back. Jug, the beautiful horn, would wave back
and forth so high we all envied him his connection, or he'd stomp
softly to the edge of the stage whispering those raucous threats. Jay
first turned the mark around, opened the way further for the completely

nihilistic act. McNeeley, the first Dada coon of the age, jumped and stomped and yowled and finally sensed the only other space that form allowed. He fell first on his knees, never releasing the horn, and walked that way across the stage. We hunched together drowning any sound, relying on Jay's contorted face for evidence that there was still music, though none of us needed it now. And then he fell backwards, flat on his back, with both feet stuck up high in the air, and he kicked and thrashed and the horn spat enraged sociologies.

That was the night Hip Charlie, the Baxter Terrace Romeo, got wasted right in front of the place. Snake and four friends mashed him up and left him for the ofays to identify. Also the night I had the grey bells and sat in the Chinese restaurant all night to show them off. Jay had set a social form for the poor, just as Bird and Dizzy proposed it for the middle class. On his back screaming was the Mona Lisa with the mustache, as crude and simple. Jo Stafford could not do it. Bird took the language, and we woke up one Saturday whispering Ornithology. Blank verse.

And Newark always had a bad reputation, I mean, everybody could pop their fingers. Was hip. Had walks. Knew all about The Apple. So I suppose when the word got to Lynn what Big Jay had done, he knew all the little down cats were waiting to see him in this town. He knew he had to cook. And he blasted all night, crawled and leaped, then stood at the side of the stand, and watched us while he fixed his sky, wiped his face. Watched us to see how far he'd gone, but he was tired and we weren't, which was not where it was. The girls rocked slowly against the silence of the horns, and big hats pushed each other or made plans for murder. We had not completely come. All sufficiently eaten by Jay's memory, "on his back, kicking his feet in the air, Ga-ud Dam!" So he moved cautiously to the edge of the stage, and the gritty muslims he played with gathered close. It was some mean honking blues, and he made no attempt to hide his intentions. He was breaking bad. "Okay, baby," we all thought, "Go for yourself". I was standing at the back of the hall with one arm behind my back, so the overcoat could hang over in that casual gesture of fashion. Lynn was moving, and the camel walkers were moving in the corners. The fast dancers and practicers making the whole hall dangerous. "Off my suedes, motherfucker." Lynn was trying to move us, and even I did the one step I knew, safe at the back of the hall. The

hippies ran for girls. Ugly girls danced with each other. Skippy, who
ran the lights, made them move faster in that circle on the ceiling,
and darkness raced around the hall. Then Lynn got his riff, that
rhythmic figure we knew he would repeat, the honked note that would
be his personal evaluation of the world. And he screamed it so the
veins in his face stood out like neon. "Uhh, yeh, Uhh, yeh, Uhh, yeh",
we all screamed to push him further. So he opened his eyes for a
second, and really made his move. He looked over his shoulder at the
other turbans, then marched in time with his riff, on his toes across
the stage. They followed; he marched across to the other side, repeated,
then finally he descended, still screaming, into the crowd, and as the
sidemen followed, we made a path for them around the hall. They
were strutting, and all their horns held very high, and they were only
playing that one scary note. They moved near the back of the hall,
chanting and swaying, and passed right in front of me. I had a little
cup full of wine a murderer friend of mine made me drink, so I
drank it and tossed the cup in the air, then fell in line behind the
last wild horn man, strutting like the rest of them. Bubbles and Rogie
followed me, and four eyed Moselle Boyd. And we strutted back and
forth pumping our arms, repeating with Lynn Hope, "Yeh, Uhh, Yeh,
Uhh". Then everybody fell in behind us, yelling still. There was confusion and stumbling, but there were no real fights. The thing they
wanted was right there and easily accessible. No one could stop you
from getting in that line. "It's too crowded. It's too many people on
the line!" some people yelled. So Lynn thought further, and made to
destroy the ghetto. We went out into the lobby and in perfect rhythm
down the marble steps. Some musicians laughed, but Lynn and some
others kept the note, till the others fell back in. Five or six hundred
hopped up woogies tumbled out into Belmont Avenue. Lynn marched
right in the center of the street. Sunday night traffic stopped, and
honked. Big Red yelled at a bus driver, "Hey, baby, honk that horn
in time or shut it off!" The bus driver cooled it. We screamed and
screamed at the clear image of ourselves as we should always be.
Ecstatic, completed, involved in a secret communal expression. It would
be the form of the sweetest revolution, to hucklebuck into the fallen
capitol, and let the oppressors lindy hop out. We marched all the way
to Spruce, weaving among the stalled cars, laughing at the dazed white
men who sat behind the wheels. Then Lynn turned and we strutted

back towards the hall. The late show at the National was turning out, and all the big hats there jumped right in our line.

Then the Nabs came, and with them, the fire engines. What was it a labor riot? Anarchists? A nigger strike? The paddy wagons and cruisers pulled in from both sides, and sticks and billies started flying, heavy streams of water splattering the marchers up and down the street. America's responsible immigrants were doing her light work again. The knives came out, the razors, all the Biggers who would not be bent, counterattacked or came up behind the civil servants smashing at them with coke bottles and aerials. Belmont writhed under the dead economy and splivs floated in the gutters, disappearing under cars. But for awhile, before the war had reached its peak, Lynn and his musicians, a few other fools, and I, still marched, screaming thru the maddened crowd. Onto the sidewalk, into the lobby, half-way up the stairs, then we all broke our different ways, to save whatever it was each of us thought we loved.

HYPOCRITE(S)

Is/fear.
>   At noise (beneath
the floor. Streets.
>   The very air.
You shout, or steal. The motion sure, the air, like sea pulled up. They'd
cry in church so easy, so wooden & smelled up. Lemon oil, just behind
the piano another room. A door, just behind the last pew. The trustees
filed in smiling. After they'd brought in the huge baskets of money.
They'd smile & be important. Their grandsons would watch from the
balcony (if you were middleclass baptists & had some women with
pince-nez.) Mrs. Peyton was one, but she stank & died skinny in a
slum. They'd smile tho. Mr. Blanks. Mr. Russ. A dark man with a
beautiful grey mustache. Also a weasely man (not the same one who'd
announce things. Deacon Jones. The same as the song. The one who
"threw the whiskey in the well".
>   Bernice was a big usherette. Graves.
They came in together & were beneath us. She smiled at me and wd
have fucked at 13. Her mother watched me. Her mother was sly.
Her mother was fat. Her mother liked that green statue of lincoln.
Her mother gave me cookies and sd "I married my first boyfriend".
I wanted to know where the fuck he was. With lincoln, or working
in the Adam's hat store. Easters they'd drag you in and make you
buy pegs.
>   And black Betty. Stuck up, because she had
"spanish" boyfriends. (The golden boys, i.e., Teddy, Sonnyboy,
Calvin, "and them") but the real reason I cdn't figure out. Her mother
was burned and her sister stayed in the service. Shadows on those
pavements. Boston Street, oil lamps, Orson Wells. A huge tailor.
>   They
were all friends. Rufus the bootblack, low man on the totem pole. He
had phone booths. Next to the florist. (The smart ones? I guess they
thot that. Collier was the name. She was pretty at first but turned pale
as wet wind. She disappeared one afternoon.

The old pimply faced
one went to some college and came back with bucks. His brother,
younger, in the same high school as me and Jimmy. But he got out
when it was plastic and Allen wore cardigans. He loved me because
he knew I'd sucked his cousin off. (They were in league with the
undertaker with the bar ear. Hayes. So, the hayeses, the colliers, Aubry,
a woman with a child in the insurance projects. They were all connected. By blood, I guess. By ideas. By Jackie Robinson.

There was
also a spookier branch . . . included a pretty girl you'd see on shade
calendars. The same ones they had in their florist shop. Roses and
mixed daisies. Cheap flowers. Middleclass flowers.

Also, a mystery man who lived near the flower box. The refrigerator. I
loitered there but he didn't respond. He knew about picnics and girls
with rubber soles and good hair. He didn't tell me. He was Warren
Slaten's style. Exposing me to softball in the suburbs and then showing
up corny like that years later (in a nigger show) wi th a japanese
pool cue and out of style clothes. A Square. And his mother worked
in Kline's. Still, if you could say "South Munn Ave.", instead of Dey
St. or Hillside Place or Belmont Ave., you had some note. You could
watch ofays play tennis. You could come late to scout meetings and
be made patrol leader of the flying eagles.
LeRoy was in it. Also Rudy. (Damn that he got in sideways, the baxter
terrace mob. They had it going different. Not softball, not with the
beautiful molded southern grass shiny money dear friend of sun walking smooth so far to talk quiet and knowing what it was to be something to live away and not know them. To not be me. To not know,
finally, what it is that ran me. To come to this. To what you see
here dying. To be that, and to be that, as I am, for you, for you all,
for all space. was slum (Rudy) that was the difference. That I knew
that . . . & we had erected by whatever guise . . . forget Morris . . .
how he did escape is worth knowing tho Barry got out, but that's
understandable. His temperament was like mine when I go abstract
and people talk nonsense to me.

BUT NOT EVER FOR ANY OF US AGAIN THE LOVELY WORLD
OF WARREN SLATEN OR THE REALLY BEAUTIFUL PETTI-
GREWS.

And Rudy's mother was ugly and looked up to my grandmother, so that made him lower. Place. Place each thing, each dot of life. Each person, will be PLACED. DISPOSED OF.

Rudy and LeRoy were a team. Also "Red". That must have dragged them. To live in Baxter Terrace yet be made to join the "fags" troop because they went to the same church.

So they tried to take over as far as athletics, &c. Only Rudy was any good tho . . . and still not much compared to Baxter or my friends. So we controlled that easy. And I outside, still, without touching any of them. A long walk home, & they used my name as if I was old and my wife had gone out "walking".

It took place in a sunday school. The declensions. The age. Tomson, his whole top head caved in like Martin's publisher. And his step son big mouth teddy (the bastard was shorter that I and weak as a bitch. Mark, his real son, was mongoloid). liked my sister. He and later his friend (the music teacher) Freddy. A "closet queen". They both hunted easter eggs in the church yard, and even planned to fuck fred's sister so I cdn't.

Get in close with me. If you're in mountains. Or weird smells pack your head. Cereals. Cold water. "Gloom", Harvey called me. "Hi, Gloom". (If I knew what that meant. Or what became of him. His socks and shoes. His relatives. It wd be easy enough to predict the future. The past. The fireplaces and whores of the cemeteries of your linoleum.) This is tether. Push towards (SOME END.

It is static. It is constant. It is water. It is her lips. It is Aristotle's coughs in the tent all night in the snow. Why the old man lived to freeze us. His "reserve". Sandy, his name was. The same as the young wavy head jew I jabbed silly at camp. Also good body punches in the 2nd round brought down his guard. When he went down my first instinct was to run. But his brother congratulated me and thot he could kick my ass because he got a letter for band.

We did a lot of things those years. Now, we do alot of things. We drink water from streams. We walk down hoping to fuck mulattos when they bathe. We tell lies to keep from getting belted, and watch a faggot take a beating in the snow from our lie.

Our fear.

Mut the zipper. Mutt the zipper. Packed lunches, on norfolk street, beans franks. The bus. Also a stone quarry. (That whole side I knew later, midnights, after work in a paint factory. You walk at night, fine. You show up. You sit. You alright. But you never be no doctor. (Hilary talking).

ORA- Why you sit in the dark & fight me when I tickle?

SKIPPY- Boy, I'll beat your ass in Miss Powell's class, cause Johnny-boy and I are friends and "Jones" did that dopey funny book about guys robbing everybody. I live in a cloak room. I live where you tried to get rid of those Ledgers.

KNOWLES- Baroom, Baroom, Baroom-Baroom-Baroom. Sho, I'll stop or climb. Or smile, or hit, or fuck (maybe, I guess, because the inkspots were popular and he had that correct trill). Miss Golden gave you a "D" in dependability and she hated something in you.

MURRAY- Nothing to it. Just be around and need a clean nose and hit people on the back of the head. Don't look for me now. It's too sociological and'd make you cry. You playground step. "Brains".

BECKY- (Ha,Ha, with colored teeth and tight ass girl friend. That was cross town. The masonic temple she gave me hunter and coke and it tasted like it does now.) Spread my legs on the 9 Clifton. Let you in for somethings. A new building to incest. Hymn to later masturbation. You could have had me, if you'd come down. Gone Down.

LOVE- Ah bullshit.

MORRIS- (Later) Boy, this cat is something. Is my dead sister. The car crashed her huge eyes. My father's big buick. You rich running. Pigeon toes, you got us in to the Troops. (And those buildings, even tho delores, and the two crazy ones, football players and midgets) were crumbling. Were red, at the corner where my grandmother made "pageboys". Miss Still, was the lady she worked for. The other street, where Willie lived, continued to the lot and the women's detention home you could forget if you only looked at the tile store or the abandoned ice house full of amonnia. Jr. Bell fell thru the floor. Jr. Bell died in the lake. Jr. Bell fucked Eunice before I did, or you. (In an alley behind the Zarros house, also crumbling grey behind Central . . . You pressed together.

OTIS- We athletes. We bowlegged. We got crooked peckers. We see'd you get stuck in the ass in a tent. We wanted some and forgot later because you ran so fast and could twist past the line for 12. I still know Whatley and he still thinks you're a punk.

GAIL- I'm fat, but Sammy likes it. Sammy and Wen Shi (&tomson). They dig. because their heads are sawed off. I like Diane(a). Not her friends or spooky dead father. She's old fashioned. You like her, LeRoi? Huh? Marcelline ain't (whisper) shit.

MARCELLINE- I don't even know what the hell you mean. I had boy-friends and one even vomited in my mouth. New Years, you never understood it. Did you jockstrop bluejacket "foots"?

SAMMY- I'm drafted and cool and wear an apron and we went to Coney last night.

JACKIE BLAND- You see me doing one thing (even tho you heard about me humping some chick in a condemned house) and you think you got something on me. Shit. I'm nigger stan kenton. I'm crazy. I got long arms and helped you whistle to juliet in the laundry (before they tore it down).

NAT P.- Intermission Riff. Is that what you know about Floyd Key and Allen Polite? You mean you never been to North Newark and met Scram and the cocksmen. Boy, we cool even tho we teach school now and disappeared in our powder blue coats. (Billy can play better than you heard. You know Wayne? He played with us. You mean you never made the Los Ruedos? Wow. I ran track too, Man, and waved my arms in sheer pinnacality.

JAN MANVILLE, MINNIE HAWKS, JUDSON, ALEX G.'S WIFE,- Sylvia was part of our scene and you know she was hip. What about Holmes? He's a doctor now, and you know you admired him. He could run and liked to talk about sports. Caesar taught you to hurdle. He had great form. He's a doctor now too. All of us are somewhere. We own trees.

THE BRANTLEY BROS.- I'm a writer. I go to games. I knew you when. I was impressed. I'm weird in Newark. I limp like a tackle. I knew everybody. You wished alot of times you could have talked with my sister. You know we don't understand what you mean by all this!

Yrs t.,
Caiaphas

THIEVES

(Was I to have made this far journey,
only to find the very thing which I had
fled?   -Gauguin, *Noa Noa*)

Space is cheap salves. A trombone in a penthouse. Madness over
the phone. Dispute, if the thief live. If he be climbing thru our
smashed windows his voice dragged in silk stockings on the radio;
Greasy Head? The metal can clunks in the head, the radio says "duh,
duh, duh-duh". Soft, tho. As pure impression—pure distinction.

The
Blind mice. Three of A Kind. To make ready. witches. B. for five. wives.
letters. strikes. bases. women. The Magi, are popular. Are broken glass.
vases, crisp, some soft faggot voice drowning the night.

It was a hall.
Jazz, is that vulgar. Hooks, in the air, like sun. Tuesday's blue metal
adolescence. Mutt the zipper, again, the fireplaces. Guns on Christmas.
Strange vanishing toys. The brown house. Registers (old new? a closet
behind the red chair.

* * * * *

The room was deformed. A heavy jowl, smell, softer hands than
streets. The moon is bitter. crushing the bannister.

A girl named Lor-
raine who used to go as our cousin—and then her tits came. She was
a tall "zaaroom" face. Zebra. Mattie McClean. Her blouse back was
loose. She had another name. Thin glasses, like some oyster ostrich
humping. A grey house, next to Lorraine's red johns manville. Her
mother and she looked the same except her mother was quieter, but
they had the same hair. Lorraine smiled nasty. And smelled up the
pool. Even lied about the nature of dances. And fumbled excitement
near the park. (Lies or ignorance) birds like tar smile.

This jumble of houses' collars. Shined shoes. Show biz. BILLY- 'O.K.
vibe player, Blow!" ARNIE- Years later, the drain glows. Rhythms.

Passports. We take our train to your astronomies. We evacuate sound.
THE PAINTER- You Rat! It could be run out. It could be yellow &
black. It could have garages. It could be disinterested in its cement
(or the years of cars that roll over my grandfather's grave.

PEGGY ANN- pigtails are for ugly girls. Snapshots, cotton dresses.
To buy is to listen. To be had/caught/applauded in the smoke of our
sound. In our Negro ulsters selling pot. In our language scared at the
shadows of our crimes. DONALD- You're listening to the Symphony
Sid Program.
          But that, I told you musicians, the rooms we spoke of,
that wind. Mere purity and light. This is sudden. Her red fingers. This
is slanting here. To me (houses tilt down into my memory. Cars.
Insides of mouths. I WANT YOU TO MEET MY FAMILY. (rooms,
aside, as this is. The door stands open. It did then and my fat
uncle strides in. He is 6ft 4″ and knew these things in the Spring
of my thoughts.
          Cardboard suitcases, essays. Walked in broke and
humble. On Cornelia St. "She looks like a little mouse." Larry or I
made that remark. The windows were dull. Cold slush in their mouths.
Nothing got thru those clubs. The street would flow black, and a moon.
     Trees wherever you are is irrelevent. TALLEY- Muscles, some biog-
raphies. Nobody knows nuthin. You got nuthin on me, but my upbring-
ing.

Which in effect, is where we come in. To prefer phonecalls, tassels on
their shades (even from the street in Gramercy). Bohemians around
too. Certainly she is beautiful, to be a lesbian, to be in stone, to be
so close to my house.
          Violence to my body. To my mind. Closed in.
To begin at the limit. Work in to the core. Centre. At which there is —
nothing. The surface of thought. Pure undulation at the mid-year,
turned yellow as deserts, suns.
          Cement room. stones, in place. Fell
there, perfect. For echoes, murders. Blood looked strange on the street.
     And there was that guy who wanted to fight my father about
the game. Spencer, his name was. Tall & agile & dark. Skinny
with long legs, low dangling hands on third base. I heard the

language when I ran down to coach. Right near the fence, I could
look across the street, and sometimes Danny would be out there,
and I call him to the game. Usually the Davises (secret gypsies
later making it as respectable shades). Algernon or Lonel (lionel),
or pooky or fat (Jerome). Frank was the oldest, went away to
Japan & got married. One girl, Evelyn, got fat and was transferred
near the golf courses.

The woman, "Miss Davis" was the cruelest
woman I know. Like Puerto Rican old women, the lower lip curls
like dogs. Hatred or pure sight. Beast Fucci, wait like rachitic Algy
for my baseball suit. Brown coarse gravel (if he thot my life was
chrome. The orange house (Rev. Red's) large and not that first plunge
into scum. Dead allies.

. You defend them. But it is not the alley, or
Elaine Charles. (She backed down, in some kind of pit. "It's too big."
And I thought from that that white women had small holes. Racing
car drivers. Pooky had the correct helmet, and Orlando would threaten
him with it. He (Orlando) led the outriders. But merely elements of
the street's imagination. I was centre. He had strength and hair that
would lay flat under tonics. And he rages with his snakes. His dirtiness. His pretenses at fucking. "Board" (Bud) was his other name.
And I called him board and found out only later it was his mother's
twisted lips. Even after they caught him with that loot.

THE SECRET SEVEN: (met under our porch and gave parties- eating kits among the wet earth odors, rusted wet nails, footsteps.)

EDDIE CLARK (cf. Vestibule)
ALGERNON DAVIS (Board's brother) NORMAN SCOTT (cd run
even with saddle head. Complete dust. Loosing, a slum in my own
fingers. Earlier he made us laugh . . . "You mean those lidda mens?"
Elks, we'd said. He was good w/ the little boys in Ringaleerio (as
the whites say they sd different. Not our fays, they took their mark
from us. Pooky wd say "rigaleerio" because his nose was stuffed.
Dried snot on its edges. But Augie would say "ringy". Let's play
ringy. He played w/ norfolk & jay st. white factions as Keneir, Herbie
Teufel, Johnny (who had strange staring fits the negroes were scared
of), "White Norman" (to differentiate between he and Scotty) & sometimes the Zarros Bros. Charlie Johnny William and Frank. Frank was

little for a long time but suddenly grew up big. Up thru the silent
pavements. His brother I always had to watch. Augie idolized him.
He was tough & fast & silent. Charlie Zarros was a scary name then.
My sister Cassandra ELAINE. A confed-
erate, lankier, bulging knees. Fast & that bitter decision to resist sweet
life. Stale as death, her tears clog the hours.
The scar (a flab of cut skin like a halfmoon on her cheek. Like a
photo a dead girl would clutch. Cry, those stale tears of time. An
inch. A sudden light collapses around us. Illuminated we are "Dr.
Caligari" or Orlando Davis. Beasts among reptiles. The huge flame of
blasphemed God. Fucci screams from his lair, and we know, finally, his
hurt name.

But she made good on all levels, except her lips were cold. And
pouted—never like me, laughing wildly — or losing fights to J.D. in
thick winter cold. (My father was ashamed that day. My hands were
cold. "Frozen" Lois Jones screamed. Roy, his hands are frozen. Angel
love him. Type. Move the blue file cabinets. She breaks down under
pressure. Under this pressure (cool as blue steel in life, and to the
others, like Algy's — cruel. That power necessary — To Sustain
Life. (Forever.)

ORLANDO & ME. (Pre-conscious era. Bones of lost civilizations: the
weird car I said I "built". Cd repair, from sheer radios. Listening to
my lips chap. Wet patches on the paper factory. All the alleys back
there. A maze. To disappear was what we wanted. To go out from
here. Romantics. We wanted to split, the porch, even then. Beneath
to caverns, slim romances.
The seventh person never came. Oh, of course, it was DANNY WIL-
SON. (and his mother sad & cruel as italians. Hunted & hurt by perverted sons.)
LEROI, ELAINE, ORLANDO, NORMAN, EDDIE,
ALGY & DANNY WILSON. (fat afternoon saint. Eater of peanut
butter & visitor at his sister's myriad "wettins".
THE EARLY PRE-
DIASPORA CLAN (removed now from its beginnings. To the splints,
slants, lies of later times. From that, e.g., KICK THE CAN. RED
ROVER (the theme "Red Rover, Red Rover, I dare you to come over")
usually at night, the moon low, a telephone pole just in front our

steps. The Centre. 19 Dey St. With a pole, right there, for Hi-Go-Seek.
HI-GO-SEEK. WAR. (i.e., not the cards,
but the street game where you mark the streets into countries.
MITCHELL 25921. (call me!) poor boy never had no phone till then.
About the time the money vanished off the buffet & I sat weeping
and peeing thru all the showings of THE FIGHTING SULLIVANS.)
That's how Algy got my suit, my mother's wrath.
                                               I * DECLARE *
WAR * ON * ETHIOPIA! (cd be anybody. Peggy Davis even, when
she played. They took names of anywhere. Augie wd take Italy sometimes. But everybody wanted to be America.)

                              Menu
14 packs of Kits
3 packages of Koolaide (grape or orange)
7 chocolate covered graham crackers
7 Mary Janes
                       (these were staples. And the parties were well planned
usually by Elaine, or Orlando who liked to eat. A few outsiders got
invited.
           Junior Bell- O.k., you got me! I'm dead & a black myth.
Poems should be written about me. The myth of the cities Rise. (black
shadow against blue lake, floats face down in the eternity of condums.)
                              RISE. against their dead bones.
Restored to corridors, busrides. The simple dark.
                                               Eunice Reardon-
Of course I know what happened. And I know that we weren't fucking
(you & I) that night in Charlie's yard. We had on all our clothes.
You pulled that stunt on your cousin. And used Jr.'s name as some
"symbol" of all evil. The black arts.

NEWARK ST. (snakes writhe in the ditch, binding our arms. Our
    minds are strong. Our minds.)
    From one end to the other (Thos. Hardy begins, beneath chains,
shaking off sun, appearing a huge pier where our brains are loaded.)
Its boundaries were Central Ave. To Sussex Ave. (1 block). This is
centre I mean. Where it all, came on. The Rest is suburb. The rest is
outside this hole. Snakes die past this block. Flames subside.

(Add Sussex Ave. To Orange St. . . . because of Jim Jam & Ronnie & the cross-eyed girl who asked all new jersey to "do nasty".

(The slum LeRoy lived there also. 3 other Leroys. Two Griffiths (who sd they were cousins. One, the tall dark one, had a brother Robert who went from wet, cowardice — which never completely subsided— to hipster violence. THE GREEKS. As some liason or at least someone who wdn't get done in. Like Murray. THE DUKES.

Where television and wine were invented. That strange wrecked house Carl (beautiful praxiteles) lived. Strange his life twisted. Charlie & he (& me too that warm summer we played & walked stiff legged). But they split up because he moved to a strange sad place. Made new friends. Treated us offhandedly. We never forgave him.

Carl Howard, his brothers, one of whom played brilliant ball. The short one with the bullet head. And for the great BURRY'S CO. team. He pitched. Carl played 3rd base for us. But he fell in with the Robt. Treat Crowd.

(Where they all teach now.) In silence at the leaves. In deference to their mad forgotten lover.

JD STARLING, "STARING" JOHNNY, EUNICE & BILLY REARDON, JR. BELL, (old drunks 25, who still played on occasion & heroes to us, i.e., CHARLIE BOOZE & his brother, the slick head, Calvin. No, something else. A fabled pitcher.) FRANK CUMMINGS tucked his legs up but never made first string Central. Academic player for the playgrounds. I was faster & got more long gainers down the sides. "Comstu here" he said in "german" to impress us.

CHARLIE (and helen) PETERSEN. He was legendary black, but somehow made stupid awkward slow. Good natured but rusty. Disappeared when the new generation (Slanty eyes who had it in for me & his sister Spotty Mae). Cambell their name was. Fast and southern.

THE ALDRIGES- Vivian (ubangi lips, later a tart, stupid whore. Rubber lips I called her also), Lawrence, the smart one. He probably works in the post office or collects debts for jews. Sammy (I hated. I wanted to blot out & kill when J.D. found out I was afraid of him (Sammy). Because the big-

boys let me sit with them on the steps because I could insult anybody
& win dozens constantly. "Your Mother's A Man". Separate, and
sometimes abstruse. My symbols hung unblinked at. The surface
appreciated, and I, sometimes, frustrated because the whole idea didn't
get in . . . only the profanity.)

And Lafayette, who set cats on fire.

That section of the street changed. Sociologists! Morons! Just past
those cherry trees. Mary Ann Notare lived at the corner. & from there
on Italians. Suddenly & without warning, they were all over. Those
clean houses at the corner. How it slipped past me. What could they
have said about me. Those old women sitting on the porch. The pizzeria
on sussex & norfolk I never understood. (Until Morris moved there
later). The Armory was a block away from that busstop. Years later I
met Morris in his house after the summer cotillion. Respectable distance
of years, educations. He had his finger cut off while I was in school.
I saw him again crippled . . . wanting to know my new friends, Bum-
bling because he still wanted to play first base and by then we (the
swag wearing middle class spades of the town) were dancing. He (&
Leon & Snooky & Love & Earl) had come into it late. They were
around the early belly rubbing days & only earl, because he bought
a cadillac, could begin to understand our stance. Our new heads.

Ellipse. These sudden autumns.

DIANE DI PRIMA

THE POET

You gotta love he said. The world is full of children of sorrow and I am always sad.

He was watching this cat beat up his chick in the street.

Sure man I said. The children of sorrow.

The chick had nothing on but her bra and pants and she was kneeling on the sidewalk.

All over the world he said the children are weeping. I weep with all the children in the world.

Great I said.

The cat kept saying get up get up you fucking whore but the chick just knelt on the sidewalk.

I weep he said and my tears are part of all the children's tears.

A lot of people stood around watching. They didn't say anything.

You don't understand he said. Then he said you're very hard.

The fuzz was driving down the avenue and they pulled up to dig the scene.

Don't you love he said.

Sure I said. I love all kinds of things.

And the children he said. Don't you love all the lost children.

The cops put the cat into the car. He was still yelling you fucking whore.

Shit man I said. I told you.

The chick was still kneeling there. She picked up her clothes.

No he said that's not what I mean.

She stood there holding her dress. Then she put on her coat and walked away.

That's not enough he said. You gotta love. I love all the lost children.

I know I said. And you weep.

SOME FOOL THING

Anyway I said you can always be a painter.

Brad picked up his coffee and clinked the ice around. That was a nice move he said.

Sure I said. That's a nice limp. Byronesque. I wasn't getting anywhere.

Brad blew the paper off his straw and it hit the back of my chair. He said the french make such wonderful movies.

For christ sake I said. If you're tired of dancing give it up can't you without ripping up your tendons.

Brad said I'm not tired of dancing.

Great I said then go to the doctor.

All dancers hurt their ankles said Brad. He put on his clever professional look.

Yes I said. Most of them go to the doctor.

Brad put his ankle on the bench and looked at it. It just has to heal he said. Doctor can't do anything.

They have this new thing now I said. Called x-rays. Find out all kinds of things.

There's nothing to find out Brad said.

He put down his coffee and started cruising the next table.

There was this little blonde trick who was laying it on.

I got up and went to the toilet. When I got back Brad was talking to the little blonde. I figured he was all set so I finished my coffee.

Wait a minute Brad said. He picked up the check. When we got outside I said you didn't have to leave.

Christ he said. I have better taste than that. He was laughing.

We took the bus to Brad's place. He lives on the fifth floor and we took it slow on the stairs.

Brad put up the cots. Then he took off the bandage and looked at his ankle for a long time. Neither of us said anything.

I turned off the light. Brad said are you still mad at me.

No I said. There was a light on across the street I could see him.

I'm not mad I said. I love you and I'm scared.

I'll be all right Brad said. Then he said I'm scared too.

I went over to the cot and kissed him. His skin was cold and loose, I pushed the hair off his face and grinned.

Don't go and do some fool thing I said. I was very tired.

THE VISITOR

Well he said so you're Lee. He stood in the doorway.

Yes I said. I didn't know him. I'm Lee.

I've been wanting to meet you he said. Jackie told me about you.

Oh I said. Come in.

He came in and sat down on the bed.

The kid who's in Rockland I said. How is she.

She's fine he said. He smiled. I mean she really is fine. She likes it there he said.

Great I. said. He gave me the creeps. Look I said what did you want to see me about?

That's where I met Jackie he said. In Rockland. In occupational therapy. We made things.

O I said.

You write poetry he said. He looked at me.

Yeah I said.

Jackie showed me some poetry you wrote he said. You sent it to her in a letter.

Did I? I said. I didn't remember.

He said yeah you sent it to her. Then he said why do you write poetry.

I didn't say anything. I had stopped thinking about that one a long time ago.

I used to write poetry he said.

Did you? I said.

Yeah he said. I used to write all the time.

Why did you stop? I said. I didn't know what else to say.

I burned it all he said. Just before I went to Rockland.

Oh I said.

Jackie gave me your address he said. It was on the envelope. Then he said I can't see why anybody does anything.

I said shit man you gotta do something. I said it very loud.

He sat there a while. It was getting dark. I turned on all the lights in the house.

Then he said I started doing it again.

You did? I said.

Yes he said. Sometimes I just do it. I can't help it. Then he said I haven't burned any of it yet.

That's good I said. I figured he still meant poetry. I'd like to see some of it.

Maybe I'll stop when I get a job he said. Do you think so?

I didn't say anything.

I hope so he said it's so stupid to write.

I'd really like to see some of your stuff I said to him.

It's nice of you he said. I liked your stuff. Jackie showed me.

He got up and put his coat on. I wrote a lot yesterday he said. Fourteen hours.

He went to the door. I guess I'll stop soon he said or else I'll burn it again. He sort of laughed. I opened the door for him.

Maybe I'll burn it again he said.

Bring it up sometime I said. I'd like to read it.

He was in the hallway but he stopped and looked at me.

I really would like to read it I said to him.

Yeah he said.

SOUTHWEST

---

texture of reeds caught in the mouth, the hair blowing, lips like a double mandala. your brown frock. tight across the shoulders. whose hands on your hips (flanks)? a piece of chalk between yr teeth, like a cigarette, flaunting. how many eyes lurking inside yr eyeballs. the flowers that grow downwards, chewing into the frame, you stand by the window on a platform, awaiting the seamonster. andromeda, circe, hippolytos. walking slowly home. riding whip trailing behind them, marking the sand. chewing its way. biting thru, out of the mother the foetus emerged in the sunlight. which instantly blinded. the orange had warts all over it, he went down on her for the last time. assuredly she was dead. pursuit of a theory. they learned to live under the snow as other mammals (mammals) live under the water. excreting an oil which allowed them to pass easily thru. the glistening tunnels. the sculpture.

how beautiful you are he said, she kept turning into a brick wall. and back again, indiscriminately. the light on her teeth, sheen, gave her away always. to carry the world like that, on yr back, the straight lines weigh the most. to have it carved into yr skin. after carving FUCK all over her body, her newmade wellsummered skin she threw herself off the roof. in redhook. the sea monster was waiting. they do not use the stairs, the spirits of your ancestors, they. do not. use. the stairs. the winter is coming when we shall eat even the seed. creeping down to the storeroom, opening the forbidden casks. the seedcorn, the seedcorn, and demeter dust in an urn. sprawling w/big bellies, eating the roasted corn. the wisps of the longdead will not stand guard much longer.

undead is a word that you cannot say w/out sneering. the turn of the teeth, the sign painted on the door. pitch, for the spring gods and to lay the spirits. carrying home salt codfish from the markets, stiff on the shoulders, the short men taking long steps. they take no thought when they tan the hide of an ox, he said, and lay back in bed. sturdy legs, in the gardens, in sunlight, another spring. the courtesy of a lion, bowing so low. what color am i when i lie beside you? how many worlds do you make it? the stone steps, ninety nine

of them at least. to climb alone. in the old days, they said, nine hundred and ninety nine. when the women were hardy. that temple long
demolished.

in the dark did she lie on the ground, doze off? the drugs keeping her awake, she actually listened for footsteps. bride of dionysius,
no way around that. did she lie all night on the stone in front of
the altar. was it the waiting of which she cd not speak. a cold the
king cdn't touch, the god had made it. the dark, the stone, her hair.
pipelines of silence.

my foot in a pointed shoe measures off the sidewalk, doorway to
taxi cab, where small dogs bark. precise instructions in the acetelyne
torch. he caught my glove in midair. rapunzel, he said, that's all. nevertheless we waited for it, four days. thru the opening of the casks,
small girls came in. saying 'do you have anything about st valentine'
. . . was it st lucy carries her eyes in a dish. and you do not eat
bread on her day, or wash. and the one where you bless the salt,
which one was that? fingering my grandmother's rosary, what i
thought was my grandmother's rosary.

the fig tree was not killed deliberately, it died. THE FIG TREE
WAS NOT KILLED DELIBERATELY, IT DIED. not like the grape
vines, torn up, 'damn things so hard to get rid of'. my great uncle's
hands as he planted them, 'now you live here'. torn up for a flagstone
path torn up again. because there were too many grapes. the collie,
the old men coughing in the twilight. shoes in a bad way a wool cap
over their ears.

her breast came to my shoulder, she did not tower above me. i have
no other reason to doubt your word. trailing vines, anemones, shells
of cicadas. under the bluish grasses. the fairy folk. tuel - hole or
chimney, middle english. what dews have gathered, whitish on the
hem. seagulls above the river, both white, both grey. THE FIELD
ITSELF turning, the seagulls turning. the water.

but the sun shines later than it used to. nor have i lost as many as
you think. turning her shoulder to him, a light rain falling. mizzle.
the willows stood with their branches pulling upwards. as if in fright.
they walked in a furrow, not knowing what they did. in silence, over
the plowed earth. the lake, with eggs lined up along the bank. comorant
herons, popinjay, turns, flamingos. walking in single file, the eggs
lined up. abandoned, exposed in a row, and waiting to hatch.

he worked in a quarry, one of the mouths of hades. into which, from time to time newborn infants were thrown. the blood & slime making the stone much harder to handle, the buzzards wheeling. overhead hungry, but never daring to land. they drew up three wooden folding chairs and perched. crossing their legs. their ankles exquisite, no way to choose between them.

slumped on the couch & never saying a word. the smell of pot in his clothes, his skin was sallow. i had expected it. and talked about messina, the olive orchards, bent slowly from the waist and kissed his hands. which lay in his lap. he looked at the nape of my neck, this utmost pressure.

if she cracked her knuckles, or sang, if she changed her clothes. the altar boy they fought over, with knives. blonde & frankly irish. aloof. in their bobby sox, on the stoops, in the area ways. chewing gum & shuffling, the glint in their green eyes. sloppy joe sweaters, the pageboy hair, the knives. brownstones & hedges, grass, that kind of light.

the light blue dress they buried her in, the snow in my shoes. i shall never get used to coffins, especially the handles. the functional house, workspace and privacy. but he stands in the doorway & offers me mad magazine. he leaves his shoes here, he offers me free cocaine. he has grown to the doorpost, the ivy on him & it.

i remember the time i saw you put him to bed. how he wept, the old man, and kissed you, you were not angry. my eyes were painted green, i looked away. you took off his shoes, your face was in the light.

in its cask of gold, the valentine, the emblem. pure as a wall. the golden girls he sold me, strong knees, dismaying hands. with which they loosed their hair. and somewhat snagged, the otter in the doorway. sniffing up what skirts. on the mirror a piece of calico like fluff. what you cannot cook in a spoon. unscrewing light bulbs, tensing himself for the pun. with feeble steps he trailed the dying rabbits. under the desert sun. they lifted their skirts and pissed on the calico. coming in just now, the sun just coming up, the smells. paris at daybreak, there are fleas in the hotel. charming he said, but the vase came apart in his fingers. in the white desert where all the sand in cocaine. lying down there to die, and shooting your horse. the ultimate sandstorm, the cactus walking away, the trees from somewhere else, that it should not rain.

if you came to my room thru a garden would it be different? picking your way on the paths and lifting your head. your stance like

a faun and smirking, the line of your forehead. if you came to my
room thru ruins, the palms of your hands turned outwards, a new
electricity in them, your ears. alive, with a separate awareness, like
a cat's. if you came to my room with a football under your arm. if
there were a cradle in my room. or a coffin. if we turned down a
gas jet just above the bed. if there were a panther chained to the
wall. if there were rats. if you climbed a wall to get here. if you
made albas. dante & bruno, sepia lithographs. framed in mahogany,
the great carved bedstead.

if it were possible to live there. if we had seen an animal at
least. a crow, a white wolf. not even seals in that water. we sat on
the beach under a shelf of ice. not speaking, not touching not even
dressed for the weather. surf on the icebergs, and my kind beast
had gone.

in the pits, the mouths of hades, the white flowers grow, the women
stoop in their veils to pull them up. by the roots, that the plant
may die as the god has died. aloof, their knees cold from squatting
the whitedew a frost on their fingers. sunflowers, tiger lilies shot
toward the sky. a different sky & no concern of theirs. the flying
shrimp that prey on other birds. nesting in waterfalls. the line they
walk. the language their young speak audible on venus. where pericles
uses the vein in his left ankle. why did you sell him to the silver
mines? the pretty one, and just because you were chicken. spinoza.
jimmy waring. socrates. who murdered once too often. blinking at
the light like a subway cat, a cave fish. the armies of alligators marching up manhattan. retreating like a snail about to be coked. 'i like the
blues best, it's my favorite color.' the city fathers hacking away @
the hudson, and out the sound the goodies in a strong-box. de sapio's
head on a stake in washington square. "what do you mean bread
lines? this here's for meat loaf."

i will see you again when you can stay all night. oiling up by the
open window, the spring wind on your flesh. your large wrists. the
ground moved like a snake and shut us in. what was she dying of, in
mosaic halls? feeling for the stair, on the way to some kind of theatre.
lying down on the floor, holding on to door jamb. doing everything
possible to slow the process. rain was predicted. the tempo of distress.

pink plaster flamingoes emerge from holes in the earth. in the
backyards, all over brooklyn, they guard the roses. false fronts on
the flat old houses. my grandmother's rosary, with one bead missing,

the links mended with wire. bone hairpins, the smell of her skin. my cruelty presses into the palms of my hands. i dont know how to dive, i climb the ladder. thinking all the time if i cd fly. who swung on the gallows, waiting for the rain. only the laughter floated up so high. skimming along the ground the sobs of the women. threading the broken pearls, their eyesight going. stopping to rub their hands on a greasy towel. smirking & turning to light a cigarette. the line-up he said i'll manage when we come to it. chug-a-lug. under green lights, blue mirrors, maroon carpets. wallpaper striped w/gladiolus patterns. rubbing the toe of his boot along the bar. john tom mix fles, with his six shooter in the doorway. picking the roaches off the window sill. without taking aim, while talking over his shoulder, in spanish, to the superintendent.

    he said i'm foreman and if i can't steal, then none of you guys are gonna. the earth turning blue. a new kind of lichen, turns the soil to glue. in which nothing will grow. roaches live off of it, but they are white. driving over them, on the hill, in a jaguar. the whitewalls spattered, a thin high cry in the air. she kept on adjusting her veil, the rearview mirror detached, for putting on lipstick. the dashboard had a contraption for cooking h. she oiled up, smiled a little, and ate a sandwich. in the back seat the child was pulling a doll apart. limb from limb, and tossing fingers out of windows. some kind of song she sang, doing it, the words were obscure, he chased him, running, clear to avenue e. bernard baruch drive, and thru the housing projects. transvestite tho he was he had been a track star. the meat was screaming, he kept throwing chunks of it away. or was it another black goat? its legs were skinny. had poliomyelitis when just a kid. finally he threw the whole thing over a hedge. and lay panting under it. his hat gave him away. or a walking stick whispering arabic nouns. something he hadnt expected, in any case. but the head of lettuce walked over at just the right moment, saying, "sir, allow me to ransom this wretched man" oozing all the time, and getting brown. earth climate doesn't agree with this kind of life. his heels caught in his skirt as he stood up, and the dying goat had chewed a hole in his skull. he curtsied apologetically. three cops came over to find out what the trouble was. they gave him the daily news award for bravery. the head of lettuce took him by the hand and they walked slowly out of sight together.

would you believe it she said a water beetle, and eating roses right
out of the milk bottle. they'll do anything he said for a little excitement. but carrion crows she said on the white house lawn? he said
are you thru with the paper. she shot him twice.

deliberately stripping the deer of their fangs a gloved hand came
nearer the trees
in the pink bowl the water trembled a little. he dropped in his rings
and blew his nose in his fingers. immediately the silver snarling trum-
pets. mustangs and chimney sweeps, bards, cholera, dismay; meat
overcooked, decision on every face. how could you not be holy after
this? next time the metronome was used as a hatrack. thus were the
thieves confounded, his narrow cape barely covering his red knees, he
pulled the paper out of his rectum without blushing and read the
edict. pages ran by with airwick, the groom threw himself into the
fire. if only you'd eat the apples before they're rotten your teeth
would slide more agreeably on mine. the clocks on his socks were a
dead giveaway for the angels. departing ultimately with the chimney-
piece.

holding a pebble under his tongue he spoke to the comorant. where
the blue water splashed. the insufficiency of mallards among the sea-
weed. concerning particularly the lost. a lad in middy blouse
approaches shyly. this is no way for tortoises. there are pink flowers
blooming along the bank, are they azaleas? the sun shines too. why
do you keep on turning your face away? pederast, dont be ashamed,
we do not condemn you. see, he holds out a tulip, his lips play, there
is no amusement in his eyes. in his young boy's sailor suit, and that
silly hat.

in the palms of her hands the white stones nested. curving archly
and pressing against the life line. she parted her lips to smile, birds
flew from between her teeth. and what fluid on her thighs, when she
rose from bed? in the early morning, the dawn now yellow now blue.
on the linen curtains, the light, her light hands moving. to let the
light in, the bird on her windowsill. regardless of the snow. passer,
deliciae meae puellae. what timing dictated her nakedness, the tones
of her flesh. the violets, driving men mad, where the thigh met the
torso? how the sheets rustled before she drew them aside. the hands
that moved on her ceiling, fluttering, slender. marking the signals,
and then she leaned on her elbow. reading in bed, she did not smoke,

the beer poured out across the floor. foam as of seasurge, the dust
that lay like a tideline. the bridge of pebbles across her while she slept.
fording a deep stream. taut ends of her silence curving, the bow never
unstrung. her shoulders like white rocks jutting, the sheets lapping at
them.

in her hand, in the silver mirror, a one-eyed beast. who did not
even smile. the draperies walked toward her, she was surrounded. dust
storms in the boudoir, fired mist, the songs of monkeys. the oysters
are yawning, they open and close their eyes. she follows the footsteps
farther down the beach. lying to herself all the while. It Is Consum-
mated, the telegrams he shd get in africa. and all the rest of them,
wherever they are. pausing a while to look down into a pit. the shape
of a bowl. from which they do not emerge the dwellers in anger.
bending forever, offering no one their hands. hearing faintly their
music, she does not edge away. fingering always the cracked plate
she has brought with her. where is the bread for the offering, the
whole grain, is this not the place. the phase of the moon keeps changing the sun does not rise. there is wind on the edges, where the
horizon is. the smell of frying sausage, she turns her head. the smell
of roasting meat, the wrong offering. withdrawing a little from the
open pit. they wanted vegetation, the green plants. that we should lie
down in them, make love, and worship. that the green herbs, dripping
with come, be tossed in the sea. lying again to herself she took out a
knife. tossing that and her sandals into the open pit. a flock of crabs
flies in the air above the dunes. uttering frightful cries and dropping
rubies. a god alights on her shoulder, then stands beside her. vulture-
headed. he takes her wrist, and gives her an indian burn.

deformed, and hunchbacked. he carries a pack on his back. there
is a ring in his nose. he follows her everywhere. farting into the
clean air on the village streets. not even the children run after, the
cobbles are covered w/slime where he passes. like a snail. they call
him the snailman. as for the woman, they simply shake their heads.
she does not look over her shoulder, she does not hurry. some say
she is sleepwalking, some say he is her dream. they make a circuit
of villages, in wales. the same ones, summer and winter. he does not
try to sell them anything. there's a child who says she saw them on the
grass. that he was horned, that they lay side by side. in the snow
she wears no cloak, she is serene.

RUSSELL EDSON

Selections from GULPING'S RECITAL

From *Father & Son* (4th Section)

. . . Speaking of using the shoulders of others, (either for recreation or specific utility), it is brought to my mind a certain rather lyrical military adventure of mine.

Not to say father's was any the less, but rather to draw a parallel that points up our similarities, precious as is the blood kinship between father and son.

The use of the shoulders of others seems to be a family trait . . .

At any rate, they were carrying my corpse, whose name was Buddy Butch, through the forest of The Old Man.

Unknown to them, I think their names were Pink and Pratt, I was quite alive; sleeping and waking by turns; lighting cigarettes, putting them out on the shoulders of my bearers.

My code name was Buddy Butch. I was on a secret mission into enemy territory.

It seemed expedient to play dead at the boundary, most of my body on enemy territory, so as to make the enemy think I came from their side.

I was lifted up by two soldiers. At the time my eyes were closed. And then I could not tell whether I was traveling back into my own land or being borne into enemy territory.

I was watching the stars with my ears wide for gossip; for it had occured to our soldiery that gossip is more important than military facts, which are likely to bore one to death, especially if one knows very little about the subject, which is the case with our military.

323

Rather, juicy bits of hearsay nourish tedious hours spent at General Intelligence, or swatting flies grown so thick lately around Colonel Muff's desk.

I must tell Colonel Muff not to eat carrion. Or, during office hours, he shouldn't. It's an unpleasant thing at any hour.

I shouldn't have tasted it were it not for the fact that he outranks me. Or does he?

Self, are you a General? A King? That's even better.

Sergeant Pluck has a nasty way about him.

Captain Girlish . . . Well, alright, but I don't like his long eyelashes. Should tell him not to wear carnations on his chest. It looks girlish for a military man to look like a flowers queen. I mean, it's alright to wear roses in your hair in the evening, or highheeled slippers in dress parade, or perhaps a little rouge. But, my goodness, a flower-print gown, even if the weather is so warm; and, *I really do need a fan* -Such airs!

How I came up -Not by looking pretty for the generals. Crossing and uncrossing my legs a dozen times to attract attention to my legs.

The hell with it, ability is what counts.

Not that I discount romance, or looking nice.

Working in the latrines, I always had the scent of, well, just a trace, mind you, of an expensive perfume.

It was well known that I spent most of my pay on fine perfume. I felt it was worth it as far as my morale and dignity were concerned.

They called me *Skunk* -A back door compliment? It has to be that, otherwise it's an insult.

Then I rose from the ranks. General Moon approached me one day and promoted me to King. No, wait, Private First Class. I entered the Intelligence.

General Moon suspected his wife of some moral inconsistency, which I was commissioned to check out, which later involved myself in such a way as to put the blame squarely on General Moon; which proved to be another stepping-stone in my career.

By hook or crook I should've made it, since my star is lucky. Otherwise it wouldn't be, which is contrary to the course of my career, which clearly shows that if we have stars at all mine is lucky.

In other words, I either have a star or I don't. If I must be saddled with one, it is forced to be lucky even if it isn't. If it isn't lucky it can't exist.

. . . Eating carrion. Why? Because the great birds are known to be in their off-moments eaters of rotten meat; and Colonel Muff thinks of himself as being a great eagle?

No, he is a lame chicken who saves a dime on hamburger by eating decayed entrails and pieces of newspaper. A juicy murder to chew on; he says there's a little blood if you chew hard enough. But it is always yesterday's newspaper -He seems to have little chance of getting away from carrion.

. . . Sergeant Pluck wants to be a general. You can tell by the way he shoves the generals around.

He told General Moon to get off the General's swivel chair so that Sergeant Pluck could attend to the General's business. All day long General Moon brooded. Sergeant Pluck has a nasty way about him.

These two under me are talking about Corporal Smooch's underwear. It sounds choice.

They know I'm not dead, which makes things easier. I had begun to get lonely.

Soon they will put me down and make me walk. Or will they pretend to think I'm dead to keep me off guard? What's the difference? The night is beautiful and I enjoy riding on their shoulders.

I look up wondering which star is mine; while branches full of birds float by. (Or, are they bats?)

Silver leaves made silver by the moon. Fences trailing off behind us down the road. An occasional cow in a silver field. A house with a string of smoke rising out of it.

. . . Captain Girlish and his jade brooch . .

Alright, alright, roses in your hair in the evening. Highheels are not unbecoming the uniform; strapless heels can add a certain flare. A touch of rouge -But not carnations in Central Intelligence. They never learn.

If these two rogues carrying me think I don't know they know I'm playing dead, they're sadly mistaken. I not only know it, but I enjoy their knowing it, because I hate secrets. When you have a secret you know you must tell it.

Secrets are designed to draw attention to themselves, which of course leads to their revelation.

Things are designed to become precisely what they are not. Otherwise they shouldn't exist at all.

Now these rogues seem to expect that I shall be happy in a hole that they are standing by. It would be cozy I must admit, but I'm not ready to go underground . . . Or, are they calling my bluff?

They know I know they know I live. Well then, let's see how far they intend to carry this mischief. Their commanding officer shall receive an angry note by messenger. And I assure you, by tea time I shall be invited to imbibe rare wines as an apology, which I shall refuse for the sake of beer, which is quite a favorite with me.

Of girls -suddenly they spring to mind like birds of the summer before.

No doubt I shall be married before my life is out . . .

Now I must really concentrate . . .

This gossiping with oneself is all very well with a glass of tea on a summer's eve, when the birds are becoming quiet.

An occasional shriek, as if someone had his claws stepped on in a nest. Or an anxious flutter, as if having one's claws stomped on weren't enough, but now accompanying it the discomfort of having to unfold one's wings to ward off a dangerous fall. Yet, one feels that finally there is room for all . . .

I sip my tea again and smile. Why not? If it weren't for these mosquitoes . . . But the fumes of the rose . . . Eternity sums itself in this sweet moment . . .

What we are after in our official capacity is gossip. Some blow to man's international sense of morality. Something that will stir the old woman in every general.

Every young supple girl whom you might well marry, must become time, the old woman with vertical wrinkles surrounding her mouth . . .

*   *   *

From *Flower* (5th Section)

. . . We were set out against the enemy, dressed in the colors of of the wood. The vegetable pretense.

We console ourselves with shrubs, for we cannot tell them from men.

Oh yes, we are crying. Not having asked to be born we have no wish to undo our births. In fact, we are asking to be born.

Though born without our consent, we are now giving our consent.

It is when we break from our neutrality that we risk the contradiction.

Is birth and death an arc separate from the circle?

We are asking to be born.

Disguised as vegetation we are trying to be men.

Yes, we are crying. Blowing my nose into an oak leaf, reminding myself of mother with handkerchief at my farewell. I could not tell whether or no she was smothering laughter. It seemed she was upset by an indigestion conveniently wrought to hide from herself the grief that she felt, yet having the appearance of undisguised grief; which has the effect of satisfying everyone, both my mother and strangers.

Except that I could not help noticing vomit running out of her handkerchief.

No, actually, I think thinking back, it was an old tramp smelling strongly of liquor was vomiting.

No, it was not mother. Mother was roaring with laughter to see her little soldier going forth.

My life is independent of mother, It has its own wish to be. It is in a way in competition with mother, as with other life.

It was not mother, I think, but a tramp who vomited surreptitiously into his sleeve.

Now the shrubs no longer console us in our advance, for the enemy, too, has on the colors of the wood. Every shrub and blade of grass bears the sign of the assassin.

Even I, in the wood moving, am dangerous to myself.

If I lie quietly as insects crawl on my lips, and think only of mother, I may survive like the trees and the constancy of the brook.

An open charge has an unasked to be born feeling about it.

But here, sneaking up on the enemy, and destiny closely observed . . .

I am afraid to be born and yet somehow afraid not to be.

And somehow the question of man, aside from his death of his crisis . . . the question of man, which, of course, is his death, which is his crisis. Somehow more than the present battle or the camouflaged flesh . . .

Perhaps it is the heat and the uncertainty of the grass and the danger of trees . . .

I think of mother, casting my anchor.

. . . I am not afraid of death -Only I don't want some sonofabitch to kill me.

I hate to be startled. It makes my heart beat fast, and gives me the discomfort of fearing death intensely for a moment. It destroys my calm appraisal of man's fate as regards his death. My biology asserts itself; and it scares me to think I will scream and kick when death really comes.

Fear proves to me that I am really afraid. I am afraid to be afraid, which does not stop me from fearing. And it grows -Fear breeds the fear of itself.

. . . And still, the fear of being *that* afraid -Until one will tremble like a fool.

Any blade of grass may swell into a bayonet. No less than the miraculous becoming of my penis.

And it may rain.

Rain!

. . . It is to rain in summertime.

Tell us how it is to die in the summertime.

For it will rain . . .

Listen: It is listening for the rain.

When will it rain?

It will rain on Sunday, when I wandered through the place I had never been before, and heard the thorn-vine rasp its spurs on the grey house.

The light of the day is milky, then it will rain on the hayfork.

The brook is full of vaginas of silver, softly it moves with clefts and folds through the leaf dark of the wood.

The deep breath of sleep through cedar and pine.

What is it to die in the summer?

For it will rain soon, and it is very far from home in a quiet avenue of some turning in a place we had never been before.

When it will rain, he whispers is a grey house.

When in the electric rain of August, and hell zigzags across the meadow, he whispers deep under time. For that is long ago, and the door swings loosely in the high grass around the stoop.

And what is it in summertime to die?

It is to hear laughter in a garden, and the cannonblast of distant thunder; and to wonder when it will rain; and bright butterflies fluttering in the cloud-dark of the garden, and that heavy sigh that precedes the desperate weeping. It is waiting now for the rain.

For that is a long time ago and deeply under time, as we are waiting.

And the door swings loosely in the high grass.

Where I was was in a place I had never been before.

And when you die is that when it will rain?

It will rain on the hayfork.

The hands are bones.

The rain erases GULPING from the stone.

The wind is moving in a tree, and now it must surely rain.

All is silver blindness, for it is surely raining in the meadow where the hayfork becomes dust.

* * *

From *The Marriage* (9th Section)

Miss Wimp and George Gulping in Circus X. Yes, in Circus X.

I am born. The child is Fuzzy Ann.

Shall I tell you secrets about my parents?

My father is a doctor. No, he is a general. Yes, and a doctor, too. On weekends he is a general, and all during the week a doctor. He is a poet.

Let me talk about their sex . . .

I should begin: Why we lost the war. And why we had still to lose it.

As a child I was Private Fuzzy Ann, General Gulping's man; attached to the household of the General. Heir apparent by the line of my father.

My mother was also a man -one of those rare cases of a rooster laying an egg. A secret kept with the aid of disguise; known only to the family, family retainers, their families, friends; written of at length in many medical journals.

But in fact, kept secret with the other fact; that my father, the General, was a woman.

My title of Private, honorary, at best.

But now, in the time of war, in spite of tears and handkerchiefs that create an ocean of white-caps on the waters of grief, so to speak . . .

Yes, and so I am to do a man's task. I am a soldier. My duty entails being attached to the General's household; so that things are no different, until I wonder if there is a war.

If there is a war, it is going badly; because father always makes mistakes.

I can say with all due respect, anything he puts his hand to will eventually end in tears. That he will be brought, all tangled in maps and telephone cords, to his room, weeping and sighing.

And he will be put to bed without supper for his lack of self-control.

With despair so touching, it is true, as he picks his nose with abandonment, asking why it is he and not the enemy General who must be disgraced by starvation -And couldn't he have a cookie or two, or, perhaps, a leg of lamb to tide him over until morning?

Until mother must resort to slapping and hissing at father; who, in the mean time, has wet his khakis, not to mention his shirt front with slobber and tears. And his nervous ear-cleaning and ass-scratching, until he must be slapped nearly unconscious and placed in a restraining sheet.

It is very interesting, the inside life of a great man, which my father is. As is seen in the great triumphs of the battlefield which end in routs, scheduled to bring his men home in time for lunch. Which the enemy are prone to call disorderly retreats. And which, on consideration, might well be characterized as: Men running for their lives to lunch. Either running from bullets, or running to lunch, or both -Which would be a great strategem in its accomplishment, in that, movement can, at its beginning and at its end, in two places, at its extremes, do a double service . . .

Or, am I swayed by the love of father, which I deny for the sake of objectivity. Which is to say, I love no one; nor hate -Not any judgement or conclusion.

I watch. I wait. I understand.

And then, father hiding in the attic among cobwebs, in the dust. Introspective, and afraid to come down, as it were, into life.

The ceilings discolored from the General's urination.

He is heard talking to the mice, who also live in the attic.

We shout up occasionally, Are you alive, sir?

And then father sighs down, Alive, but more nearly dead. But really dead, and just a little alive. On the percentage basis, and for simplicity, I think *dead* is the word.

And then we might say, Oh, then roast pork and blackeyed peas couldn't interest you?

And then he is heard to move as he cries, Out of my way if you value your lives. I shall eat you out of house and home. My appetite is fairly big, my dangerous foes.

Mother quickly boards up the attic entrance, through which father breaks through, with all introspection forgotten, crying, Hi ya, Miss Wimp. Supper ready?

And right down into the kitchen he goes. And, very soon mother and father are on the floor, with the roast sliding around and them fighting for it.

Meanwhile the enemy is charging, and the house is on fire, and father has wet his khakis. And all is being lost, until finally all is lost; and father must be retired to his room.

*   *   *

From *The Soldier* (10th Section)

Father down in the cellar.

Father leaning over maps.

A Corporal had a grey rat he was petting.

Captain Mommy was polishing his boots.

The Corporal said, Hey General, this rat wants to bite you.

Be a good boy, replied father.

But he wants to bite you, General. He's hungry, screamed the Corporal.

I could have you court-martialled, yelped father.

But, General Gulping, just one little bite. Just a tiny nip, no bigger than a rat's jaw, you selfish pig, roared Corporal Jasmine.

Captain Mommy, Mommy, whimpered father, please don't let Corporal Jasmine put a rat on me.

Captain Mommy said to Corporal Jasmine, You know better than to tease the General. You're in the army, and we're under fire. The General's studying maps and plans. The war depends on him. And then a silly little Corporal wants to put a rat on the great General. I can hardly believe this is true. Now tell the General you're sorry. Go ahead . . .

But this rat's hungry. He said he was, screamed the Corporal.

General, the Captain implored, how about it, just one little bite, to quiet the Corporal.

No, no, cried father, beginning to go into a tantrum.

The Corporal was saying to the rat, Sic 'em, go on, sic 'em.

The rat was baring its teeth.

Father was screaming, Mommy, mommy, Captain Mommy, quickly, it's going to bite me.

Captain Mommy trying to soothe him said, There, there, General, the Corporal was just having a little game. It's alright, you can continue the war . . . Easy, General, easy, sweetheart, it's alright.

And Corporal Jasmine said, I was just fooling; this rat won't bite you. He likes you. See, he's wagging his tail.

Father sobbing, I thought he was going to bite me . . . sob . . .

General, Captain Mommy said, before you go back to the war, I wonder if you would kiss my boots? They're so shiny, I wonder if you wouldn't just kiss them?

I will not, said father. A man in my position can't go around kissing the boots of a Captain, even if they are so nice and shiny.

Then Corporal Jasmine said, May this hungry rat bite you?

Father said, I will kiss Captain Mommy's boots if he protects me from the dangerous infection of the rat's bite.

Captain Mommy said, Please leave me out of your affairs with the rat. I merely want you, as a personal favor to me, to kiss my shiny boots. I want you to grovel before me, as if I were your superior;

while I know you are mine. I would get a particular enjoyment if you would bow down and kiss my boots.

I can't very well, said father, since I went to West Point, and have become a very important person. And this is why I can't allow the rat to bite me, either. I must maintain a certain dignity, because people would say, What kind of General is he, letting a rat bite him, and bowing before his Captain's boots to kiss them. (Which are beautiful, I must admit, and do deserve kissing; and which tempt me more than I would like to say.)

Oh, come on, General, Captain Mommy whimpered, who will know, except us? And you can count on us to keep the secret, as long as you pay us a thousand a week. Come on, here in the privacy of this cellar . . . bow down to my boots, and let the rat bite you . . .

Well, said father, perhaps I might just peck one of your white gloves. Something quite casual, as if I were stooping to pick up a piece of paper from the floor, and my face brushed against your glove, quite by accident.

No, General, said the Captain, that will not do.

Perhaps I'll blow a kiss to your boots. That'll be quite romantic, yelped father.

No, General, Captain Mommy said, that will not do. You must get on your knees and say, *Your Royal Highness, will you permit me to kiss your boots?* Nothing else will do.

But, I am the General, and you are but a lowly Captain. How dare you even suggest I kiss your boots? Although, again, I admit the prospect of kissing those shiny wonders does seem attractive. I must say, again, you have no right expecting your commanding officer to bow before you.

General, General, cried Corporal Jasmine, the rat's sick. He needs food.

The Corporal was holding the famished rat in his hands. He approached the General. General, let him nibble on your double chin, for only five minutes.

No, no, get that thing out of here.

Please, General, put him inside your shirt, so he can sink his teeth into your lush flesh, implored the Corporal.

Mommy, Mommy, do something with that incorrigible boy, crooned father.

I'm quits, said Captain Mommy. What kind of a general are you, anyway, that you can't do a captain a personal favor? If you had kissed my boots you would now be busily at your maps, conducting the war. But, as it is now -Well, General, you can plainly se you have no friends. You might be able to win the rat over by giving him a meal; but, as for me, if you kissed my boots now, it would only seem as if you were trying to make me feel good; and that wouldn't do at all, because I've a very large ego; and, when a general kisses my boots, I like to feel he's doing it only because my un-advertised importance demands it.

Father whimpered, if I let the rat chew on the back of my neck for ten minutes, will you, Corporal Jasmine, be nice to me until the end of the war?

Oh no, the Corporal said, now it's too late. Now the rat knows exactly what sort of a person you are.

Please, begged father, please let me put the rat inside my clothes.

Unh unh, said the Corporal. If the rat were dying . . . No siree, the rat doesn't want that kind of gift.

Won't either of you let me do anything for you? pleaded father. Look, I'll cut my hand and feed the rat some blood, to awaken his appetite. Captain, I'll not only kiss your boots, I'll kiss your ass; and you can pass wind if you want to. Oh, but please let me mortify myself.

Listen General, said Captain Mommy, we'll serve you in our official capacities, fair enough; but, as to liking you, well, that is quite another thing. And, I don't mind telling you, when we're in contact with the troops again, it shall make the rounds that you refused to kiss my boots, and refused to feed a hungry rat. How do you think it'll sound to the mothers back home; that you refused to let a rat bite you? And, how do you think the officers under you will feel, when they find out that you wouldn't kiss my shiny boots? And the fact that, all through the battle I did nothing else but shine them, hoping the General would notice, and bow down before me and kiss my boots to distraction.

Look, said father, as he lifted some soggy sewerage from the floor, I'm pouring filth on the General. I'm turning him into a regular K.P. fellow.

The Corporal screamed, General, you are beginning to smell! You are basically foul despite all your medals to the contrary.

The General, interjected Captain Mommy, is not the fellow I should like to be wrecked on a desert island with.

Why doesn't the General inspire love?, pleaded father.

He might inspire pity, yet, he is too disgusting. His weakness is not pitiable. It makes one angry. One wishes to hurt. Even to ruin the shine on one's boots with the General's blood -If you get what I mean, General, said Captain Mommy.

Yes, yes, screamed father. One wishes to destroy by great pain an awkward situation that has no dignity -Like a fat General full of medals.

General, roared Corporal Jasmine, the rat has just fainted!

Oh my, he must be all tuckered out, murmured father with womanly concern.

And now, General, commanded Captain Mommy, I would like to hit you on the head with a brick. Or, perhaps, pull out your hair.

Oh yes, you must do something terrible to me, I understand. It all stems from the fact that I didn't stoop and kiss your lovable boots; and then, when I was ready to, I had lost the right to.

I'm going to kill you, General, said Captain Mommy.

Please do not hurt a hair on my head, cried father.

I'm going to kill all that digestive plumbing that pushes out the front of your uniform, whined Captain Mommy.

Corporal Jasmine, screamed father, I order you to kill Captain Mommy before I can say Jack and the beanstalk!

If you will comfort the rat; sway it in your arms and sing to it, replied Corporal Jasmine.

Of course, give me the little fellow! There, there, you dirty rat, you louse-infested, disease-carrying pest. . . . *When the wind blows* . . . Now what's the matter wid da itty bitty shit-stained rodent?, crooned father. Now hurry up, Corporal Jasmine, kill Captain Mommy before I can say Jack and the beanstalk.

Don't you dare touch me. And, if you get a speck of dirt on my handsome footwear . . . if you mar the shine, even so much as by trying to spruce up by looking in the mirror-effect of these lovely, and most awe-inspiring -these beautiful examples of artistic achievement, these art-treasures of lovable leather; if you dare, I shall most certainly stamp them with impatience at your philistine attitude towards this century's greatest cultural achievement, said Captain Mommy.

Oh dear, screamed father, I think I love this rat! I think I must kiss it, or forever thirst for its lips.

Now wait, General, roared the Corporal, it's only a child. Sure, I understand that in times of war social customs get out of joint, and that one may be dead tomorrow, and all; but you're far too ugly to engage this animal in the complications of housekeeping. Which means, getting the children off to school, picking you up at the station, dodging the exterminator, trying to look pretty for you; and at the same time keeping contact with other rats. In fact, living two lives, one in the living room, and one in the walls.

Of course you're right, whimpered father, I could only bring misery to my little bride. And, incidentally, I think this rat's a male, anyway. I see now that it would never work out.

Corporal Jasmine said, And now I'll kill Captain Mommy.

Before you do, said Captain Mommy, I should like to make a verbal will, that, on the event of my death shall be shouted throughout the world:

I, Captain Mommy, being of sound mind and body, wearing the most exquisite boots, (they really are!) . . . Having entered the military world for the sole purpose of securing the right to wear cavalry boots, (without people saying, as they do of civilians, *he's putting on airs*). And, having spent my entire career in the polishing of same, feel now loath to be parted from such glistening leather. (Indeed, more bright than sunshine; which may be the exaggeration that love exacts.) Therefore, I consign all pensions, or monies resulting from activities that make me recipient of such monies, etc., to the care and maintenance of said glorious, almost unholy in their unnatural beauty, boots. Also, I stipulate that they be exhibited in the Royal London Museum, the Metropolitan of New York, and the Louvre of Paris; and that only high persons view these precious and most darling boots in the private offices of the museum directors. And that, under no condition shall they be used as footwear, even if it is raining. But that, on the occasion of a coronation they be present, and be carried on a red pillow, signifying their importance. And that they be referred to as *Their Highness!* And, that the Queen of England pose with them on her lap. And, that the President of the United States address odes to these boots over the radio. And, further, that even in the event of my untimely death, they not be removed from my feet. Signed (verbally), Captain Mommy.

Very commendable, Captain. Very fine; you're a true soldier, sighed father, as he collapsed . . .

* * *

MICHAEL RUMAKER

THE USE OF THE UNCONSCIOUS IN WRITING

Story can be, obliquely, a map of the unconscious, its terrain and peopling. The physical can be made to yield psychic responses.

The unconscious nests the actual.

The landscapes which draw one are the landscapes of the self. Actual or imagined, the unconscious one posits itself on the physical one, invisibly permeating it. Each moving, in the act of writing, concurrently, creates an open structure in which one is free to invent, bound neither strictly to unconscious nor to conscious, but drawing from each — an interchange of the powers of each in which the tactile lifts as the psychic contents respond. All is believable within the framework of the story since all is created between those two poles of force.

It's as tho experience resides in the unconscious as layers of silt — each the essence of the actual event heaped in layers of memory and non-memory.

It's as tho the unconscious stores up, gathers into itself, as a slow accumulation, all our experiences. The more poignant, the more deeply does it imprint itself there. There is that other, as a residue, which we can't account for personally — there, in the unconscious as a kind of carryover of non-memory which we inherit with our blood at birth. It seems this residue only manifests itself according to the degree of intensity we bring to bear upon our own lives as the cross-forces of life touch us — as we act and are acted upon. It will sleep, if we sleep.

The psyche, in quietness, absorbs the energy of its contents, a thickening process that gathers for charges. They will be manageable or unmanageable according to how equipped and prepared we are.

The process is a conscious working at the substance of the unconscious whenever it manifests itself, in dream or in wakefulness. As a ruined site, tripe rests, indiscriminately, amongst valuable content there. Quality will depend on the closeness of sifting, will depend on how close and precise one has made known to the self its contents. That no barrier, impasse, is ducked. That one also is involved in his known and in the known world about him.

If the unconscious has appeared in writing, it has been mainly by accident. Here is a rich field of content. To be acted upon consciously. To be made known.

Seized by the sight of an object, an intensity of seeing, brings up other, psychic contents charged with meaning beyond what the eye, as instrument, registers to the brain.

Tho the root is in language and what men say, what their bodies do — yet, this other thing, which is unseen, quiet and unquiet, needs also its own equivalent language to make it known — by image, images as precise as those found to present the actual.

To get the thing there, in the words, with that same swift heightening, that sharp penetration, which strikes meaning from an object. But that the object remain the object, stated as such, with the same spareness and preciseness which is the heart of intuition. That the object be allowed or made to yield its meaning but not be despoiled. That is, not used simply for self-expression.

Not so simple. Too often the temptation is to imbue the object with personal meanings and effusions which force the object to be mouthpiece for the expression of the writer's reminiscences, ideas, private bellyaches, etc. — the qualities and characteristics of the object set aside, the object itself disturbed, taken out of its context to serve the writer merely as an instrument to express himself. Whereas the writer must act upon the object in such a way that it gets said, and the other, under meaning, without its being tampered with. The object must remain in its own context, as you, the writer, must also. Objects in a story must be given no more than their weight — that their lift or drop in the prose be equal to their substance — that the writer develops a sensitivity to the degrees of intensity with which they strike the psyche — that a point is reached where he can say, and know, 'Yes, there, there I go in.'

This is the quality of flatness: to present the thing no more than it is. It is not to equal objects, people, out, in a dull stringing. There must be intensity. There must be sensitivity.

In such a story meanings get there which aren't put there consciously. And if not consciously, they must stem from the unconscious. Meanings don't get there by accident. There is also operant an under-logic — not the conscious one — that brings about an interlocked structure of things within the story, in the face of the consciously willed one. It's as tho this intense preoccupation with the physical, with the self and with story, sets up an involitional force which is the unconscious, its contents moving parallel with the known contents as the narrative progresses. A rhythm, as car gears meshing, grabbing and jibing, each causing the other to move, to prompt and to yield the substance and power of each — an absolute rhythm of movement, instantaneous, going.

ROBERT CREELEY

PREFACE TO GOLD DIGGERS

Had I lived some years ago, I think I would have been a moralist, i.e., one who lays down, so to speak, rules of behaviour with no small amount of self-satisfaction. But the writer isn't allowed that function anymore, or no man can take the job on very happily, being aware (as he must be) of what precisely that will make him.

So there is left this other area, still the short story or really the tale, and all that can be made of it. Whereas the novel is a continuum, of necessity, chapter to chapter, the story can escape some of that obligation, and function exactly in terms of whatever emotion best can serve it.

The story has no time finally. Or it hasn't here. Its shape, if form can be so thought of, is a sphere, an egg of obdurate kind. The only possible reason for its existence is that it has, in itself, the fact of reality and the pressure. There, in short, is its form — no matter how random and broken that will seem. The old assumptions of beginning and end — those very neat assertions — have fallen way completely in a place where the only actuality is life, the only end (never realized) death, and the only value, what love one can manage.

It is impossible to think otherwise, or at least I have found it so. I begin where I can, and end when I see the whole thing returning. Perhaps that is an obsession. These people, and what happens to them here, have never been completely my decision — because if you once say something, it will lead you to say more than you had meant to.

As the man responsible, I wanted to say what I thought was true, and make that the fact. It has led me to impossible things at times. I was not obliged, certainly, to say anything, but that argument never made sense to me.

December 14, 1953

JACK KEROUAC

ESSENTIALS OF SPONTANEOUS PROSE

SET-UP. The object is set before the mind, either in reality, as in sketching (before a landscape or teacup or old face) or is set in the memory wherein it becomes the sketching from memory of a definite image-object.

PROCEDURE. Time being of the essence in the purity of speech, sketching language is undisturbed flow from the mind of personal secret idea-words, *blowing* (as per jazz musician) on subject of image.

METHOD. No periods separating sentence-structures already arbitrarily riddled by false colons and timid usually needless commas — but the vigorous space dash separating rhetorical breathing (as jazz musician drawing breath between outblown phrases) — "measured pauses which are the essentials of our speech" — "divisions of the *sounds* we hear" — "time and how to note it down".

SCOPING. Not 'selectivity' of expression but following free deviation (association) of mind into limitless blow-on-subject seas of thoughts, swimming in sea of English with no discipline other than rhythms of rhetorical exhalation and expostulated statement, like a fist coming down on a table with each complete utterance, bang! ((the space-dash) — Blow as deep as you want — write as deeply, fish as far down as you want, satisfy yourself first, then reader cannot fail to receive telepathic shock and meaning-excitement by same laws operating in his own human mind.

LAG IN PROCEDURE. No pause to think of proper word but the infantile pileup of scatalogical buildup words till satisfaction is gained, which will turn out to be a great appending rhythm to a thought and be in accordance with Great Law of timing.

TIMING. Nothing is muddy that *runs in time* and to laws of *time* — Shakespearian stress of dramatic need to speak now in own unalterable way or forever hold tongue — *no revisions* (except obvious rational mistakes, such as names or *calculated* insertions in act of not-writing but *inserting*).

CENTER OF INTEREST. Begin not from preconceived idea of what to say about image but from jewel center of interest in subject of image at *moment* of writing, and write outwards swimming in sea of language to peripheral release and exhaustion — Do not afterthink except for poetic or P. S. reasons. Never afterthink to "improve" or defray impressions, as, the best writing is always the most painful personal wrung-out tossed from cradle warm protective mind — tap from yourself the song of yourself, *blow!* — *now!* — *your* way is your only way — "good" — or "bad" — always honest. ('ludicrous') spontaneous, 'confessional' interesting, because not 'crafted.' Craft *is* craft.

STRUCTURE OF WORK. Modern bizarre structures (science fiction etc.) arise from language being dead, "different" themes give illusion of "new" life. Follow roughly outlines in outfanning movement over subject, as river rock, so mindflow over jewel-center need (run your mind over it, *once*) arriving at pivot, where what was dim formed 'beginning' becomes sharp-necessitating "ending" and language shortens in race to wire of timerace of work, following laws of Deep Form, to conclusion, last words, last trickle — Night is The End.

MENTAL STATE. If possible write 'without consciousness' in semi-trance (as Yeats' later 'trance writing') allowing subconscious to admit in own unhibited interesting necessary and so 'modern' language what conscious art would censor, and write excitedly, swiftly, with writing-or-typing-cramps, in accordance (as from center to periphery) with laws of orgasm, Reich's "beclouding of consciousness." *Come* from within, out — to relaxed and said.

WILLIAM BURROUGHS
NOTE ON VAUDEVILLE VOICES

In writing this chapter I have used what I call "the fold in" method that is I place a page of one text folded down the middle on a page of another text (my own or someone else's)—The composite text is read across half from one text and half from the other— The resulting material is edited, re-arranged, and deleted as in any other form of composition—This chapter contains fold ins with the work of Rimbaud, T.S. Eliot, Paul Bowles, James Joyce, Michael Portman, Peter Weber, Fabrizio Mondadori, Jacques Stern, Evgeny Yevtushenko, some newspaper articles and of course my own work—

THE CUT UP METHOD

At a surrealist rally in the 1920's Tristan Tzara the man from nowhere proposed to create a poem on the spot by pulling words out of a hat. A riot ensued wrecked the theatre. André Breton expelled Tristan Tzara from the movement and grounded the cut ups on the Freudian couch.

In the summer of 1959 Brion Gysin painter and writer cut newspaper articles into sections and rearranged the sections at random. *Minutes To Go* resulted from this initial cut up experiment. *Minutes To Go* contains unedited unchanged cut ups emerging as quite coherent and meaningful prose.

The cut up method brings to writers the collage which has been used by painters for fifty years. And used by the moving and still camera. In fact all street shots from movie or still cameras are by the unpredictable factors of passers by and juxtaposition cut ups. And photographers will tell you that often their best shots are accidents . . . writers will tell you the same. The best writing seems to be done almost by accident but writers until the cut up method was made explicit— (all writing is in fact cut ups. I will return to this point)—had no way to produce the accident of spontaneity. You can not will spontaneity. But you can introduce the unpredictable spontaneous factor with a pair of scissors.

The method is simple. Here is one way to do it. Take a page. Like this page. Now cut down the middle and cross the middle. You have four sections: 1   2   3   4 . . . one two three four. Now rearrange the sections placing section four with section one and section two with section three. And you have a new page. Sometimes it says much the same thing. Sometimes something quite different—(cutting up political speeches is an interesting exercise)—in any case you will find that it says something and something quite definite. Take any poet or writer you fancy. Heresay, or poems you have read over many times. The words have lost meaning and life through years of repetition. Now take the poem and type out selected passages. Fill a page with excerpts. Now cut the page. You have a new poem. As many poems as you like. As many Shakespeare Rimbaud poems as you like. Tristan Tzara said: "Poetry for everyone." And André Breton called him a cop and expelled him from the movement. Say it again: "Poetry is for everyone." Poetry is a place and it is free to all cut up Rimbaud and you are in Rimbaud's place. Here is a Rimbaud cut up.

"Visit of memories. Only your dance and your voice house. On the suburban air improbable desertions . . . all harmonic pine for strife. The great skies are open. Candor of vapor and tent spitting blood laugh and drunken penance. Promenade of wine perfume opens slow bottle. The great skies are open. Supreme bugle burning flesh children to mist."

Cut ups are for everyone. Any body can make cut ups. It is experimental in the sense of being *something to do*. Right here write now. Not something to talk and argue about. Greek philosophers assumed logically that an object twice as heavy as another object would fall twice as fast. It did not occur to them to push the two objects off the table and see how they fall. Cut the words and see how they fall. Shakespeare Rimbaud live in their words. Cut the word lines and you will hear their voices. Cut ups often come through as code messages with special meaning for the cutter. Table tapping? Perhaps. Certainly an improvement on the usual deplorable performance of contacted poets through a medium. Rimbaud announces himself to be followed by some excruciatingly bad poetry. Cutting Rimbaud's words and you are assured of good poetry at least if not personal appearance.

All writing is in fact cut ups. A collage of words read heard overhead. What else? Use of scissors renders the process explicit and subject to extension and variation. Clear classical prose can be composed entirely of rearranged cut ups. Cutting and rearranging a page of written words introduces a new dimension into writing enabling the writer to turn images in cineramic variation. Images shift sense under the scissors smell images to sound sight to sound sound to kinesthetic. This is where Rimbaud was going with his color of vowels. And his "systematic derangement of the senses." The place of mescaline hallucination: seeing colors tasting sounds smelling forms.

The cut ups can be applied to other fields than writing. Doctor Neuman in his *Theory of Games and Economic Behavior* introduces the cut up method of random action into game and military strategy: assume that the worst has happened and act accordingly. If your strategy is at some point determined . . . by random factor your opponent will gain no advantage from knowing your strategy since he can not predict the move. The cut up method could be used to advantage in processing scientific data. How many discoveries have been made by accident? We can not produce accidents to order. The cut ups could add new dimension to films. Cut gambling scene in with a thousand gambling scenes all times and places. Cut back. Cut streets of the world. Cut and rearrange the word and image in films. There is no reason to accept a second rate product when you can have the best. And the best is there for all. "Poetry is for everyone" . . .

Now here are the previous paragraphs cut into four sections and rearranged:

ALL WRITING IS IN FACT CUT UPS OF GAMES AND ECONOMIC BEHAVIOR OVERHEARD? WHAT ELSE? ASSUME THAT THE WORST HAS HAPPENED EXPLICIT AND SUBJECT TO STRATEGY IS AT SOME POINT CLASSICAL PROSE. CUTTING

AND REARRANGING FACTOR YOUR OPPONENT WILL GAIN
INTRODUCES A NEW DIMENSION YOUR STRATEGY. HOW
MANY DISCOVERIES SOUND TO KINESTHETIC? WE CAN NOW
PRODUCE ACCIDENT TO HIS COLOR OF VOWELS. AND NEW
DIMENSION TO FILMS CUT THE SENSES. THE PLACE OF
SAND. GAMBLING SCENES ALL TIMES COLORS TASTING
SOUNDS SMELL STREETS OF THE WORLD. WHEN YOU CAN
HAVE THE BET ALL: "POETRY IS FOR EVERYONE" DOCTOR
NEUMAN IN A COLLAGE OF WORDS READ HEARD INTRO-
DUCED THE CUT UP SCISSORS RENDERS THE PROCESS GAME
AND MILITARY STRATEGY, VARIATION CLEAR AND ACT
ACCORDINGLY. IF YOU POSED ENTIRELY OF REARRANGED
CUT DETERMINED BY RANDOM A PAGE OF WRITTEN WORDS
NO ADVANTAGE FROM KNOWING INTO WRITER PREDICT
THE MOVE. THE CUT VARIATION IMAGES SHIFT SENSE
ADVANTAGE IN PROCESSING TO SOUND SIGHT TO SOUND.
HAVE BEEN MADE BY ACCIDENT IS WHERE RIMBAUD WAS
GOING WITH ORDER THE CUT UPS COULD "SYSTEMATIC
DERANGEMENT" OF THE GAMBLING SCENE IN WITH A TEA
HALLUCINATION: SEEING AND PLACES. CUT BACK. CUT
FORMS. REARRANGE THE WORD AND IMAGE TO OTHER
FIELDS THAN WRITING.

NOTES ON THE AUTHORS

WILLIAM EASTLAKE has had three novels published: *Go in Beauty, The Bronc People,* and *Portrait of the Artist with Twenty-Six Horses.* His stories have appeared in Harper's, Hudson Review, Evergreen Review, The Saturday Evening Post, New World Writing, and other magazines. Although he was born in New York City, he lives on a ranch in Cuba, New Mexico.

EDWARD DORN lives in Pocatello, Idaho with his wife and three children. He has had a book of poems published, *The Newly Fallen,* and his poems have been published in many magazines, as well as in the anthology *The New American Poetry.* His prose has appeared in The Black Mountain Review, Measure, Yugen, and other magazines. He has recently finished a novel, *Rite of Passage.*

DOUGLAS WOOLF's published books are *The Hypocritic Days, Fade Out,* and *Wall to Wall.* He was born in New York City in 1922, but he has lived in the West and Southwest most of his adult life. He is now living in Denver, Colorado. His stories have appeared in Second Coming, Kulchur, Evergreen Review.

PAUL METCALF's novel, *Will West,* was published by Jonathan Williams' Jargon Press in 1955. He has just moved to Massachusetts from North Carolina.

JOHN RECHY's first book, *City of Night,* has just been published. His short fiction has appeared in Evergreen Review, Nugget, The Nation. He lives in El Paso, Texas, where he was born in 1934.

MICHAEL RUMAKER had his first novel, *The Butterfly,* published in 1962. His stories have appeared in The Black Mountain Review, Evergreen Review, Measure, Redbook. Since graduating from Black Mountain College, he has lived in and around New York City.

ROBERT CREELEY is very well known as a poet. His selected works, *For Love,* was published in 1962. Seven volumes of his poetry had been previously published. A book of his short stories, *Gold Diggers,* appeared in 1945, and his first novel, *The Island,* will appear this year. He lives in Albuquerque, New Mexico.

FIELDING DAWSON's work has appeared in a great many literary magazines—Yugen, Black Mountain Review, Neon, etc. *Crazy Kat* and *Elizabeth Constantine,* two small books of stories, have been published. He attended Black Mountain College and is now living in New York City.

HUBERT SELBY, JR. was born in 1928 in Brooklyn, New York. His work has appeared widely including New Direction 17, The Provincetown Review, Black Mountain Review, Neon, and Yugen. Grove Press will shortly publish his first book *Last Exit to Brooklyn.* He is currently at work on a new novel. He moved to Manhattan from Brooklyn some time ago.

JACK KEROUAC, born in 1922, became quickly famous with the publication of *On the Road* in 1957. He had one novel published before that, *The Town and The City.* He has published nine books since then, including a book of poetry, *Mexico City Blues.* His most recent novel to appear is *Big Sur.* He lives on Long Island with his mother.

WILLIAM BURROUGHS' best known work is *Naked Lunch.* He followed it with *The Exterminator, The Soft Machine* and *Novia Express.* Works in progress include *Vaudeville Voices* and *The Ticket That Exploded.* Most of his recent activity has been centered around Paris and Tangiers.

LeROI JONES has had published a book of poetry, *Preface to a Twenty Volume Suicide Note,* and a non-fiction sociological study, *Blues People,* which appeared this year. A book of fiction, *The System of Dante's Hell,* is to be published shortly by Grove Press. He lives in New York City with his wife and two girl children.

DIANE DI PRIMA was born in Brooklyn, New York in 1933. Her last book was *Dinners and Nightmares* which included fiction and poetry. Her first book of poetry was *This Kind of Bird Flies Backward*. She has also edited a book of fables, *Various Fables From Various Places*. A new volume of her poetry, *The New Handbook of Heaven*, is due to be published soon. She recently returned to New York City from California.

RUSSELL EDSON now lives in Stamford, Connecticut. He has had two books published, *Appearances* and *A Stone is To Throw*. Jonathan Williams' Jargon Press is scheduled to bring out the complete *Gulping's Recital*.